A-Level Year 2
Chemistry

Exam Board: Edexcel

Revising for Chemistry exams is stressful, that's for sure — even just getting your
notes sorted out can leave you needing a lie down. But help is at hand...

This brilliant CGP book explains **everything you'll need to learn** (and nothing
you won't), all in a straightforward style that's easy to get your head around.
We've also included **exam questions** to test how ready you are for the real thing.

There's even a free Online Edition you can read on your computer or tablet!

How to get your free Online Edition

Go to **cgpbooks.co.uk/extras** and enter this code...

2263 3665 1430 1752

This code only works for one person. If somebody else has used
this book before you, they might have already claimed the Online Edition.

CGP

A-Level revision? It has to be CGP!

Contents

Topic 18 — Organic Chemistry III

Topic 19 — Modern Analytical Techniques II

Practical Skills

Do Well In Your Exams

Published by CGP

Editors:
Katie Braid, Katherine Faudemer, Robin Flello, Emily Howe, Paul Jordin and Sophie Scott.

Contributors:
Mike Bossart, Rob Clarke, Ian H. Davis, John Duffy, Paddy Gannon, Lucy Muncaster, Jane Simoni, Derek Swain, Paul Warren and Chris Workman.

ISBN: 978 1 78294 342 6

With thanks to Jan Greenway for the copyright research.

Cover Photo © **Laguna Design**/Science Photo Library

Clipart from Corel®
Printed by Elanders Ltd, Newcastle upon Tyne.

Based on the classic CGP style created by Richard Parsons.

Calculations Involving K_c

The equilibrium constant is about to become a constant presence in your life — just you wait and see...

K_c is the **Equilibrium Constant**

You learnt in Year 1 that K_c, the equilibrium constant, is calculated from the **ratio** of product concentration to reactant concentration. This means that if you know the **molar concentration** of each substance **at equilibrium**, you can work out K_c. A particular value of K_c will be constant for a given **temperature**.

For the general reaction $aA + bB \rightleftharpoons dD + eE$, $K_c = \dfrac{[D]^d [E]^e}{[A]^a [B]^b}$

> The lower-case letters a, b, d and e are the relative mole ratios of each substance.

So for the reaction $H_{2(g)} + I_{2(g)} \rightleftharpoons 2HI_{(g)}$, $K_c = \dfrac{[HI]^2}{[H_2]^1 [I_2]^1}$. This simplifies to $K_c = \dfrac{[HI]^2}{[H_2][I_2]}$.

1) Actually, this definition of K_c only applies to **homogeneous equilibria**, i.e. ones where all the products and reactants are in the **same phase**. If you've got more than one phase in there — a **heterogeneous equilibrium** — not everything is necessarily included in the expression for K_c.

2) You don't include **solids** or **pure liquids** in the expression for K_c when you're dealing with heterogeneous equilibria. This is because their concentrations **stay constant** throughout the reaction.

You Might Need to **Work Out** the **Equilibrium Concentrations**

You might have to figure out some of the **equilibrium concentrations** before you can find K_c:

Example: 0.20 moles of phosphorus(V) chloride decomposes at 600 K in a vessel of 5.00 dm³. The equilibrium mixture is found to contain 0.080 moles of chlorine. Write the expression for K_c and calculate its value, including units. $PCl_{5(g)} \rightleftharpoons PCl_{3(g)} + Cl_{2(g)}$

First find out how many moles of PCl_5 and PCl_3 there are at equilibrium:

> The **equation** tells you that when **1 mole of PCl_5** decomposes, **1 mole of PCl_3** and **1 mole of Cl_2** are formed. So if 0.080 moles of chlorine are produced at equilibrium, then there will be **0.080 moles** of PCl_3 as well. 0.080 moles of PCl_5 must have decomposed, so there will be (0.20 − 0.080 =) **0.12 moles** left.

Divide each number of moles by the volume of the flask to give the molar concentrations:

$[PCl_3] = [Cl_2] = 0.08 \div 5.00 =$ **0.016 mol dm⁻³** $[PCl_5] = 0.12 \div 5.00 =$ **0.024 mol dm⁻³**

Put the concentrations in the expression for K_c and calculate it: $K_c = \dfrac{[PCl_3][PCl_2]}{[PCl_5]} = \dfrac{[0.016][0.016]}{[0.024]} = \textbf{0.011}$

Now find the units of K_c: $K_c = \dfrac{(\text{mol dm}^{-3})(\text{mol dm}^{-3})}{(\text{mol dm}^{-3})} = \textbf{mol dm}^{-3}$ So $K_c =$ **0.011 mol dm⁻³**

K_c can be used to Find **Concentrations** in an **Equilibrium Mixture**

Example: When the reaction between ethanoic acid and ethanol was allowed to reach equilibrium at 25 °C, it was found that the equilibrium mixture contained 2.0 mol dm⁻³ ethanoic acid and 3.5 mol dm⁻³ ethanol. K_c of the equilibrium is 4.0 at 25 °C. What are the concentrations of the other components?

$$CH_3COOH_{(l)} + C_2H_5OH_{(l)} \rightleftharpoons CH_3COOC_2H_{5(l)} + H_2O_{(l)}$$

Put all the values you know in the K_c expression: $K_c = \dfrac{[CH_3COOC_2H_5][H_2O]}{[CH_3COOH][C_2H_5OH]} \Rightarrow 4.0 = \dfrac{[CH_3COOC_2H_5][H_2O]}{2.0 \times 3.5}$

Rearranging this gives: $[CH_3COOC_2H_5][H_2O] = 4.0 \times 2.0 \times 3.5 = 28.0$

From the equation, you know that an equal number of moles of $CH_3COOC_2H_5$ and H_2O will form, so:

$[CH_3COOC_2H_5] = [H_2O] = \sqrt{28} =$ **5.3 mol dm⁻³**

Calculations Involving K_c

The **Equilibrium Constant** Can Be Calculated from **Experimental Data**

A simple experiment that can be carried out in the laboratory involves the following reaction:

$$Fe^{2+}_{(aq)} + Ag^+_{(aq)} \rightleftharpoons Fe^{3+}_{(aq)} + Ag_{(s)}$$

The silver nitrate provides the Ag^+ ions and the iron(II) sulfate provides the Fe^{2+} ions.

1) If you leave a mixture of iron(II) sulfate solution and silver nitrate solution in a stoppered flask at 298 K, the reaction above will eventually reach **equilibrium**.

2) You can then take samples of the equilibrium mixture and **titrate** them — this will let you work out the **equilibrium concentration** of the **Fe^{2+} ions** (there's more on redox titrations on pages 42-47).
   Normally, if you change the amounts involved in an equilibrium, the position of equilibrium changes (see your Year 1 notes).
   However, this reaction is really slow to reach equilibrium, so carrying out the titration doesn't affect the equilibrium enough to matter.

3) From this, you can work out the equilibrium concentrations of the other components, and so K_c.

Example: 500 cm³ of 0.100 mol dm⁻³ iron(II) sulfate solution and 500 cm³ of 0.100 mol dm⁻³ silver nitrate solution are placed in a stoppered flask and allowed to reach equilibrium. It's found that the equilibrium concentration of Fe^{2+} is 0.0439 mol dm⁻³ under s.t.p.. Calculate K_c for this reaction at s.t.p..

The reaction equation (see above) tells you 1 mole of Fe^{2+} reacts with 1 mole of Ag^+ to form 1 mole of Fe^{3+} and 1 mole of Ag. In this particular reaction, **solid** silver is formed. The concentration of a solid is **constant**, so you **don't** need to include it in the expression for K_c.

The **starting concentrations** of Ag^+ and Fe^{2+} are the same and equal to **0.0500 mol dm⁻³**.

The **equilibrium concentration** of Ag^+ will be the same as Fe^{2+}, i.e. **0.0439 mol dm⁻³**.

The **equilibrium concentration** of Fe^{3+} will be 0.0500 – 0.0439 = **0.0061 mol dm⁻³**.

500 cm³ of each solution is used, so you have a total of 1000 cm³ of solution. The concentration of each reactant is therefore halved since you have the same number of moles of each reactant, but in double the volume.

$$\text{So } K_c = \frac{[Fe^{3+}]}{[Fe^{2+}][Ag^+]} = \frac{0.0061}{0.0439 \times 0.0439} = 3.17$$

The units of K_c are: $\dfrac{\text{mol dm}^{-3}}{(\text{mol dm}^{-3})(\text{mol dm}^{-3})} = \text{mol}^{-1}\,\text{dm}^3$

At s.t.p., K_c = **3.17 mol⁻¹ dm³**

Practice Questions

Q1 What do the square brackets, [ ], represent in a K_c expression?

Q2 Write the expression for K_c for the following equilibrium: $Cl_{2(g)} + PCl_{3(g)} \rightleftharpoons PCl_{5(g)}$. What are the units of K_c?

Exam Questions

Q1 At 723 K, the equilibrium constant for the reaction $H_{2(g)} + Cl_{2(g)} \rightleftharpoons 2HCl_{(g)}$ is 60.
   The equilibrium concentrations of H_2 and Cl_2 are 2.0 mol dm⁻³ and 0.30 mol dm⁻³ respectively.
   What is the molar concentration of HCl at equilibrium?

   A 0.10 mol dm⁻³   **B** 0.010 mol dm⁻³   **C** 6.0 mol dm⁻³   **D** 36 mol dm⁻³   [1 mark]

Q2 Copper is shaken with silver nitrate solution to form the following equilibrium. $Cu_{(s)} + 2Ag^+_{(aq)} \rightleftharpoons Cu^{2+}_{(aq)} + 2Ag_{(s)}$
   At a certain temperature, there are 0.431 mol dm⁻³ Ag^+ and
   0.193 mol dm⁻³ Cu^{2+} at equilibrium. Calculate K_c, giving its units.   [3 marks]

Q3 Nitrogen dioxide dissociates according to the equation $2NO_{2(g)} \rightleftharpoons 2NO_{(g)} + O_{2(g)}$.
   When 42.5 g of nitrogen dioxide were heated in a vessel of volume 22.8 dm³ at 500 °C,
   14.1 g of oxygen were found in the equilibrium mixture.

   a) Calculate: i) the number of moles of nitrogen dioxide originally.   [1 mark]

                ii) the number of moles of each gas in the equilibrium mixture.   [3 marks]

   b) Write an expression for K_c for this reaction. Calculate the value for K_c at 500 °C and give its units.   [5 marks]

As far as I'm concerned, equilibria are a constant pain in the *@?!

K_c is there to be calculated, so calculate it you must — and the only way to get good at it is to practise. And then practise again, just to be on the safe side. Now now, don't start moaning — you'll thank me if it comes up in the exam.

Gas Equilibria

It's easier to talk about gases in terms of their pressures rather than their molar concentrations. If you want to do this, you need a slightly different equilibrium constant — it's called K_p (but I'm afraid it's got nothing to do with peanuts).

The **Total Pressure** is **Equal** to the **Sum** of the **Partial Pressures**

In a mixture of gases, each individual gas exerts its own pressure — this is called its **partial pressure**.

> The **total pressure** of a gas mixture is the **sum** of all the **partial pressures** of the individual gases.

You might have to put this fact to use in pressure calculations:

Example: When 3.0 moles of the gas PCl_5 is heated, it decomposes into PCl_3 and Cl_2: $PCl_{5(g)} \rightleftharpoons PCl_{3(g)} + Cl_{2(g)}$
In a sealed vessel at 500 K, the equilibrium mixture contains chlorine with a partial pressure of 2.6 atm.
If the total pressure of the mixture is 7.0 atm, what is the partial pressure of PCl_5?

From the equation you know that PCl_3 and Cl_2 are produced in equal amounts, so the partial pressures of these two gases are the **same** at equilibrium — they're both 2.6 atm.

Total pressure $= p(PCl_5) + p(PCl_3) + p(Cl_2)$

$7.0 = p(PCl_5) + 2.6 + 2.6$

So the partial pressure of $PCl_5 = 7.0 - 2.6 - 2.6 = \mathbf{1.8\ atm}$

> $p(X)$ just means partial pressure of X.
> You might see this notation used without brackets, but it means the same thing.

Partial Pressures can be Worked Out from **Mole Fractions**

A 'mole fraction' is just the **proportion** of a gas mixture that is a particular gas. So if you've got four moles of gas in total, and two of them are gas A, the mole fraction of gas A is ½. There are **two formulae** you've got to know:

> 1) Mole fraction of a gas in a mixture $= \dfrac{\textbf{number of moles of gas}}{\textbf{total number of moles of gas in the mixture}}$
>
> 2) Partial pressure of a gas = **mole fraction of gas × total pressure of the mixture**

Example: When 3.00 mol of PCl_5 is heated in a sealed vessel, the equilibrium mixture contains 1.75 mol of chlorine. If the total pressure of the mixture is 7.0 atm, what is the partial pressure of PCl_5?

From the equation above, PCl_3 and Cl_2 are produced in equal amounts, so there'll be **1.75 moles** of PCl_3 too.
1.75 moles of PCl_5 must have decomposed so (3.00 − 1.75 =) **1.25 moles** of PCl_5 must be left at equilibrium.
This means that the total number of moles of gas at equilibrium = 1.75 + 1.75 + 1.25 = **4.75**

So the mole fraction of $PCl_5 = \dfrac{1.25}{4.75} = \mathbf{0.263...}$

The partial pressure of PCl_5 = mole fraction × total pressure = 0.263... × 7.0 = **1.8 atm**

The **Equilibrium Constant K_p** is Calculated from **Partial Pressures**

K_p is an equilibrium constant that you can calculate dealing with equilibria involving **gases**.
The expression for K_p is just like the one for K_c — except you use partial pressures instead of concentrations.

> For the equilibrium $aA_{(g)} + bB_{(g)} \rightleftharpoons dD_{(g)} + eE_{(g)}$: $K_p = \dfrac{p(D)^d p(E)^e}{p(A)^a p(B)^b}$

> There are no square brackets because they're partial pressures, not molar concentrations.

To calculate K_p, you just have to put the partial pressures in the expression. You work out the **units** like you did for K_c.

Example: Calculate K_p for the decomposition of PCl_5 gas at 500 K: $PCl_{5(g)} \rightleftharpoons PCl_{3(g)} + Cl_{2(g)}$
The partial pressures of each gas are: $p(PCl_5) = 1.8$ atm, $p(PCl_3) = 2.6$ atm, $p(Cl_2) = 2.6$ atm

$K_p = \dfrac{p(Cl_2)p(PCl_3)}{p(PCl_5)} = \dfrac{2.6 \times 2.6}{1.8} = 3.755... = \mathbf{3.8}\ (2\ s.f.)$

The units for K_p are worked out by putting the units into the expression instead of the numbers, and cancelling (like for K_c): $K_p = \dfrac{\text{atm} \times \text{atm}}{\text{atm}} = \text{atm}$. So, $K_p = \mathbf{3.8\ atm}$

Gas Equilibria

K_p can be Used to Find **Partial Pressures**

You might be given the value of K_p and have to use it to calculate **equilibrium partial pressures**.

> **Example:** An equilibrium exists between ethanoic acid monomers, CH_3COOH, and dimers, $(CH_3COOH)_2$.
> At 160 °C, K_p for the reaction $(CH_3COOH)_{2(g)} \rightleftharpoons 2CH_3COOH_{(g)}$ is 1.78 atm.
> At this temperature the partial pressure of the dimer, $(CH_3COOH)_2$, is 0.281 atm.
> Calculate the partial pressure of the monomer in this equilibrium and state the total pressure
> exerted by the equilibrium mixture.
>
> First, use the chemical equilibrium to write an expression for K_p: $K_p = \dfrac{p(CH_3COOH)^2}{p((CH_3COOH)_2)}$
> This rearranges to give: $p(CH_3COOH)^2 = K_p \times p((CH_3COOH)_2) = 1.78 \times 0.281 = 0.500...$
> $$p(CH_3COOH) = \sqrt{0.500...} = 0.707... \text{ atm}$$
> So the total pressure of the equilibrium mixture = $0.281 + 0.707... = $ **0.988 atm**

Add the two partial pressures together to get the total pressure.

K_p for **Heterogeneous** Equilibria Still **Only Includes Gases**

You met the idea of homogeneous and heterogeneous equilibria back in Year 1.
Up until now we've only thought about K_p expressions for **homogeneous equilibria**.
If you're writing an expression for K_p for a **heterogeneous equilibrium**, only include **gases**.

> **Example:** Write an expression for K_p for the following reaction: $NH_4HS_{(s)} \rightleftharpoons NH_{3(g)} + H_2S_{(g)}$.
>
> The equilibrium is **heterogeneous** — a solid decomposes to form two gases.
> Solids don't get included in K_p, so $K_p = p(NH_3)\,p(H_2S)$.

There's no bottom line as the reactant is a solid.

Practice Questions

Q1 What is meant by partial pressure?

Q2 How do you work out the mole fraction of a gas?

Q3 Write the expression for K_p for the following equilibrium: $NH_4HS_{(g)} \rightleftharpoons NH_{3(g)} + H_2S_{(g)}$

Exam Questions

Q1 At high temperatures, SO_2Cl_2 dissociates according to the equation $SO_2Cl_{2(g)} \rightleftharpoons SO_{2(g)} + Cl_{2(g)}$.
    When 1.50 moles of SO_2Cl_2 dissociates at 700 K, the equilibrium mixture contains SO_2 with
    a partial pressure of 0.594 atm. The mixture has a total pressure of 1.39 atm.

    a) Write an expression for K_p for this reaction.   [1 mark]

    b) Calculate the partial pressure of Cl_2 and the partial pressure of SO_2Cl_2 in the equilibrium mixture.   [2 marks]

    c) Calculate a value for K_p for this reaction and give its units.   [2 marks]

Q2 When nitric oxide and oxygen were mixed in a 2:1 mole ratio at a constant temperature
    in a sealed flask, an equilibrium was set up according to the equation: $2NO_{(g)} + O_{2(g)} \rightleftharpoons 2NO_{2(g)}$.
    The partial pressure of the nitric oxide (NO) at equilibrium was 0.36 atm. The total pressure in the flask was 0.98 atm.

    a) Deduce the partial pressure of oxygen in the equilibrium mixture.   [1 mark]

    b) Calculate the partial pressure of nitrogen dioxide in the equilibrium mixture.   [1 mark]

    c) Write an expression for the equilibrium constant, K_p, for this
        reaction and calculate its value at this temperature. State its units.   [3 marks]

I'm rather partial to a few pressure calculations — and a chocolate biscuit...

*Partial pressures are like concentrations for gases. The more of a substance you've got in a solution, the higher the
concentration, and the more of a gas you've got in a container, the higher the partial pressure. It's all to do with how
many molecules are crashing into the sides. With gases though, you've got to keep the lid on tight or they'll escape.*

Le Chatelier's Principle and Equilibrium Constants

You should already know that changing conditions can change the position of the equilibrium. That's great, but you also need to be able to predict what will happen to the equilibrium constant when you change conditions.

If **Conditions Change** the **Position of Equilibrium** Will Move

1) You learnt in Year 1 that when a reversible reaction reaches **dynamic equilibrium**, the forward reaction will be going at exactly the **same rate** as the backward reaction, so the amounts of reactants and products **won't be changing** any more. The **concentrations** of **reactants** and **products** stay **constant**.

2) If you **change** the **concentration**, **pressure** or **temperature** of a reversible reaction, you're going to **alter** the **position of equilibrium**. This just means you'll end up with **different amounts** of reactants and products at equilibrium.

3) If the change causes **more product** to form, then you say that the equilibrium shifts to the **right**. If **less product** forms, then the equilibrium has shifted to the **left**.

4) You also met Le Chatelier's principle in Year 1, which lets you predict how the **position of equilibrium** will change if a **condition changes**. Here it is again:

> If there's a change in **concentration**, **pressure** or **temperature**, the equilibrium will move to help **counteract** the change.

The removal of his dummy was a change that Maxwell always opposed.

5) So, basically, if you **raise the temperature**, the position of equilibrium will shift to try to **cool things down**. And if you **raise the pressure or concentration**, the position of equilibrium will shift to try to **reduce it again**.

6) The **size** of the equilibrium constant tells you where the equilibrium lies. The **greater** the value of K_c or K_p, the further to the **right** the equilibrium lies. **Smaller** values of K_c and K_p mean the equilibrium lies further to the **left**.

Temperature Changes **Alter** the Equilibrium Constant

1) From Le Chatelier's principle, you know that an **increase** in temperature causes more of the product of an **endothermic** reaction to form so that the extra heat is absorbed. Le Chatelier also states that a **decrease** in temperature causes more of the product of an **exothermic** reaction to form.

2) The equilibrium constant for a reaction depends on the **temperature**. Changing the temperature alters the position of equilibrium and the **value** of the equilibrium constant.

Example: The reaction below is exothermic in the forward direction. If you increase the temperature, the equilibrium shifts to the left to absorb the extra heat. What happens to K_p?

Exothermic ⟶

$$2SO_{2(g)} + O_{2(g)} \rightleftharpoons 2SO_{3(g)} \quad \Delta H = -197 \text{ kJ mol}^{-1}$$

⟵ Endothermic

An exothermic reaction releases heat and has a negative ΔH. An endothermic reaction absorbs heat and has a positive ΔH.

If the equilibrium shifts to the left, then less product will form. By looking at the expression for the equilibrium constant, you can see that if there's less product, the value of K_p will decrease.

This reaction is between gases, so it's easiest to use K_p, but it's exactly the same for K_c and the other equilibrium constants you'll meet in this course.

$$K_p = \frac{p(SO_3)^2}{p(SO_2)^2 p(O_2)}$$

There's less product and more reactant, so the number on the top gets smaller and the number on the bottom gets bigger. This means K_p must have decreased.

3) The general rule for what happens to an equilibrium constant when you change the **temperature** of a reaction is that:

- If changing the temperature causes **less product** to form, the equilibrium moves to the **left**, and the equilibrium constant **decreases**.
- If changing the temperature causes **more product** to form, the equilibrium moves to the **right**, and the equilibrium constant **increases**.

Le Chatelier's Principle and Equilibrium Constants

Concentration and Pressure Changes Don't Affect the Equilibrium Constant

Concentration

The value of the **equilibrium constant** is **fixed** at a given temperature. So if the concentration of one thing in the equilibrium mixture **changes** then the concentrations of the others must change to keep the value of K_c the same.

> E.g. $CH_3COOH_{(l)} + C_2H_5OH_{(l)} \rightleftharpoons CH_3COOC_2H_{5(l)} + H_2O_{(l)}$
>
> If you **increase** the concentration of **CH_3COOH** then the equilibrium will move to the **right** to get rid of the extra CH_3COOH — so more $CH_3COOC_2H_5$ and H_2O are produced. This keeps the **equilibrium constant** the same.

Pressure

Increasing the **total pressure** increases the **partial pressures** (or concentration) of each of the products and reactants. The equilibrium shifts to the side with **fewer moles** of gas to decrease the pressure. The overall effect is that K_p and K_c are **unchanged**.

> E.g. $2SO_{2(g)} + O_{2(g)} \rightleftharpoons 2SO_{3(g)}$
>
> There are 3 moles on the left, but only 2 on the right. So an **increase in pressure** would shift the equilibrium to the **right**. The equilibrium constant however doesn't change.

So, to summarise, concentration and pressure **don't** affect the **values** of K_c or K_p. Changes to concentration and pressure **do** change the **amounts** of products and reactants present at equilibrium, but the **ratio** of reactants to products stays the same (leaving K_c or K_p unchanged). Changes in **temperature** not only alter the **amounts** of products and reactants present at equilibrium, but also **change** the **value** of the equilibrium constants.

> **Catalysts** have **NO EFFECT** on the **position of equilibrium**, so don't affect the value of K_c (or K_p). They **can't** increase **yield** — but they **do** mean equilibrium is approached **faster**.

Practice Questions

Q1 If you raise the temperature of a reversible reaction, in which direction will the reaction move?

Q2 Does temperature change affect the equilibrium constant?

Q3 Why doesn't concentration affect the equilibrium constant?

Exam Questions

Q1 At temperature T_1, the equilibrium constant K_c for the following reaction is 0.67 mol^{-1} dm^3.

$$N_{2(g)} + 3H_{2(g)} \rightleftharpoons 2NH_{3(g)} \qquad \Delta H = -92 \text{ kJ mol}^{-1}$$

a) When equilibrium was established at a different temperature, T_2, the value of K_c increased. State which of T_1 or T_2 is the lower temperature and explain why. [3 marks]

b) The experiment was repeated exactly the same in all respects at T_1, except a flask of smaller volume was used. How would this change affect the yield of ammonia and the value of K_c? [2 marks]

Q2 The reaction between methane and steam is used to produce hydrogen. The forward reaction is endothermic.
$$CH_{4(g)} + H_2O_{(g)} \rightleftharpoons CO_{(g)} + 3H_{2(g)}$$

a) Write an equation for K_p for this reaction. [1 mark]

b) Which of the following will cause the value of K_p to increase?

A Increasing the temperature.   **B** Using a catalyst.

C Decreasing the pressure.   **D** Decreasing the temperature. [1 mark]

The performers at the equilibrium concert were unaffected by pressure...

Predicting how the equilibrium position shifts if the conditions change isn't always simple. E.g. if you increase the pressure and temperature of the reaction between SO_2 and O_2 (see the last two pages), the increase in pressure would want to shift the equilibrium to the right but the increase in temperature would want to push it to the left. Tricky...

Acids and Bases

The scientific definition of an acid has changed over time — originally, the word acid just meant something that tasted sour. But, in 1923, Johannes Nicolaus Brønsted and Martin Lowry came along and refined the definition.

An Acid **Releases** Protons — a Base **Accepts** Protons

Brønsted-Lowry acids are **proton donors** — they release **hydrogen ions** (H^+) when they're mixed with water. You never get H^+ ions by themselves in water though — they're always combined with H_2O to form **hydroxonium ions, H_3O^+**.

$$HA_{(aq)} + H_2O_{(l)} \rightarrow H_3O^+_{(aq)} + A^-_{(aq)}$$

Brønsted-Lowry bases are **proton acceptors**. When they're in solution, they grab **hydrogen ions** from water molecules.

$$B_{(aq)} + H_2O_{(l)} \rightarrow BH^+_{(aq)} + OH^-_{(aq)}$$

HA is any old acid and B is just a random base.

Acids and Bases can be **Strong** or **Weak**

1) **Strong acids dissociate** (or ionise) **almost completely** in water — **nearly all** the H^+ ions will be released. **Hydrochloric acid** is a strong acid:

$$HCl \rightarrow H^+ + Cl^-$$

These are really both reversible reactions, but the equilibrium lies extremely far to the right.

   Strong bases (like sodium hydroxide) **dissociate almost completely** in water too:

$$NaOH \rightarrow Na^+ + OH^-$$

2) **Weak acids** (e.g. ethanoic acid) dissociate only very **slightly** in water — so only small numbers of H^+ ions are formed. An **equilibrium** is set up which lies well over to the **left**:

$$CH_3COOH \rightleftharpoons CH_3COO^- + H^+$$

   Weak bases (such as ammonia) **only slightly protonate** in water. Just like with weak acids, the equilibrium lies well over to the **left**:

$$NH_3 + H_2O \rightleftharpoons NH_4^+ + OH^-$$

Acids and Bases form **Conjugate Pairs**

1) Acids **can't** just throw away their protons — they can only get rid of them if there's a **base** to accept them. In this reaction the **acid**, HA, **transfers** a proton to the **base**, B:

$$HA_{(aq)} + B_{(aq)} \rightleftharpoons BH^+_{(aq)} + A^-_{(aq)}$$

2) It's an **equilibrium**, so if you add more **HA** or **B**, the position of equilibrium moves to the **right**. But if you add more **BH⁺** or **A⁻**, the equilibrium will move to the **left**. This is all down to **Le Chatelier's principle** (see page 6).

3) Conjugate pairs are species that are linked by the **transfer** of a **proton**. They're always on opposite sides of the reaction equation.

A species is just any type of chemical — it could be an atom, a molecule, an ion...

4) The species that has **lost** a proton is the **conjugate base** and the species that has **gained** a proton is the **conjugate acid**. For example...

- When an acid's added to water, the equilibrium shown on the right is set up.
- In the **forward reaction**, HA acts as an **acid** as it **donates** a proton. In the **reverse reaction**, A⁻ acts as a **base** and **accepts** a proton from the H_3O^+ ion to form HA.
- HA and A⁻ are called a **conjugate pair** — HA is the **conjugate acid** of A⁻ and A⁻ is the **conjugate base** of the acid, HA. **H_2O** and **H_3O^+** are a conjugate pair too.

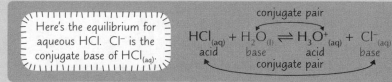

conjugate pair

acid   base   acid   base
$$HA + H_2O \rightleftharpoons H_3O^+ + A^-$$
conjugate pair

- The acid and base of a conjugate pair are linked by an **H⁺**, e.g. $HA \rightleftharpoons H^+ + A^-$ or this: $H^+ + H_2O \rightleftharpoons H_3O^+$

Here's the equilibrium for aqueous HCl. Cl⁻ is the conjugate base of $HCl_{(aq)}$.

conjugate pair
$$HCl_{(aq)} + H_2O_{(l)} \rightleftharpoons H_3O^+_{(aq)} + Cl^-_{(aq)}$$
acid   base   acid   base
conjugate pair

- An equilibrium with **conjugate pairs** is also set up when a **base** dissolves in water.
- The base, B, takes a proton from the water to form **BH⁺** — so B is the **conjugate base** of BH⁺, and BH⁺ is the **conjugate acid** of B. H_2O and OH⁻ also form a **conjugate pair**.

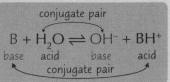

conjugate pair
$$B + H_2O \rightleftharpoons OH^- + BH^+$$
base   acid   base   acid
conjugate pair

Acids and Bases

Acids and Bases React in *Neutralisation Reactions*

1) When **acids** and **bases** react together, a salt and water are produced:

Example: The reaction of hydrochloric acid and sodium hydroxide.

$$HCl_{(aq)} + NaOH_{(aq)} \rightarrow H_2O_{(l)} + NaCl_{(aq)}$$
acid   base   water   salt

2) If the concentration of H^+ ions from the acid is equal to the concentration of OH^- ions from the base, then a **neutral solution** is produced — this is one where $[H^+] = [OH^-]$. All of the H^+ ions from the acid and the OH^- ions from the base react to form water.

If $[H^+]$ is greater than $[OH^-]$ the solution is acidic, and if $[OH^-]$ is greater than $[H^+]$ the solution is basic (or alkaline).

3) There's a **change** in **enthalpy** when **neutralisation** reactions happen — the enthalpy change of **neutralisation**.

> The **standard enthalpy change of neutralisation** is the enthalpy change when solutions of an **acid** and a **base** react together, under standard conditions, to produce **1 mole** of **water**.

Neutralisation reactions are always exothermic, so enthalpy changes of neutralisation are always negative.

4) As you saw on the last page, **weak acids** and **weak bases** only dissociate slightly in solution — it's a **reversible reaction**. When they're involved in neutralisation reactions, their H^+ ions (for acids) or OH^- ions (for bases) get used up quickly, as there are only a **few** of them in solution. The acid or base is therefore **constantly dissociating more** to replace the H^+/OH^- ions in solution and maintain the equilibrium (see your Year 1 notes for more on concentration and equilibrium). This requires enthalpy, so the standard enthalpy change of neutralisation for weak acids and weak bases includes **enthalpy** to do with the **reaction** between H^+ and OH^- **ions**, and enthalpy to do with **dissociation**. The enthalpy of dissociation varies, depending on the acid and base involved, so the standard enthalpy change of neutralisation for reactions involving weak acids or weak bases **varies**.

5) On the last page, you also saw that **strong acids** and **strong bases** fully dissociate in solution. When they react together in neutralisation reactions, there's **no dissociation enthalpy** for the acid or base — just **enthalpy** for the **reaction** of the H^+ and OH^- ions. Therefore, since this reaction is always the same, the standard enthalpy of neutralisation is **very similar** for all the reactions of strong acids with strong bases.

$$H^+_{(aq)} + OH^-_{(aq)} \rightarrow H_2O_{(l)}$$

Practice Questions

Q1 Give the Brønsted-Lowry definitions of an acid and a base.

Q2 Give the definition of: a) a strong acid,   b) a weak acid.

Q3 Write the equilibrium for hydrochloric acid dissolving in water and identify the conjugate pairs.

Q4 What is a neutral substance?

Exam Questions

Q1 Hydrocyanic acid, $HCN_{(aq)}$, is a weak acid with a faint smell of bitter almonds. It is extremely poisonous.

   a) Write the equation for the equilibrium set up when it dissolves in water. [1 mark]

   b) What can you say about the position of this equilibrium? Explain your answer. [2 marks]

   c) What is the conjugate base of this acid? [1 mark]

Q2 A student is investigating the standard enthalpy change of neutralisation of some acid/base reactions.

   a) Define the standard enthalpy change of neutralisation. [2 marks]

   b) The student knows that the standard enthalpy change of neutralisation for the reaction of potassium hydroxide and nitric acid (a strong acid) is -57.1 kJ mol^{-1}. He predicts that the standard enthalpy change of neutralisation of the reaction of potassium hydroxide and ethanoic acid (a weak acid) will be the same. Is the student correct? Explain your answer. [3 marks]

I'm going to neutralise my hatred of acids and bases with a nice cup of tea...

Don't confuse strong acids with concentrated acids, or weak acids with dilute acids. Strong and weak are to do with how much an acid dissociates. Concentrated and dilute are to do with the number of moles of acid you've got per dm^3.

pH

Get those calculators warmed up — especially the log function key.

The **pH Scale** is a Measure of the **Hydrogen Ion Concentration**

The **concentration of hydrogen ions** can vary enormously, so some clever chemists decided to express the concentration on a **logarithmic scale**.

$$pH = -\log_{10}[H^+]$$

The pH scale normally goes from **0** (very acidic) to **14** (very alkaline/basic). **pH 7** is regarded as being **neutral**.

For Strong **Monoprotic** Acids, [H⁺] = Acid Concentration

1) Hydrochloric acid and nitric acid ($HNO_{3(aq)}$) are **strong acids** so they dissociate fully.
They're also **monoprotic**, so each mole of
acid produces **one mole of hydrogen ions**.
This means the H⁺ concentration is the **same**
as the acid concentration. Here's an example:

> **Example:** Calculate the pH of 0.050 mol dm⁻³ nitric acid.
>
> $[H^+] = 0.050 \Rightarrow pH = -\log_{10}(0.050) = \textbf{1.30}$

2) You also need to be able to work out **[H⁺]** if you're given the **pH** of a solution.
You do this by finding the **inverse log of –pH**, which is **10^{-pH}**.

> **Example:** An acid solution has a pH of 2.45. What is the hydrogen ion concentration, or [H⁺], of the acid?
>
> $[H^+] = 10^{-2.45} = \textbf{3.5} \times \textbf{10}^{-3} \textbf{ mol dm}^{-3}$

Polyprotic Acids Can Lose More Than One Proton

1) You saw above that **monoprotic** acids only have **one proton** that they can release into solution.

2) But some acids, such as sulfuric acid (H_2SO_4), are **polyprotic** — this means they have **more than one proton** that they can release into solution.

3) Each molecule of a **strong diprotic acid** releases **two protons** when it dissociates.

4) Calculating the **[H⁺]**, and therefore the **pH** of **polyprotic acids** is a bit trickier, as more than one mole of hydrogen ions is released per mole of acid — you won't be asked to do this in the exam though, so don't panic.

To Find the **pH** of a **Weak Acid** You Use **K_a** (the **Acid Dissociation Constant**)

Weak acids (like CH_3COOH) **don't** dissociate fully in solution, so the [H⁺] **isn't** the same as the acid concentration. This makes it a **bit trickier** to find their pH. You have to use yet another **equilibrium constant**, K_a (the acid dissociation constant).

- For a weak aqueous acid, HA, you get the following equilibrium: $HA_{(aq)} \rightleftharpoons H^+_{(aq)} + A^-_{(aq)}$

- As only a **tiny amount** of HA dissociates, you can assume that $[HA_{(aq)}] \gg [H^+_{(aq)}]$ so $[HA_{(aq)}]_{start} \approx [HA_{(aq)}]_{equilibrium}$.

- So if you apply the equilibrium law, you get: $K_a = \dfrac{[H^+][A^-]}{[HA]_{start}}$

  See page 12 for more about the dissociation of water.

- You can also assume that dissociation of the **acid** is much greater than dissociation of **water**. This means you can assume that all the H⁺ ions in solution come from the **acid**, so $[H^+_{(aq)}] \approx [A^-_{(aq)}]$.

  The units of K_a are mol dm⁻³. So $K_a = \dfrac{[H^+]^2}{[HA]}$

  This expression is fine for calculations, but if you're asked for the expression of K_a, remember to give the one above ($K_a = [H^+][A^-]/[HA]$).

The assumptions made above to find K_a only work for **weak acids**.
Strong acids **dissociate more** in solution, so the difference between $[HA]_{start}$ and $[HA]_{equilibrium}$ becomes **significant**, so the assumption that $[HA]_{start} = [HA]_{equilibrium}$ is no longer **valid**.

pH

To Find the pH of a *Weak Acid*, You Use K_a

K_a is an **equilibrium constant** just like K_c (see page 2). It applies to a particular acid at a **specific temperature** regardless of the **concentration**. You can use this fact to find the **pH** of a known concentration of a weak acid.

> **Example:** Calculate the hydrogen ion concentration and the pH of a
> 0.02 mol dm⁻³ solution of propanoic acid (CH_3CH_2COOH).
> K_a for propanoic acid at this temperature is 1.30×10^{-5} mol dm⁻³.
>
> First, write down your expression for K_a and rearrange to find [H⁺].
>
> $$K_a = \frac{[H^+]^2}{[CH_3CH_2COOH]} \implies [H^+]^2 = K_a[CH_3CH_2COOH] = 1.30 \times 10^{-5} \times 0.02 = 2.60 \times 10^{-7}$$
> $$\implies [H^+] = \sqrt{(2.60 \times 10^{-7})} = \textbf{5.10} \times \textbf{10}^{-4} \textbf{ mol dm}^{-3}$$
>
> You can now use your value for [H⁺] to find pH: $pH = -\log_{10} 5.10 \times 10^{-4} = \textbf{3.29}$

You Might Have to Find the *Concentration* or K_a of a *Weak Acid*

You don't need to know anything new for this type of calculation. You usually just have to find **[H⁺]** from the pH, then fiddle around with the K_a **expression** to find the missing bit of information.

This bunny may look cute,
but he can't help Horace
with his revision.

> **Example:** The pH of an ethanoic acid (CH_3COOH) solution was 3.02 at 298 K.
> Calculate the molar concentration of this solution.
> K_a of ethanoic acid is 1.75×10^{-5} mol dm⁻³ at 298 K.
>
> First, use the pH to find [H⁺]: $[H^+] = 10^{-pH} = 10^{-3.02} = \textbf{9.55} \times \textbf{10}^{-4} \textbf{ mol dm}^{-3}$
>
> Then rearrange the expression for K_a and plug in your values to find [CH_3COOH]:
>
> $$K_a = \frac{[H^+]^2}{[CH_3COOH]} \implies CH_3COOH = \frac{[H^+]^2}{K_a} = \frac{(9.55 \times 10^{-4})^2}{1.75 \times 10^{-5}} = \textbf{0.0521 mol dm}^{-3}$$

Practice Questions

Q1 Explain what is meant by the term 'diprotic acid'?

Q2 Explain how to calculate the pH of a strong monoprotic acid from its concentration.

Q3 Explain how to calculate the pH of a weak acid from its concentration and K_a.

Exam Questions

Q1 a) What's the pH of a solution of the strong acid, hydrobromic acid (HBr),
if it has a concentration of 0.32 mol dm⁻³? [1 mark]

b) Hydrofluoric acid (HF) is a weaker acid than hydrochloric acid.
Explain what that means in terms of hydrogen ions and pH. [1 mark]

Q2 The value of K_a for the weak acid HA, at 298 K, is 5.60×10^{-4} mol dm⁻³.

a) Write an expression for K_a. [1 mark]

b) Calculate the pH of a 0.280 mol dm⁻³ solution of HA at 298 K. [2 marks]

Q3 The pH of a 0.150 mol dm⁻³ solution of a weak monoprotic acid, HX, is 2.65 at 298 K.
Calculate the value of K_a for the acid HX at 298 K. [3 marks]

pH calculations are pH–ing great...

No, I really like them. Honestly. Although they can be a bit tricky. Just make sure you learn all the key formulae. Oh and not all calculators work the same way, so make sure you know how to work logs out on your calculator. There's loads more on pH coming up, and lots more calculations (eek), so make sure you've nailed this page before you move on.

The Ionic Product of Water

More pH calculations to come, but this time they're to do with bases. If only that meant they were basic — they're actually quite tricky. But fear not, there are loads of examples over the next two pages to guide you through K_w...

The Ionic Product of Water, K_w, Depends on the Concentration of H^+ and OH^-

Water can act as an **acid** by **donating** a proton — but it can also act as a **base** by **accepting** a proton. So, in water there'll always be both **hydroxonium ions** and **hydroxide ions** swimming around at the **same time**. So the following equilibrium exists in water:

$$H_2O_{(l)} + H_2O_{(l)} \rightleftharpoons H_3O^+_{(aq)} + OH^-_{(aq)}$$ or more simply: $$H_2O_{(l)} \rightleftharpoons H^+_{(aq)} + OH^-_{(aq)}$$

And, just like for any other equilibrium reaction, you can apply the equilibrium law and write an expression for the **equilibrium constant**: $$K_c = \frac{[H^+][OH^-]}{[H_2O]}$$

Water only dissociates a **tiny amount**, so the equilibrium lies well over to the **left**. There's so much water compared to the amounts of H^+ and OH^- ions that the concentration of water is considered to have a **constant** value.

So if you multiply K_c (a constant) by $[H_2O]$ (another constant), you get a **constant**. This new constant is called the **ionic product of water** and it is given the symbol K_w.

The units of K_w are always $mol^2\ dm^{-6}$.

$$K_w = [H^+][OH^-]$$

It doesn't matter whether water is pure or part of a solution — this equilibrium is always happening, and K_w is always the same at the same temperature.

For **pure water**, there's a **1:1** ratio of H^+ and OH^- ions due to dissociation. This means $[H^+] = [OH^-]$ and $K_w = [H^+]^2$. So if you know K_w of pure water at a certain temperature, you can calculate $[H^+]$ and use this to find the pH.

The fact that K_w always has the **same value** for pure water or an aqueous solution at a **given temperature** is really useful, as you're about to discover...

$$\boxed{\text{At } 25\ ^\circ C\ (298\ K),\ K_w = 1.0 \times 10^{-14}\ mol^2\ dm^{-6}}$$

Use K_w to Find the pH of a Strong Base

1) Sodium hydroxide (NaOH) and potassium hydroxide (KOH) are **strong bases** that **fully dissociate** in water:

$$NaOH_{(s)} \xrightarrow{H_2O} Na^+_{(aq)} + OH^-_{(aq)}$$ $$KOH_{(s)} \xrightarrow{H_2O} K^+_{(aq)} + OH^-_{(aq)}$$

2) They donate **one mole of OH^- ions** per mole of base. This means that the concentration of OH^- ions is the **same** as the **concentration of the base**. So for 0.02 mol dm^{-3} sodium hydroxide solution, $[OH^-]$ is also **0.02 mol dm^{-3}**.

3) But to work out the **pH** you need to know **$[H^+]$** — this is linked to **$[OH^-]$** through the **ionic product of water**, K_w:

4) So if you know K_w and $[OH^-]$ for a **strong aqueous base** at a certain temperature, you can work out **$[H^+]$** (then the **pH**).

Example: Find the pH of 0.10 mol dm^{-3} NaOH at 298 K, given that K_w at 298 K is 1.0×10^{-14} mol^2 dm^{-6}.

1) First put all the values you know into the expression for the ionic product of water, K_w:

$$1.0 \times 10^{-14} = [H^+][0.10]$$

2) Now rearrange the expression to find $[H^+]$:

$$[H^+] = \frac{1.0 \times 10^{-14}}{0.10} = 1.0 \times 10^{-13}\ mol\ dm^{-3}$$

3) Use your value of $[H^+]$ to find the pH of the solution:

$$pH = -\log_{10}[H^+] = -\log_{10}(1.0 \times 10^{-13}) = \textbf{13.00}$$

The Ionic Product of Water

$pK_w = -log_{10} K_w$ and $K_w = 10^{-pK_w}$

pK_w is calculated from K_w. And, since under standard conditions K_w is always 1.0×10^{-14}, pK_w is always:

$$pK_w = -log_{10}K_w = -log_{10}(1.0 \times 10^{-14}) = \textbf{14.00}$$

The advantage of pK_w values is that they're a decent size so they're easy to work with.

$pK_a = -log_{10} K_a$ and $K_a = 10^{-pK_a}$

Since K_a is different for different acids, pK_a is a bit trickier than pK_w.
pK_a is calculated from K_a in exactly the same way as **pH** is calculated from **[H⁺]** — and vice versa.

Example: i) If an acid has a K_a value of 1.50×10^{-7} mol dm³, what is its pK_a?

$$pK_a = -log_{10}(1.50 \times 10^{-7}) = \textbf{6.824}$$

ii) What is the K_a value of an acid if its pK_a is 4.32?

$$K_a = 10^{-4.32} = \textbf{4.8} \times \textbf{10}^{-5} \textbf{ mol dm}^{-3}$$

The smaller the pK_a, the stronger the acid (just like for pH).

$pK_{oink} = -hog_{10}K_{oink}$

Just to make things that bit more complicated, you might be given a **pK_a** value in a question to work out concentrations or pH. If so, you just need to convert pK_a to K_a so that you can use the **K_a expression**.

Example: Calculate the pH of 0.0500 mol dm⁻³ methanoic acid (HCOOH).
Methanoic acid has a pK_a of 3.75 at this temperature.

$$K_a = 10^{-pK_a} = 10^{-3.75} = 1.77... \times 10^{-4} \text{ mol dm}^{-3}$$

First you have to convert the pK_a to K_a.

$$K_a = \frac{[H^+]^2}{[HCOOH]} \longrightarrow [H^+]^2 = K_a \times [HCOOH] = 1.77... \times 10^{-4} \times 0.0500 = 8.91... \times 10^{-6}$$

$$[H^+] = \sqrt{(8.91... \times 10^{-6})} = 2.98... \times 10^{-3} \text{ mol dm}^{-3}$$

$$pH = -log_{10}(2.98... \times 10^{-3}) = \textbf{2.53}$$

You might also be asked to work out a pK_a value from concentrations or pH. In this case, you just work out the K_a value as usual and then convert it to pK_a.

Practice Questions

Q1 Give the equation for the ionic product of water.

Q2 What equation would you use to work out pK_w from K_w?

Exam Questions

Q1 At 298 K, a solution of sodium hydroxide contains 2.50 g dm⁻³. K_w at 298 K is 1.0×10^{-14} mol² dm⁻⁶.

    a) What is the molar concentration of the hydroxide ions in this solution? [2 marks]

    b) Calculate the pH of this solution. [2 marks]

Q2 Calculate the pH of a 0.0370 mol dm⁻³ solution of sodium hydroxide at 298 K.
K_w, the ionic product of water, is 1.0×10^{-14} mol² dm⁻⁶ at 298 K. [2 marks]

Q3 Benzoic acid is a weak acid that is used as a food preservative. It has a pK_a of 4.20 at 298 K.
Find the pH of a 1.60×10^{-4} mol dm⁻³ solution of benzoic acid at 298 K. [3 marks]

An ionic product — when your trousers have no creases in them...

You know things are getting serious when maths stuff like logs start appearing. It's fine really though, just practise a few questions and make sure you know how to use the log button on your calculator. And make sure you've learned the equations for K_w, pK_w AND pK_a. And while you're up, go and make me a nice cup of tea, lots of milk, no sugar.

Experiments Involving pH

You thought that was all there was to know about pH? Sorry to disappoint, but you're only halfway through this topic...

You Can **Measure** the pH of a Solution Using a **pH Meter**

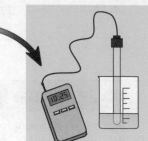

1) A **pH meter** is an electronic gadget you can use to tell you the **pH** of a solution.

2) pH meters have a **probe** that you put into your solution and a **digital display** that shows the reading.

3) Before you use a pH meter, you need to make sure it's **calibrated correctly**. To do this...

   • Place the bulb of the pH meter into **deionised water** and allow the reading to settle. Now **adjust** the reading so that it reads **7.0**.

   • Do the same with a standard solution of pH 4 and another of pH 10. Make sure you **rinse** the probe with **deionised water** in between each reading.

4) You're now ready to take your **actual measurement**. Place the probe in the liquid you're measuring and let the reading **settle** before you record the result. After each measurement, you should **rinse** the probe in **deionised water**.

> You could also measure pH with a pH probe attached to a data logger. A data logger records data at set intervals for a specified amount of time.

The **pH** of Equimolar Solutions Can Tell You About the Substances

You can learn quite a lot about the nature of a chemical just by looking at its **pH**. By measuring the **pHs** of different equimolar solutions (solutions that contain the same number of moles), you can see whether a substance is an acid, base or a salt, and whether it is strong or weak.

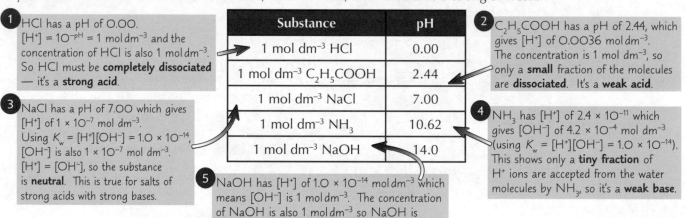

1 HCl has a pH of 0.00. $[H^+] = 10^{-pH} = 1\ mol\,dm^{-3}$ and the concentration of HCl is also $1\ mol\,dm^{-3}$. So HCl must be **completely dissociated** — it's a **strong acid**.

2 C_2H_5COOH has a pH of 2.44, which gives $[H^+]$ of $0.0036\ mol\,dm^{-3}$. The concentration is $1\ mol\,dm^{-3}$, so only a **small** fraction of the molecules are **dissociated**. It's a **weak acid**.

3 NaCl has a pH of 7.00 which gives $[H^+]$ of $1 \times 10^{-7}\ mol\,dm^{-3}$. Using $K_w = [H^+][OH^-] = 1.0 \times 10^{-14}$, $[OH^-]$ is also $1 \times 10^{-7}\ mol\,dm^{-3}$. $[H^+] = [OH^-]$, so the substance is **neutral**. This is true for salts of strong acids with strong bases.

4 NH_3 has $[H^+]$ of 2.4×10^{-11} which gives $[OH^-]$ of $4.2 \times 10^{-4}\ mol\,dm^{-3}$ (using $K_w = [H^+][OH^-] = 1.0 \times 10^{-14}$). This shows only a **tiny fraction** of H^+ ions are accepted from the water molecules by NH_3, so it's a **weak base**.

5 NaOH has $[H^+]$ of $1.0 \times 10^{-14}\ mol\,dm^{-3}$ which means $[OH^-]$ is $1\ mol\,dm^{-3}$. The concentration of NaOH is also $1\ mol\,dm^{-3}$ so NaOH is **completely dissociated** — it's a **strong base**.

Substance	pH
1 mol dm⁻³ HCl	0.00
1 mol dm⁻³ C₂H₅COOH	2.44
1 mol dm⁻³ NaCl	7.00
1 mol dm⁻³ NH₃	10.62
1 mol dm⁻³ NaOH	14.0

You Can Use **Masses** and **pH** to Work Out K_a

You can use **experimental data** to work out K_a for weak acids. The example below shows you how this works.

Example: 1.31 g of ethanoic acid (CH_3COOH) are dissolved in 250 cm³ of distilled water to create a solution of ethanoic acid. The solution has a pH of 2.84. Calculate the acid dissociation constant for ethanoic acid.

1) First, you need to work out the number of moles of ethanoic acid that are in the solution.

$$\text{moles} = \text{mass} \div M \implies \text{moles} = 1.31 \div [(2 \times 12.0) + (4 \times 1.0) + (2 \times 16.0)] = 0.02183...\ \text{moles}$$

2) Then, calculate the concentration of the ethanoic acid solution.

$$\text{concentration} = \frac{\text{moles} \times 1000}{\text{volume (cm}^3)} \implies \text{concentration} = \frac{0.02183... \times 1000}{250} = 0.0873...\ \text{mol dm}^{-3}$$

3) You can use the pH to work out $[H^+]$ at equilibrium: $[H^+] = 10^{-pH} = 10^{-2.84} = 0.00144...$

4) For weak acids, $K_a = \dfrac{[H^+]^2}{[HA]}$, so $K_a = \dfrac{[0.00144...]^2}{[0.0873..]} = 0.00002392... = \mathbf{2.4 \times 10^{-5}}$

> Remember, for weak acids $[HA]_{start} = [HA]_{equilibrium}$.

Experiments Involving pH

When Acids are **Diluted** their pH **Changes**

Diluting an acid reduces the **concentration of H⁺** in the solution. This **increases the pH**. The table shows the pH of a strong and a weak acid at different concentrations.

Concentration of Acid (mol dm⁻³)	HCl pH at 298 K	C_2H_5COOH pH at 298 K
1	0	2.44
0.1	1	2.94
0.01	2	3.44
0.001	3	3.94

Strong Acid — Hydrochloric Acid (HCl)

Diluting a **strong acid** by a **factor of 10** increases the pH by **1**.

It's easy to see this for yourself. Remember that for a strong acid, [H⁺] = [acid], so **pH = –log₁₀[acid]**.

Just try sticking [acid] = 1, 0.1, 0.01, etc. into this formula.

These results may seem a bit random, but they're true. It's all in the maths...

Sir John used teaH calculations to work out the optimum concentration of tea in the perfect cuppa.

Weak Acid — Propanoic Acid (C_2H_5COOH)

Diluting a **weak acid** by a **factor of 10** increases the pH by **0.5**.

Again, you can see this for yourself if you like by sticking numbers into the right formula, but it's a lot more fiddly this time...

Rearranging $K_a = \frac{[H^+]^2}{[Acid]}$ gives $[H^+] = \sqrt{K_a[acid]}$, and then $pH = -log_{10}\sqrt{K_a[acid]}$

Stick [acid] = 1, 0.1, 0.01, etc. into this formula to find the pH each time. The pH will always change by 0.5, no matter what value you use for K_a.

E.g. To get the figures in the table above, K_a of propanoic acid is 1.31×10^{-5}.
So $[C_2H_5COOH]$ = 1 mol dm⁻³ gives [H⁺] = 3.6×10^{-3} which gives pH = **2.44**
$[C_2H_5COOH]$ = 0.1 mol dm⁻³ gives [H⁺] = 1.14×10^{-3} which gives pH = **2.94**

Practice Questions

Q1 What pH would you expect a 1.0 mol dm⁻³ solution of a base that completely dissociates in solution to have?

Q2 What would happen to the pH of a strong acid if you diluted it by a factor of 100?

Exam Questions

Q1 A student is measuring the pH of three 2.0 mol dm⁻³ solutions, A, B and C, to investigate the extent of their acidity or basicity. The pHs of A, B and C, at standard temperature and pressure are 3.20, 13.80 and 6.80 respectively.

a) Suggest a piece of equipment that she could use to accurately measure the pH of the solutions. [1 mark]

b) In A, B and C, only one mole of hydrogen or hydroxide ions are released per mole of acid or base. Comment on whether A, B or C dissociates most in solution. Show your working. [4 marks]

Q2 1.22 g of benzoic acid, C_6H_5COOH, are dissolved in 100 cm³ of distilled water to create a standard solution of benzoic acid. The pH of the solution is 2.60 at 298 K.

a) Calculate a value for K_a for the acid at this temperature. [5 marks]

b) Use the value of K_a that you have calculated to find the [H⁺] of a 0.0100 mol dm⁻³ solution of this acid. [2 marks]

c) Calculate the pH of the 0.0100 mol dm⁻³ solution of the acid at 298 K. [1 mark]

d) Show that the pH of a 1.00 mol dm⁻³ solution of the acid is 2.1 at 298 K. [2 marks]

e) Without further calculations, predict the pH of a 0.001 mol dm⁻³ solution of benzoic acid at 298 K. Explain your answer. [2 marks]

The perfect dilution — 1 part orange squash to 10 parts water...

Remember, if you dilute a weak acid by a factor of 10, you'll increase its pH by 0.5. But diluting a strong acid by a factor of 10 will increase the pH by a whole 1. Don't get them mixed up, it might cost you valuable marks...

Titration Curves and Indicators

If you add base to acid the pH changes in a squiggly sort of way.

Use *Titration* to Find the *Concentration* of an *Acid* or *Base*

You met titrations back in Year 1, so here's just a quick reminder of how to do them.

1) Measure out some **base** using a pipette and put it in a flask, along with some **indicator**.

2) **Rinse** a burette with some of your **standard solution** of acid. Then **fill** it with your standard solution.

3) Do a rough titration to get an idea where the **end point** is (the point where the base is **exactly neutralised** and the indicator changes colour). To do this, take an initial reading to see how much acid is in the burette to start off with. Then, add the **acid** to the base — giving the flask a regular **swirl**. Stop when your indicator shows a permanent colour change (the end point). Record the final reading from your burette.

4) Now do an **accurate** titration. Run the acid in to within 2 cm³ of the end point, then add the acid **dropwise** until you reach the end point.

5) **Work out** the amount of acid used to **neutralise** the base (the **titre**).

6) **Repeat** the titration a few times, making sure you get a similar answer each time — your readings should be within 0.1 cm³ of each other. Then calculate a **mean titre** (see page 123), ignoring any anomalous results.

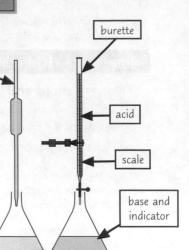

You can also do titrations the other way round — adding base to acid.

Titration Curves Plot *pH* Against *Volume* of *Acid* or *Base* Added

1) **Titrations** let you find out **exactly** how much base is needed to **neutralise** a quantity of acid.

2) All you have to do is plot the **pH** of the titration mixture against the **amount of base** added as the titration goes on. The pH of the mixture can be measured using a pH meter and the scale on the burette can be used to see how much base has been added.

3) The **shape** of your plot looks a bit different depending on the **strengths** of the acid and base that are used.

4) Here are the titration curves for the different combinations of **equimolar** strong and weak monoprotic acids and bases:

You may see titration curves called pH curves.

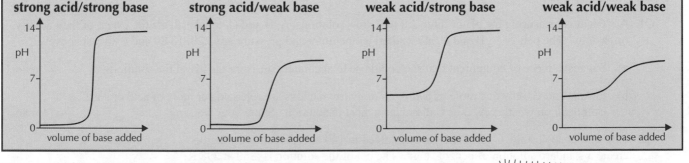

You can explain why each graph has a particular shape:

If you titrate a base with an acid instead, the shapes of the curves stay the same, but they're reversed.

- The **initial** pH depends on the **strength** of the **acid**. So a strong acid titration will start at a much **lower** pH than a weak acid.

- To start with, addition of **small** amounts of base have **little impact** on the pH of the solution.

- All the graphs (apart from the weak acid/weak base graph) have a bit that's almost vertical — this is the **equivalence line**. The point at the **centre** of the equivalence line is the **equivalence point** or **end point**. At this point $[H^+] \approx [OH^-]$ — it's here that all the acid is just **neutralised**. When this is the case, a tiny amount of base causes a sudden, big change in pH.

- The change in pH is also **less pronounced** when **strong acids** are added to **strong bases** (or vice versa), compared to when **strong acids** are added to **weak bases** (or strong bases are added to weak acids).

- The **final** pH depends on the strength of the **base** — the **stronger** the base, the **higher** the final pH.

Titration Curves and Indicators

Titration Curves Can Help you Decide which Indicator to Use

1) When carrying out a titration, you'll often need to use an **indicator** that changes **colour** to show you when your sample has been **neutralised**.

2) You need your indicator to change colour exactly at the **end point** of your titration. So you need to pick one that changes colour over a **narrow pH range** that lies entirely on the **vertical part** of the titration curve.

3) **Methyl orange** and **phenolphthalein** are **indicators** that are often used for acid-base titrations. They each change colour over a **different pH range**:

E.g. For this titration, the curve is vertical between **pH 8** and **pH 11** — so a very small amount of base will cause the pH to **change** from 8 to 11.

So you want an indicator that changes **colour** somewhere between pH 8 and pH 11.

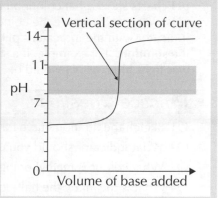

Name of indicator	Colour at low pH	Approx. pH of colour change	Colour at high pH
Methyl orange	red	3.1 – 4.4	yellow
Phenolphthalein	colourless	8.3 – 10	pink

methyl orange

- For a **strong acid/strong base** titration, you can use **either** of these indicators — there's a rapid pH change over the range for **both** indicators.

- For a **strong acid/weak base** only **methyl orange** will do. The pH changes rapidly across the range for methyl orange, but not for phenolphthalein.

- For a **weak acid/strong base**, **phenolphthalein** is the stuff to use. The pH changes rapidly over phenolphthalein's range, but not over methyl orange's.

- For **weak acid/weak base** titrations there's no sharp pH change, so **neither** of these indicators works. In fact, there aren't **any** indicators you can use in weak acid/weak base titrations, so you should just use a pH meter.

Another Great Use for Titration Curves — Finding the pKₐ of a Weak Acid

1) You can work out pK_a of a weak acid using the titration curve for a **weak acid/strong base titration**. It involves finding the **pH** at the **half-equivalence point**.

2) **Half-equivalence** is the stage of a titration when **half** of the acid has been neutralised — it's when half of the equivalence volume of **strong base** has been added to the **weak acid**.

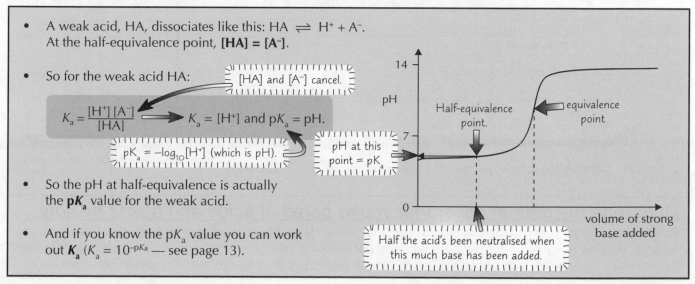

- A weak acid, HA, dissociates like this: HA $\rightleftharpoons$ H⁺ + A⁻. At the half-equivalence point, **[HA] = [A⁻]**.

- So for the weak acid HA:

  [HA] and [A⁻] cancel.

  $$K_a = \frac{[H^+][A^-]}{[HA]} \longrightarrow K_a = [H^+] \text{ and } pK_a = pH.$$

  pK_a = $-\log_{10}[H^+]$ (which is pH).

  pH at this point = pK_a

- So the pH at half-equivalence is actually the **pK_a** value for the weak acid.

- And if you know the pK_a value you can work out K_a ($K_a = 10^{-pK_a}$ — see page 13).

Half the acid's been neutralised when this much base has been added.

TOPIC 12 — ACID-BASE EQUILIBRIA

Titration Curves and Indicators

You Can Follow pH Changes with a pH Chart

pH charts show what colour an indicator appears at different pHs. You can compare the colour of a solution containing an indicator with the indicator's pH chart to determine the pH of the solution. For example, if a solution containing thymol blue was light blue, its pH would be somewhere between 8 and 10.

1 2 3 4 5 6 7 8 9 10 11 12 13 14

pH chart for thymol blue

Practice Questions

Q1 Sketch the titration curve for a weak acid/strong base titration.

Q2 What indicator should you use for a strong acid/weak base titration — methyl orange or phenolphthalein?

Q3 What colour is methyl orange at pH 2?

Q4 What is meant by the half-equivalence point?

Exam Questions

Q1 1.0 mol dm^{-3} NaOH (a strong base) is added separately to 25 cm^3 samples of
1.0 mol dm^{-3} nitric acid (a strong acid) and 1.0 mol dm^{-3} ethanoic acid (a weak acid).
Sketch the titration curves for each of these titrations.

[2 marks]

Q2 A sample of ethanoic acid (a weak acid) was titrated against potassium hydroxide (a strong base).

From the table on the right, select the best indicator for this titration, and explain your choice.

[2 marks]

Name of indicator	pH range
bromophenol blue	3.0 – 4.6
methyl red	4.2 – 6.3
bromothymol blue	6.0 – 7.6
thymol blue	8.0 – 9.6

Q3 This curve shows the pH change as sodium hydroxide solution (a strong base) is added to a solution of ethanoic acid (a weak acid).

a) What is the pH at the equivalence point? [1 mark]

b) What volume of base had been added at this point? [1 mark]

c) Suggest an indicator to use for the titration and explain your choice. [2 marks]

d) Sketch the curve you would get if the titration was repeated using ammonia solution (a weak base) as the base. [1 mark]

e) Why couldn't you use an indicator to identify the end point of a titration between ethanoic acid and ammonia solution? [1 mark]

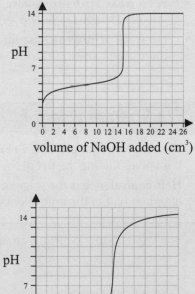

volume of NaOH added (cm^3)

Q4 This curve shows the pH change when sodium hydroxide (a strong base) is added to a 0.1 mol dm^{-3} solution of methanoic acid (a weak acid).

a) What is the pH of:

i) the equivalence point? [1 mark]

ii) the half-equivalence point? [1 mark]

b) Write an expression for K_a for the dissociation of this acid. [1 mark]

c) At the half-equivalence point what is the concentration of the acid? [1 mark]

d) Calculate the value of pK_a and K_a for the acid. [2 marks]

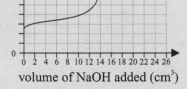

volume of NaOH added (cm^3)

I'll burette my bottom dollar that you're bored of acids and bases by now...

Titrations involve playing with big bits of glassware that you're told not to break as they're really expensive — so you instantly become really clumsy. I highly recommend not dropping your burette though. If it's smashed into hundreds or thousands of teeny weeny tiny pieces, you'll find it much harder to take readings from it. I speak from experience...

Buffers

How can a solution resist becoming more acidic if you add acid to it? Here's where you find out...

Buffers **Resist** Changes in pH

A **buffer** is a solution that **minimises** changes in pH when **small** amounts of acid or base are added.

A buffer **doesn't** stop the pH from changing completely — it does make the changes **very slight** though. Buffers only work for small amounts of acid or base — put too much in and they won't be able to cope.

Acidic Buffers Contain a **Weak Acid** and its **Conjugate Base**

Acidic buffers have a pH of less than 7 — they're made by setting up an equilibrium between a **weak acid** and its **conjugate base**. This can be done in two ways:

1) **Mix a weak acid with the salt of its conjugate base.**
   e.g. ethanoic acid and sodium ethanoate:
   - The salt **fully** dissociates into its ions when it dissolves:
     $CH_3COO^-Na^+_{(aq)} \rightarrow CH_3COO^-_{(aq)} + Na^+_{(aq)}$
   - Ethanoic acid is a **weak acid**, so only **slightly** dissociates:
     $CH_3COOH_{(aq)} \rightleftharpoons H^+_{(aq)} + CH_3COO^-_{(aq)}$

2) **Mix an excess of weak acid with a strong base.**
   e.g. ethanoic acid and sodium hydroxide:
   - **All** the base reacts with the acid:
     $CH_3COOH_{(aq)} + OH^-_{(aq)} \rightarrow CH_3COO^- + H_2O$
   - The weak acid was in **excess**, so there's still some left in solution once all the base has reacted. This acid **slightly dissociates**:
     $CH_3COOH_{(aq)} \rightleftharpoons H^+_{(aq)} + CH_3COO^-_{(aq)}$

In both cases, the following equilibrium is set up between the weak acid and its conjugate base:

Lots of undissociated weak acid $\Rightarrow CH_3COOH_{(aq)} \rightleftharpoons H^+_{(aq)} + CH_3COO^-_{(aq)} \Leftarrow$ Lots of CH_3COO^-

Addition of H^+ (acid) ←

Addition of OH^- (base) →

The equilibrium solution contains lots of undissociated acid (HA), lots of the acid's conjugate base (A⁻) and enough H⁺ ions to make the solution acidic.

It's the job of the conjugate pair to control the pH of a buffer solution. The **conjugate base** mops up any extra **H⁺**, while the **conjugate acid releases** H⁺ if there's too much base around.

- If you add a **small** amount of **acid** the **H⁺ concentration** increases. Most of the extra H⁺ ions combine with CH_3COO^- ions to form CH_3COOH. This shifts the equilibrium to the **left**, reducing the H⁺ concentration to close to its original value. So the **pH** doesn't change much.

- If a **small** amount of **base** (e.g. NaOH) is added, the **OH⁻ concentration** increases. Most of the extra OH⁻ ions react with H⁺ ions to form water — removing H⁺ ions from the solution. This causes more CH_3COOH to **dissociate** to form H⁺ ions — shifting the equilibrium to the **right**. The H⁺ concentration increases until it's close to its original value, so the **pH** doesn't change much.

Alkaline Buffers are Made from a **Weak Base** and one of its **Salts**

A mixture of **ammonia solution** (a base) and **ammonium chloride** (a salt of ammonia) acts as an **alkaline** (or **basic**) buffer. It works in a similar way to acidic buffers:

An alkaline solution is a basic solution that's soluble in water.

1) The **salt** is fully dissociated in solution: $NH_4Cl_{(aq)} \rightarrow NH_4^+_{(aq)} + Cl^-_{(aq)}$.

Lots of NH_4^+ Addition of H^+ (acid)   Lots of weak base ←

2) An equilibrium is set up between the **ammonium ions** and **ammonia**: $NH_4^+_{(aq)} \rightleftharpoons H^+_{(aq)} + NH_{3(aq)}$

Addition of OH^- (base) →

3) If a small amount of **acid** is added, the H⁺ concentration **increases** — most of the added H⁺ reacts with NH_3 and the equilibrium shifts **left**. This reduces the H⁺ concentration to near its original value. So the pH **doesn't** change much.

4) If a small amount of **base** is added, the OH⁻ concentration **increases**. OH⁻ ions react with the H⁺ ions, removing them from the solution. There are plenty of **NH_4^+** molecules around that can dissociate to generate replacement **H⁺ ions** — so the equilibrium shifts **right**, stopping the pH from changing much.

Buffers

Buffer Action can be Seen on a Titration Curve

1) You met **titration curves** back on pages 16 and 17. They show you how the **pH** of a solution **changes** as an **increasing volume** of **acid** or **base** is added.

2) The **titration curves** for weak acids with strong bases, and for strong acids with weak bases, have a **distinctive shape** due to the formation of **buffer solutions** as the reaction proceeds.

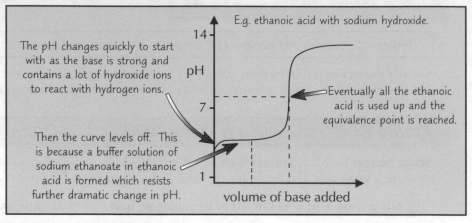

E.g. ethanoic acid with sodium hydroxide.

The pH changes quickly to start with as the base is strong and contains a lot of hydroxide ions to react with hydrogen ions.

Then the curve levels off. This is because a buffer solution of sodium ethanoate in ethanoic acid is formed which resists further dramatic change in pH.

Eventually all the ethanoic acid is used up and the equivalence point is reached.

volume of base added

Buffer Solutions are Important in the Blood

1) Blood needs to be kept at around **pH 7.4**. The pH is controlled using a **carbonic acid-hydrogencarbonate buffer system**. Carbonic acid dissociates into H^+ ions and HCO_3^- ions.

$$H_2CO_{3(aq)} \rightleftharpoons H^+_{(aq)} + HCO^-_{3\,(aq)}$$

2) If the **concentration** of **H^+ ions rises** in blood, then **HCO_3^- ions** from the carbonic acid-hydrogencarbonate buffer system will **react** with the excess H^+ ions, and the **equilibrium** will **shift to the left**, reducing the H^+ concentration to almost its original value. This stops the **pH** of **blood** from **dropping**.

3) Meanwhile, if the **concentration** of **H^+ ions falls** in blood, then more H_2CO_3 molecules from the carbonic acid-hydrogencarbonate buffer system will dissociate, and the **equilibrium** will **shift to the right**, increasing the H^+ concentration to almost its original value. This stops the **pH** of **blood** from **rising**.

4) The levels of H_2CO_3 are controlled by **respiration**. By breathing out CO_2, the level of H_2CO_3 is reduced, as it moves this equilibrium to the right.

$$H_2CO_{3(aq)} \rightleftharpoons H_2O_{(l)} + CO_{2(aq)}$$

5) The levels of HCO_3^- are controlled by the **kidneys**, with excess being excreted in the urine.

Here's How to Calculate the pH of a Buffer Solution

Calculating the **pH** of an acidic buffer isn't too tricky. You just need to know the K_a of the weak acid and the **concentrations** of the weak acid and its salt. Your calculation requires the following assumptions to be made:

- The **salt** of the **conjugate base** is **fully dissociated**, so assume that the equilibrium concentration of A^- is the **same** as the initial concentration of the salt.
- **HA** is only **slightly dissociated**, so assume that its equilibrium concentration is the **same** as its initial concentration.

The conjugate base doesn't only come from dissociation of the weak acid so $[H^+] \neq [A^-]$.

Example: At a certain temperature, a buffer solution contains 0.40 mol dm⁻³ methanoic acid, HCOOH, and 0.60 mol dm⁻³ sodium methanoate, HCOO⁻Na⁺. At this temperature, K_a for methanoic acid = 1.8×10^{-4} mol dm⁻³. What is the pH of this buffer?

Remember — these are all equilibrium concentrations.

Firstly, write the expression for K_a of the weak acid:

$$HCOOH_{(aq)} \rightleftharpoons H^+_{(aq)} + HCOO^-_{(aq)} \implies K_a = \frac{[H^+][HCOO^-]}{[HCOOH]}$$

Then rearrange the expression and stick in the data to calculate $[H^+]$:

$$[H^+] = K_a \times \frac{[HCOOH]}{[HCOO^-]}$$

$$[H^+] = 1.8 \times 10^{-4} \times \frac{0.40}{0.60} = 1.2 \times 10^{-4}\ mol\,dm^{-3}$$

If you wanted to find the concentration of an acid needed to make a buffer solution of a particular pH, using a salt of known concentration and the K_a of the acid, you could use this equation to find [acid]. Or you could use the Henderson-Hasselbalch equation on the next page...

Finally, convert $[H^+]$ to pH:

$$pH = -\log_{10}[H^+] = -\log_{10}(1.2 \times 10^{-4}) = \textbf{3.92}$$

Buffers

You Need to be Able to **Calculate Concentrations**

You may want to create a buffer with a **specific pH**.
To work out the **concentrations** of **salt** and **acid** or **base** that you'll need, you may need
to use a fancy equation, known as the **Henderson-Hasselbalch** equation. Here it is:

> This equation relies on the fact that $[HA] \approx [HA]_{start}$ and $[A^-] \approx [A^-]_{start}$.

$$pH = pK_a + \log_{10}\left(\frac{[A^-]}{[HA]}\right)$$

Nobody's gonna change my pH.

Acids and bases didn't mess with Jeff after he became buffer.

Example: A buffer is made using ethanoic acid (CH_3COOH) and an ethanoic acid salt ($CH_3COO^-Na^+$). 1.20 mol dm^{-3} of the ethanoic acid salt is used. What concentration of ethanoic acid is required so that the buffer has a pH of 4.9? Under these conditions, K_a of ethanoic acid = 1.75×10^{-5}.

You know that **$pK_a = -\log K_a$**, so you can work out the pK_a of ethanoic acid: $pK_a = -\log_{10}(1.75 \times 10^{-5}) = 4.756...$

Now, substitute your value for **pK_a**, and the **desired pH** (which you were given in the question) into the Henderson-Hasselbalch equation to work out the **ratio** of **[A$^-$]:[HA]** that you need.

> This is a log rule (from maths). You'll need to remember it to do questions like this one.

$$pH = pK_a + \log_{10}\left(\frac{[A^-]}{[HA]}\right)$$ ← This is the Henderson-Hasselbalch equation.

$$4.9 = 4.756... + \log_{10}\left(\frac{[CH_3COO^-]}{[CH_3COOH]}\right)$$

$$\log_{10}\left(\frac{[CH_3COO^-]}{[CH_3COOH]}\right) = 4.9 - 4.756... = 0.143...$$

$$10^{\log_{10}x} = x, \longrightarrow \frac{[CH_3COO^-]}{[CH_3COOH]} = 10^{0.143...} = 1.39...$$

You know that the salt **fully dissociates**, so [salt] = [A$^-$]. This lets you calculate **[HA] at equilibrium**, which is equal to **[HA] at the start** of the reaction (since ethanoic acid is a **weak acid**).

$$\frac{1.20}{[CH_3COOH]} = 1.39... \longrightarrow [CH_3COOH] = 1.20 \div 1.39...$$
$$[CH_3COOH] = \textbf{0.86 mol dm}^{-3}$$

Practice Questions

Q1 What's a buffer solution?

Q2 How can a mixture of ethanoic acid and sodium ethanoate act as a buffer?

Q3 Describe how to make an alkaline buffer.

Q4 Describe how the pH of the blood is buffered.

Exam Questions

Q1 A buffer solution contains 0.400 mol dm^{-3} benzoic acid, C_6H_5COOH, and 0.200 mol dm^{-3} sodium benzoate, $C_6H_5COO^-Na^+$. At 25 °C, K_a for benzoic acid is 6.40×10^{-5} mol dm^{-3}.

a) Calculate the pH of the buffer solution. [2 marks]

b) Explain the effect on the buffer of adding a small quantity of dilute sulfuric acid. [3 marks]

Q2 A buffer was prepared by mixing solutions of butanoic acid, $CH_3(CH_2)_2COOH$, and sodium butanoate, $CH_3(CH_2)_2COO^-Na^+$, so that they had the same concentration.

a) Write a balanced chemical equation to show butanoic acid acting as a weak acid. [1 mark]

b) Given that K_a for butanoic acid is 1.5×10^{-5} mol dm^{-3} at 298 K, calculate the pH of the buffer solution. [2 marks]

Old buffers are often resistant to change...

So that's how buffers work. There's a pleasing simplicity and neatness about it that I find rather elegant. Like watching the sun rise on a misty May morning, with only bird song for company... OK, I'll shut up now.

Lattice Energy

On these pages you can learn about lattice energy, not lettuce energy which is the energy change when 1 mole consumes salad from a veggie patch. Bu–dum cha... (that was meant to be a drum — work with me here).

Lattice Energy is a Measure of Ionic Bond Strength

Ionic compounds can form regular structures called **giant ionic lattices** where the positive and negative ions are held together by **electrostatic attractions**. When **gaseous ions** combine to make a solid lattice, energy is given out — this is called the **lattice energy**.

Here's the definition of **standard lattice energy** that you need to know:

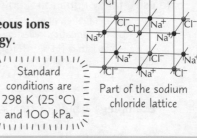

Part of the sodium chloride lattice

> The **standard lattice energy**, $\Delta_{LE}H^{\ominus}$, is the energy change when **1 mole** of an **ionic solid** is formed from its **gaseous ions** under standard conditions.

Standard conditions are 298 K (25 °C) and 100 kPa.

The standard lattice energy is a measure of **ionic bond strength**. The more **negative** the lattice energy, the **stronger** the bonding. E.g. out of NaCl and MgO, MgO has stronger bonding.

$$Na^+_{(g)} + Cl^-_{(g)} \rightarrow NaCl_{(s)} \quad \Delta_{LE}H^{\ominus} = -787 \text{ kJ mol}^{-1}$$
$$Mg^{2+}_{(g)} + O^{2-}_{(g)} \rightarrow MgO_{(s)} \quad \Delta_{LE}H^{\ominus} = -3791 \text{ kJ mol}^{-1}$$

Ionic Charge and Size Affects Lattice Energy

Energy changes are sometimes known as enthalpy changes — don't worry, they're the same thing.

1) The **higher the charge** on the ions, the **more energy** is released when an ionic lattice forms. This is due to the **stronger electrostatic forces** between the ions.

2) More energy released means that the lattice energy will be **more negative**. So the lattice energies for compounds with **2+** or **2– ions** (e.g. Mg^{2+} or S^{2-}) are **more exothermic** than those with **1+** or **1– ions** (e.g. Na^+ or Cl^-).

> E.g. the lattice energy of **NaCl** is only –787 kJ mol^{-1}, but the lattice energy of **MgCl$_2$** is –2526 kJ mol^{-1}. **MgS** has an even **higher** lattice energy (–3299 kJ mol^{-1}) because both Mg and S ions have **double charges**.

3) The **smaller** the ionic radii of the ions involved, the **more exothermic** (more negative) the **lattice energy**. Smaller ions have a higher **charge density** and their **smaller ionic radii** mean that the ions can sit **closer together** in the lattice. Both these things mean that the attractions between the ions are **stronger**.

Born-Haber Cycles can be Used to Calculate Lattice Energies

Hess's law says that the **total enthalpy change** of a reaction is always the **same**, no matter which route is taken — this is known as the conservation of energy.

You can't calculate a lattice energy **directly**, so you have to use a **Born-Haber cycle** to figure out what the enthalpy change would be if you took **another, less direct, route**.

Here's a Born-Haber cycle you could use to calculate the lattice energy of **NaCl**:

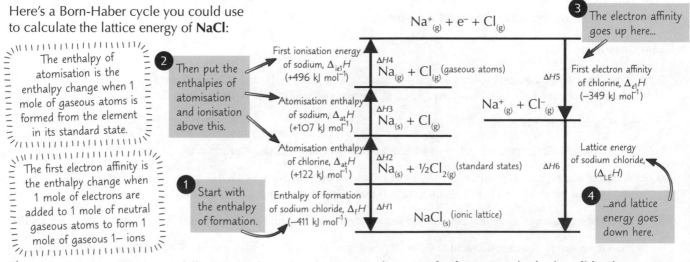

The enthalpy of atomisation is the enthalpy change when 1 mole of gaseous atoms is formed from the element in its standard state.

The first electron affinity is the enthalpy change when 1 mole of electrons are added to 1 mole of neutral gaseous atoms to form 1 mole of gaseous 1– ions

① Start with the enthalpy of formation.

② Then put the enthalpies of atomisation and ionisation above this.

③ The electron affinity goes up here...

④ ...and lattice energy goes down here.

$Na^+_{(g)} + e^- + Cl_{(g)}$

First ionisation energy of sodium, $\Delta_{ie1}H$ (+496 kJ mol^{-1})

$\Delta H4$ $Na_{(g)} + Cl_{(g)}$ (gaseous atoms)

Atomisation enthalpy of sodium, $\Delta_{at}H$ (+107 kJ mol^{-1})

$\Delta H3$ $Na_{(s)} + Cl_{(g)}$

Atomisation enthalpy of chlorine, $\Delta_{at}H$ (+122 kJ mol^{-1})

$\Delta H2$ $Na_{(s)} + \frac{1}{2}Cl_{2(g)}$ (standard states)

Enthalpy of formation of sodium chloride, $\Delta_f H$ (–411 kJ mol^{-1})

$\Delta H1$ $NaCl_{(s)}$ (ionic lattice)

First electron affinity of chlorine, $\Delta_{e1}H$ (–349 kJ mol^{-1})

$\Delta H5$

$Na^+_{(g)} + Cl^-_{(g)}$

Lattice energy of sodium chloride, ($\Delta_{LE}H$)

$\Delta H6$

There are **two routes** you can follow to get from the elements in their **standard states** to the **ionic solid**. The green arrow shows the **direct route** and the purple arrows show the **indirect route**. The energy change for each is the **same**.

From Hess's law: $\Delta H6 = -\Delta H5 - \Delta H4 - \Delta H3 - \Delta H2 + \Delta H1$
$$= -(-349) - (+496) - (+107) - (+122) + (-411) = \mathbf{-787 \text{ kJ mol}^{-1}}$$

You need a minus sign if you go the wrong way along an arrow.

Lattice Energy

Calculations involving Group 2 Elements are a Bit Different

Born-Haber cycles for compounds containing **Group 2 elements** have a few **changes** from the one on the previous page. Make sure you understand what's going on so you can handle whatever compound they throw at you.

Here's the Born-Haber cycle for calculating the lattice energy of **magnesium chloride** ($MgCl_2$):

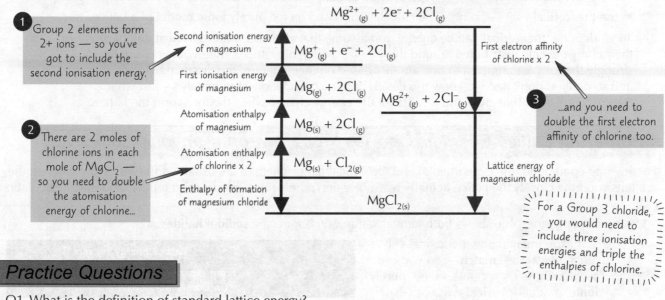

① Group 2 elements form 2+ ions — so you've got to include the second ionisation energy.

② There are 2 moles of chlorine ions in each mole of $MgCl_2$ — so you need to double the atomisation energy of chlorine...

③ ...and you need to double the first electron affinity of chlorine too.

For a Group 3 chloride, you would need to include three ionisation energies and triple the enthalpies of chlorine.

Practice Questions

Q1 What is the definition of standard lattice energy?

Q2 What does a large, negative lattice energy mean, in terms of bond strength?

Q3 Why does magnesium chloride have a more negative lattice energy than sodium chloride?

Q4 What is the definition of the enthalpy of atomisation?

Exam Questions

Q1 Using this data:

$\Delta_f H^\ominus$[potassium bromide] = –394 kJ mol⁻¹ $\Delta_{at} H^\ominus$[bromine] = +112 kJ mol⁻¹ $\Delta_{at} H^\ominus$[potassium] = +89 kJ mol⁻¹
$\Delta_{ie1} H^\ominus$[potassium] = +419 kJ mol⁻¹ $\Delta_{e1} H^\ominus$[bromine] = –325 kJ mol⁻¹

a) Construct a Born-Haber cycle for potassium bromide (KBr). [3 marks]

b) Use your Born-Haber cycle to calculate the lattice energy of potassium bromide. [2 marks]

Q2 Using this data:

$\Delta_f H^\ominus$[aluminium chloride] = –706 kJ mol⁻¹ $\Delta_{at} H^\ominus$[chlorine] = +122 kJ mol⁻¹ $\Delta_{at} H^\ominus$[aluminium] = +326 kJ mol⁻¹
$\Delta_{e1} H^\ominus$[chlorine] = –349 kJ mol⁻¹ $\Delta_{ie1} H^\ominus$[aluminium] = +578 kJ mol⁻¹
$\Delta_{ie2} H^\ominus$[aluminium] = +1817 kJ mol⁻¹ $\Delta_{ie3} H^\ominus$[aluminium] = +2745 kJ mol⁻¹

a) Construct a Born-Haber cycle for aluminium chloride ($AlCl_3$). [3 marks]

b) Use your cycle to calculate the lattice energy of aluminium chloride. [2 marks]

Q3 Using this data:

$\Delta_f H^\ominus$[aluminium oxide] = –1676 kJ mol⁻¹ $\Delta_{at} H^\ominus$[oxygen] = +249 kJ mol⁻¹ $\Delta_{at} H^\ominus$[aluminium] = +326 kJ mol⁻¹
$\Delta_{ie1} H^\ominus$[aluminium] = +578 kJ mol⁻¹ $\Delta_{ie2} H^\ominus$[aluminium] = +1817 kJ mol⁻¹ $\Delta_{ie3} H^\ominus$[aluminium] = +2745 kJ mol⁻¹
$\Delta_{e1} H^\ominus$[oxygen] = –141 kJ mol⁻¹ $\Delta_{e2} H^\ominus$[oxygen] = +844 kJ mol⁻¹

a) Construct a Born-Haber cycle for aluminium oxide (Al_2O_3). [3 marks]

b) Use your cycle to calculate the lattice energy of aluminium oxide. [2 marks]

Using Born-Haber cycles — it's just like riding a bike...

All this energy going in and out can get a bit confusing. Remember these simple rules: 1) It takes energy to break bonds, but energy is given out when bonds are made. 2) A negative ΔH means energy is given out (it's exothermic). 3) A positive ΔH means energy is taken in (it's endothermic). 4) Never return to a firework once lit.

Polarisation

And you thought you'd finished with lattice energies...

Theoretical Lattice Energies are Based on the Ionic Model

1) There are **two ways** to work out a lattice energy:
   - the **experimental** way — using **experimental enthalpy values** in a Born-Haber cycle (see previous page).
   - the **theoretical** way — doing some calculations based on the **purely ionic model** of a lattice.

2) To work out a 'theoretical' lattice energy, you assume that all the ions are **spherical** and have their **charge evenly distributed** around them — a purely **ionic** lattice. Then you work out how strongly the ions are attracted to one another based on their charges, the distance between them and so on (you don't need to know the details of these calculations, fortunately — just what they're based on). That gives you a value for the **energy change** when the ions **form** the lattice.

Comparing Lattice Energies Can Tell You 'How Ionic' an Ionic Lattice Is

For any one compound, the experimental and theoretical lattice energies are usually **different**. **How** different they are tells you **how closely** the lattice **actually** resembles the 'purely ionic' model used for the theoretical calculations.

1) For example, the table shows **both** lattice energy values for some **sodium halides**.
   - The experimental and theoretical values are a pretty close **match** — so you can say that these compounds fit the '**purely ionic**' model (spherical ions with evenly distributed charge, etc.) very **well**.
   - This indicates that the structure of the lattice for these compounds is quite close to being **purely ionic**.

	Lattice Energy (kJ mol^{-1})	
	From experimental values (in Born-Haber cycle)	From theory
Sodium chloride	−787	−756
Sodium bromide	−742	−731
Sodium iodide	−698	−686

2) Here are some more lattice energies, for **magnesium halides** this time:

	Lattice Energy (kJ mol^{-1})	
	From experimental values (in Born-Haber cycle)	From theory
Magnesium chloride	−2526	−2326
Magnesium bromide	−2440	−2097
Magnesium iodide	−2327	−1944

- The experimental lattice energies are **more negative** than the theoretical values by a fair bit.
- This tells you that the bonding is, in practice, **stronger** than the calculations from the ionic model predict.

- The difference shows that the bonding in the magnesium halides **isn't** as close to 'purely ionic' as it is with sodium halides.
- It tells you that the ionic bonds in the magnesium halides are more **polarised** — they have **some covalent character** — whereas the bonds in sodium halides have almost no polarisation and very little covalent character.

Bill was a Grizzly bear before he was polarised.

Polarisation of Ionic Bonds Leads to Covalent Character in Ionic Lattices

So, **magnesium** halides have more covalent character in their ionic bonds than sodium halides. Here's why...

1) In a sodium halide, e.g. NaCl, the **cation**, Na$^+$, has only a **small charge** (+1) so it can't really pull electrons from the anion towards itself — so the charge is distributed evenly around the ions (there's almost **no polarisation**).

2) This is pretty much what the simple **ionic model** looks like — that's why the theoretical calculations of lattice energy match the experimental ones so well for sodium halides.

3) However, the magnesium halides **don't** fit the ionic model quite so well, because charge isn't evenly distributed around the ions — the cation, Mg^{2+}, has a **bigger charge** (+2), so it can pull electrons from the anion towards itself a bit, polarising the bond.

4) In general, the greater the **charge density** of the cation (its charge compared to its volume), the poorer the match will be between experimental and theoretical values for lattice energy.

Charge Density = Charge ÷ Volume

Polarisation

Small Cations Are Very Polarising

What normally happens in ionic compounds is that the **positive charge** on the **cation** attracts electrons towards it from the **anion** — this is **polarisation**.

1) **Small** cations with a **high charge** are **very polarising** because they have a **high charge density** — the positive charge is concentrated in the ion. So the cation can pull electrons towards itself.

2) **Large anions** with a **high charge** are **polarised more easily** than smaller ones with a lower charge. This is because their electrons are **further away** from the nucleus and there is **more repulsion** between the electrons, so the electrons can be pulled away more easily towards cations.

3) If a compound contains a cation with a **high polarising ability** and an anion which is **easily polarised**, some of the anion's electron charge cloud will be dragged towards the positive cation.

4) If the compound is polarised enough, a partially **covalent bond** is formed.

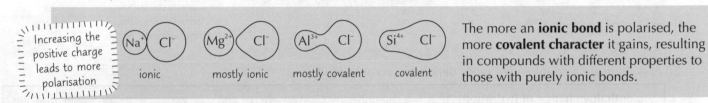

Increasing the positive charge leads to more polarisation

Na⁺ Cl⁻ ionic   Mg²⁺ Cl⁻ mostly ionic   Al³⁺ Cl⁻ mostly covalent   Si⁴⁺ Cl⁻ covalent

The more an **ionic bond** is polarised, the more **covalent character** it gains, resulting in compounds with different properties to those with purely ionic bonds.

Pauling Values Can Be Used to Work Out How Polar a Covalent Bond Is

1) **Electronegativity** is the ability of an atom to attract the bonding electrons in a **covalent** bond.

2) The **Pauling Scale** is usually used to measure the electronegativity of an atom.

3) The greater the **difference** in electronegativity, the greater the shift in electron density, and the **more polar** the bond.

4) Bonds are polar if the difference in Pauling electronegativity values is more than about 0.4.

Don't worry about remembering Pauling values — you'll be given this data in the exam.

> **Example:** Predict whether a C–Cl bond will be polar, given that the Pauling electronegativity values of carbon and bromine are C = 2.5 and Cl = 3.0
>
> The difference between the electronegativities of chlorine and carbon is: **3.0 – 2.5 = 0.5**
>
> So the bond will be **polar**. The **chlorine atom** will have a slight **negative** charge and the **carbon atom** will have a slight **positive** charge.

5) Differences in electronegativity can also be given as **% ionic character** (see your Year 1 notes).

Practice Questions

Q1 How can you tell, using lattice energies, whether an ionic compound is significantly polarised?

Q2 What sort of cation is highly polarising? What sort of anion is easily polarised?

Exam Questions

Q1 Metal/non-metal compounds are usually ionic, yet solid aluminium chloride exhibits many covalent characteristics. Explain why. [4 marks]

Q2 Consider the following compounds: MgBr₂ NaBr MgI₂

    a) These compounds have differing degrees of covalent character in their bonds. Arrange the compounds in order of increasing covalent character, and explain your reasoning. [3 marks]

    b) The theoretical lattice enthalpy of sodium iodide matches well with its experimental value but the theoretical lattice enthalpy of magnesium iodide does not match well with its experimental value. Explain this difference. [2 marks]

Lattice Energy — it's why rabbits have so many babies....

Is it ionic? Is it covalent? Who knows? Interpreting data is important when you're looking at the differences between theoretical and experimental values for lattice energies — you need to be able to explain what the data shows. Remember, the closer the two lattice energy values, the better the purely ionic model fits your compound.

Dissolving

Once you know what's happening when you stir sugar into your tea, your cuppa'll be twice as enjoyable.

Dissolving Involves Enthalpy Changes

When a solid **ionic lattice** dissolves in water these **two** things happen:

1) The bonds between the ions **break** — this is **endothermic**.
   The enthalpy change is the **opposite** of the **lattice enthalpy**.

2) Bonds between the ions and the water are **made** — this is **exothermic**.
   The enthalpy change here is called the **enthalpy change of hydration**.

The **enthalpy change of solution** is the overall effect of these two things.

Luckily for Geraldine, her lattice energy was greater than her enthalpy of hydration.

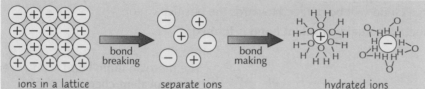

ions in a lattice   separate ions   hydrated ions

This effect happens because oxygen is more electronegative than hydrogen, so it draws the bonding electrons toward itself, creating a dipole.

So now, here are a couple more fancy **definitions** you need to know:

> The **enthalpy change of hydration**, $\Delta_{hyd}H$, is the enthalpy change when 1 mole of gaseous ions dissolves in water.
> The **enthalpy change of solution**, $\Delta_{sol}H$, is the enthalpy change when 1 mole of solute dissolves in water.

Substances generally **only** dissolve if the energy released is roughly the same, or **greater than** the energy taken in. So soluble substances tend to have **exothermic** enthalpies of solution.

Enthalpy Change of Solution can be Calculated

You can work out the enthalpy change of solution using an energy cycle.
You just need to know the **lattice energy** of the compound and the **enthalpies of hydration** of the ions.

Here's how to draw the energy cycle for working out the **enthalpy change of solution** for **sodium chloride**:

1 Put the ionic lattice and the dissolved ions on the top — connect them by the enthalpy change of solution. This is the direct route.

2 Connect the ionic lattice to the gaseous ions by the lattice energy.
The breakdown of the lattice has the opposite enthalpy change to the formation of the lattice.

$$NaCl_{(s)} \xrightarrow[\Delta H3]{\text{Enthalpy change of solution}} Na^+_{(aq)} + Cl^-_{(aq)}$$

$\Delta H1$ — lattice energy (-787 kJ mol^{-1})

$\Delta H2$ — Enthalpy of hydration of $Na^+_{(g)}$ (-406 kJ mol^{-1})
Enthalpy of hydration of $Cl^-_{(g)}$ (-364 kJ mol^{-1})

$$Na^+_{(g)} + Cl^-_{(g)}$$

3 Connect the gaseous ions to the dissolved ions by the hydration enthalpies of **each** ion. This completes the indirect route.

From Hess's law: $\Delta H3 = -\Delta H1 + \Delta H2 = +787 + (-406 + -364) = \textbf{+17 kJ mol}^{-1}$

The enthalpy change of solution is **slightly endothermic**, but there are other factors at work that mean that sodium chloride still dissolves in water.

As long as there's only one unknown enthalpy value, you can use these cycles to work out any value on the arrows. For example, if you know the enthalpy change of solution and the enthalpy changes of hydration, you can use those values to work out the lattice energy.

You can also use energy level diagrams...

This one's for working out the **enthalpy change of solution** for **silver chloride**:

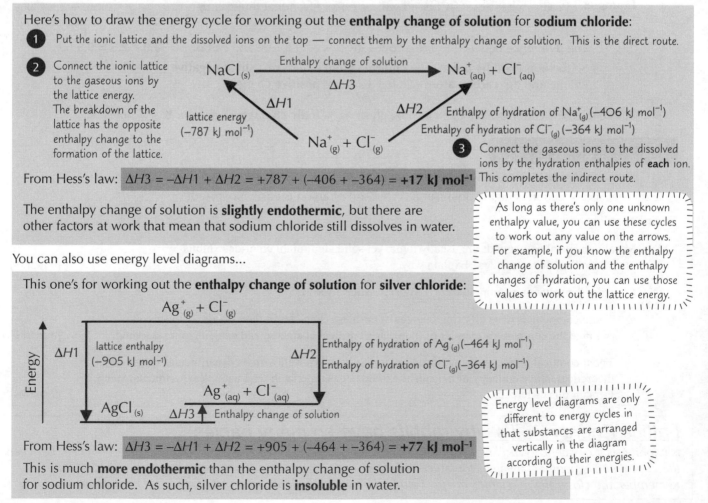

$$Ag^+_{(g)} + Cl^-_{(g)}$$

Energy

$\Delta H1$ — lattice enthalpy (-905 kJ mol^{-1})

$\Delta H2$ — Enthalpy of hydration of $Ag^+_{(g)}$ (-464 kJ mol^{-1})
Enthalpy of hydration of $Cl^-_{(g)}$ (-364 kJ mol^{-1})

$$Ag^+_{(aq)} + Cl^-_{(aq)}$$

$$AgCl_{(s)} \quad \Delta H3 \quad \text{Enthalpy change of solution}$$

From Hess's law: $\Delta H3 = -\Delta H1 + \Delta H2 = +905 + (-464 + -364) = \textbf{+77 kJ mol}^{-1}$

Energy level diagrams are only different to energy cycles in that substances are arranged vertically in the diagram according to their energies.

This is much **more endothermic** than the enthalpy change of solution for sodium chloride. As such, silver chloride is **insoluble** in water.

Dissolving

Ionic Charge and *Ionic Radius* Affect the Enthalpy of Hydration

The **two** things that can affect the lattice energy (see page 22) can also affect the enthalpy of hydration. They are the **size** and the **charge** of the ions.

Ions with a greater charge have a greater enthalpy of hydration.

Ions with a **higher charge** are better at **attracting** water molecules than those with lower charges — the electrostatic attraction between the ion and the water molecules is **stronger**. This means **more energy** is released when the bonds are **made** giving them a **more exothermic** enthalpy of hydration.

Smaller ions have a greater enthalpy of hydration.

Smaller ions have a **higher** charge density than bigger ions. They **attract** the water molecules **better** and have a **more exothermic** enthalpy of hydration.

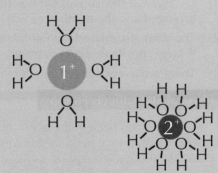

The higher charge and smaller radius of the 2+ ion create a higher charge density than the 1+ ion. This creates a stronger attraction for the water molecules and gives a more exothermic enthalpy of hydration.

E.g. a magnesium ion is smaller and more charged than a sodium ion, which gives it a much more exothermic enthalpy of hydration.

$$\Delta_{hyd}H^{\ominus}[Mg^{2+}_{(g)}] = -1920 \text{ kJ mol}^{-1}$$
$$\Delta_{hyd}H^{\ominus}[Na^{+}_{(g)}] = -406 \text{ kJ mol}^{-1}$$

Practice Questions

Q1 Describe the two steps that occur when an ionic lattice dissolves in water.

Q2 Define the enthalpy change of solution.

Q3 Do soluble substances have exothermic or endothermic enthalpies of solution in general?

Q4 Sketch an energy cycle that could be used to calculate the enthalpy change of solution of sodium chloride.

Q5 Name two factors that affect the enthalpy of hydration of an ion.

Exam Questions

Q1 a) Draw an energy cycle for the enthalpy change of solution of $AgF_{(s)}$. Label each enthalpy change. [2 marks]

   b) Calculate the enthalpy change of solution for AgF from the following data: [2 marks]

   $\Delta_{LE}H^{\ominus}[AgF_{(s)}] = -960 \text{ kJ mol}^{-1}$, $\Delta_{hyd}H^{\ominus}[Ag^{+}_{(g)}] = -464 \text{ kJ mol}^{-1}$, $\Delta_{hyd}H^{\ominus}[F^{-}_{(g)}] = -506 \text{ kJ mol}^{-1}$.

Q2 a) Draw an energy level diagram for the dissolving of $CaCl_2$ using the data below. Label each enthalpy change. [2 marks]

   $\Delta_{LE}H^{\ominus}[CaCl_{2(s)}] = -2258 \text{ kJ mol}^{-1}$, $\Delta_{hyd}H^{\ominus}[Ca^{2+}_{(g)}] = -1579 \text{ kJ mol}^{-1}$, $\Delta_{hyd}H^{\ominus}[Cl^{-}_{(g)}] = -364 \text{ kJ mol}^{-1}$

   b) Calculate the enthalpy change of solution for $CaCl_2$. [2 marks]

Q3 Show that the enthalpy of hydration of $Cl^{-}_{(g)}$ is -364 kJ mol^{-1}, given that: [3 marks]

   $\Delta_{LE}H^{\ominus}[MgCl_{2(s)}] = -2526 \text{ kJ mol}^{-1}$, $\Delta_{hyd}H^{\ominus}[Mg^{2+}_{(g)}] = -1920 \text{ kJ mol}^{-1}$, $\Delta_{sol}H^{\ominus}[MgCl_{2(s)}] = -122 \text{ kJ mol}^{-1}$.

Q4 Which of these ions will have a greater enthalpy of hydration — Ca^{2+} or K^{+}? Explain your answer. [3 marks]

Enthalpy change of solution of the Wicked Witch of the West = 939 kJ mol⁻¹...

Compared to the ones on pages 22-23 or the ones you met in Year 1, these energy cycles are a breeze. You've got to make sure the definitions are firmly fixed in your mind though. You only need to know the lattice enthalpy and the enthalpy of hydration of your lattice ions, and you're well on your way to finding out the enthalpy change of solution.

Entropy

If you were looking for some random chemistry pages, you've just found them.

Entropy *Tells you How Much* Disorder *There Is*

1) Entropy is a measure of the **disorder** of a system — it tells you the **number of ways** that **particles** can be **arranged** and the **number of ways** that the **energy** can be shared out between the particles.

2) The more **disordered** the particles are, the higher the entropy is. A **large**, **positive** value of entropy shows a **high** level of disorder.

3) There are a few things that affect entropy:

Physical State affects Entropy

You have to go back to the good old **solid-liquid-gas** particle explanation thingy to understand this. **Solid** particles just wobble about a fixed point — there's **hardly any** randomness, so they have the **lowest entropy**. **Gas** particles whizz around wherever they like. They've got the most **random arrangements** of particles, so they have the **highest entropy**.

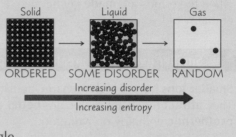

Examples:

- The **exothermic burning** of magnesium ribbon in air has a single **solid** product. One of the reactants (oxygen) is a **gas**, so in this reaction **disorder reduces** and **entropy is lowered.**

$$2Mg_{(s)} + O_{2(g)} \rightarrow 2MgO_{(s)}$$

- The reaction of **ethanoic acid** with **ammonium carbonate** produces **CO_2 gas** as a product, so in this reaction **disorder increases** and entropy is **raised.**

$$2CH_3COOH_{(aq)} + (NH_4)_2CO_{3(s)} \rightarrow 2CH_3COONH_{4(aq)} + H_2O_{(l)} + CO_{2(g)}$$

Dissolving affects Entropy

Dissolving a solid also increases its entropy — dissolved particles can **move freely** as they're no longer held in one place.

Example: Dissolving ammonium nitrate crystals in water results in an increase in entropy:

$$NH_4NO_{3(s)} \rightarrow NH_4{}^+{}_{(aq)} + NO_3{}^-{}_{(aq)}$$

A squirrel's favourite activity is to increase entropy.

More Particles means More Entropy

It makes sense — the more particles you've got, the **more ways** they and their energy can be **arranged**. So in a reaction like $N_2O_{4(g)} \rightarrow 2NO_{2(g)}$, entropy increases because the **number of moles** increases.

More Arrangements *Means More* Stability

1) Substances are actually more **energetically stable** when there's more disorder. So particles will move to try to **increase their entropy**.

2) This is why some reactions are **feasible** (they just happen by themselves — without the addition of energy) even when the enthalpy change is **endothermic**.

Example: The reaction of sodium hydrogencarbonate with hydrochloric acid is an **endothermic reaction** — but it is **feasible**. This is due to an **increase in entropy** as the reaction produces carbon dioxide gas and water. Liquids and gases are **more disordered** than solids and so have a **higher entropy**. This increase in entropy **overcomes** the change in enthalpy.

$NaHCO_{3(s)}$	+	$H^+{}_{(aq)}$	$\rightarrow$	$Na^+{}_{(aq)}$	+	$CO_{2(g)}$	+	$H_2O_{(l)}$
1 mole solid		1 mole aqueous ions		1 mole aqueous ions		1 mole gas		1 mole liquid

The reaction is also favoured because it increases the number of moles.

Entropy

You Can **Calculate** the **Entropy Change** of a System

During a reaction there's an **entropy change** (ΔS) between the **reactants** and **products** — the entropy change of the system.

$$\Delta S_{system} = S_{products} - S_{reactants}$$

The units of entropy are $J\ K^{-1}\ mol^{-1}$.

Example: Calculate the entropy change for the reaction of ammonia and hydrogen chloride under standard conditions.

$$NH_{3(g)} + HCl_{(g)} \rightarrow NH_4Cl_{(s)}$$

$S^{\ominus}[NH_{3(g)}] = 192.3\ J\ K^{-1}\ mol^{-1}$, $S^{\ominus}[HCl_{(g)}] = 186.8\ J\ K^{-1}\ mol^{-1}$, $S^{\ominus}[NH_4Cl_{(s)}] = 94.60\ J\ K^{-1}\ mol^{-1}$

1) First find the entropy of the **products**:

$S^{\ominus}_{products} = S^{\ominus}[NH_4Cl] = 94.60\ J\ K^{-1}\ mol^{-1}$

2) Now find the entropy change of the **reactants**:

$S^{\ominus}_{reactants} = S^{\ominus}[NH_3] + S^{\ominus}[HCl] = 192.3\ J\ K^{-1}\ mol^{-1} + 186.8\ J\ K^{-1}\ mol^{-1} = 379.1\ J\ K^{-1}\ mol^{-1}$

3) Finally you can subtract the entropy of the reactants from the entropy of the products to find the **entropy change** for the system:

$\Delta S_{system} = S^{\ominus}_{products} - S^{\ominus}_{reactants} = 94.60 - 379.1 = \mathbf{-284.5\ J\ K^{-1}\ mol^{-1}}$

This shows a negative change in entropy. It's not surprising as 2 moles of gas have combined to form 1 mole of solid.

A positive entropy change means that a reaction is likely to be feasible, but a negative total entropy change **doesn't guarantee** the reaction **can't** happen — **enthalpy**, **temperature** and **kinetics** also play a part in whether or not a reaction occurs.

Practice Questions

Q1 What does the term 'entropy' mean?

Q2 Arrange the following compounds in order of increasing entropy values: $H_2O_{(l)}$, $MgO_{(s)}$, $CO_{2(g)}$

Q3 Write down the formula for the entropy change of a system.

Exam Questions

Q1 a) Based on just the equation below, predict whether the reaction is likely to be feasible. Give a reason for your answer.

$Mg_{(s)} + \frac{1}{2}O_{2(g)} \rightarrow MgO_{(s)}$ [2 marks]

b) Use the data on the right to calculate the entropy change for the system above. [2 marks]

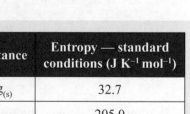

Substance	Entropy — standard conditions ($J\ K^{-1}\ mol^{-1}$)
$Mg_{(s)}$	32.7
$O_{2(g)}$	205.0
$MgO_{(s)}$	26.9

c) Does the result of the calculation indicate that the reaction will be feasible? Give a reason for your answer. [1 mark]

Q2 For the reaction $H_2O_{(l)} \rightarrow H_2O_{(s)}$:

$S^{\ominus}[H_2O_{(l)}] = 70\ J\ K^{-1}\ mol^{-1}$, $S^{\ominus}[H_2O_{(s)}] = 48\ J\ K^{-1}\ mol^{-1}$

a) Calculate the entropy change for this reaction. [1 mark]

b) Explain why this reaction might be feasible. [1 mark]

In the chemistry lab — chaos reigns...

Well, there you go. Entropy in all its glory. You haven't seen the back of it yet though, oh no. There's more where this came from. Which is why, if random disorder has left you in a spin, I'd suggest reading it again and making sure you've got your head round this lot before you turn over. You'll thank me for it... Chocolates are always welcome...

More on Entropy Change

Here we go, as promised, more entropy. Don't ever say I don't spoil you rotten...

The **Total Entropy Change** Includes the **System** and the **Surroundings**

1) As shown on page 29, during a reaction, there's an entropy change between the **reactants and products** — the entropy change of the **system**.

2) The entropy of the **surroundings** changes too (because **energy** is transferred to or from the system).

3) The **TOTAL entropy change** is the sum of the entropy changes of the **system** and the **surroundings**.

Remember, $\Delta S_{system} = S_{products} - S_{reactants}$

$$\Delta S_{total} = \Delta S_{system} + \Delta S_{surroundings}$$

Luckily, as well as for ΔS_{system}, there's a formula for calculating the change of entropy of the surroundings:

$$\Delta S_{surroundings} = -\frac{\Delta H}{T}$$

ΔH = enthalpy change (in J mol^{-1})
T = temperature (in K)

You can **Calculate** the **Total Entropy Change** for a Reaction

Example: Calculate the **total entropy change** for the reaction of ammonia and hydrogen chloride under standard conditions.

$$NH_{3(g)} + HCl_{(g)} \rightarrow NH_4Cl_{(s)} \qquad \Delta H = -315 \text{ kJ mol}^{-1} \text{ (at 298 K)}$$

$S^{\ominus}[NH_{3(g)}] = 192.3 \text{ J K}^{-1} \text{ mol}^{-1}$, $S^{\ominus}[HCl_{(g)}] = 186.8 \text{ J K}^{-1} \text{ mol}^{-1}$, $S^{\ominus}[NH_4Cl_{(s)}] = 94.60 \text{ J K}^{-1} \text{ mol}^{-1}$

First find the entropy change of the **system** — you've already done this on the previous page.

$$\Delta S_{system} = S_{products} - S_{reactants} = 94.60 - (192.3 + 186.8) = \textbf{-284.5 J K}^{-1} \textbf{ mol}^{-1}$$

Now find the entropy change of the **surroundings**:

$$\Delta H = -315 \text{ kJ mol}^{-1} = -315 \times 10^3 \text{ J mol}^{-1}$$

$$\Delta S_{surroundings} = -\frac{\Delta H}{T} = \frac{-(-315 \times 10^3)}{298} = \textbf{+1057 J K}^{-1} \textbf{ mol}^{-1}$$

The ΔH value given above is in kJ mol^{-1}, ΔH in the equation $\Delta S_{surroundings} = -\Delta H/T$ is in J mol^{-1}. You need to multiply the figure above by 1000 to convert it into J mol^{-1}.

Finally you can find the **total** entropy change:

$$\Delta S_{total} = \Delta S_{system} + \Delta S_{surroundings} = -284.5 + (+1057) = \textbf{+772.5 J K}^{-1} \textbf{ mol}^{-1}$$

Example: Calculate the **total entropy change** for ammonium nitrate crystals being dissolved in water under standard conditions.

$$NH_4NO_{3(s)} \xrightarrow{H_2O_{(l)}} NH_4^+{}_{(aq)} + NO_3^-{}_{(aq)} \qquad \Delta H = +25.70 \text{ kJ mol}^{-1} \text{ (at 298 K)}$$

$S^{\ominus}[NH_4NO_{3(s)}] = 151.1 \text{ J K}^{-1} \text{ mol}^{-1}$, $S^{\ominus}[NH_4^+{}_{(aq)}] = 113.4 \text{ J K}^{-1} \text{ mol}^{-1}$, $S^{\ominus}[NO_3^-{}_{(aq)}] = 146.4 \text{ J K}^{-1} \text{ mol}^{-1}$

Find the entropy change of the **system**:

$$\Delta S_{system} = S_{products} - S_{reactants} = (146.4 + 113.4) - 151.1 = \textbf{+108.7 J K}^{-1} \textbf{ mol}^{-1}$$

Now find the entropy change of the **surroundings**:

$$\Delta S_{surroundings} = -\frac{\Delta H}{T} = -\frac{(25.70 \times 10^3)}{298} = \textbf{-86.24 J K}^{-1} \textbf{ mol}^{-1}$$

This makes sense if you look at the equation — you'd expect an increase in the entropy of the system because a solid is dissolving to produce freely moving ions, increasing disorder.

So, the **total** entropy change is:

$$\Delta S_{total} = \Delta S_{system} + \Delta S_{surroundings} = 108.7 - 86.24 = \textbf{+22.46 J K}^{-1} \textbf{ mol}^{-1}$$

More on Entropy Change

You Can Relate **Reaction Results** to Changes in **Entropy** and **Enthalpy**

Example: Reaction between barium hydroxide and ammonium chloride.

First, place a flask on top of a piece of damp cardboard. Add to the flask **solid barium hydroxide crystals**, $Ba(OH)_2.8H_2O$, and **solid ammonium chloride**, then stir. Within about 30 seconds, the smell of ammonia becomes noticeable and a short time later, the bottom of the flask will be **frozen** to the cardboard. The **temperature drops** to well below 0 °C.

$$Ba(OH)_2.8H_2O_{(s)} + 2NH_4Cl_{(s)} \rightarrow BaCl_{2(s)} + 10H_2O_{(l)} + 2NH_{3(g)} \qquad \Delta H = +164.0 \text{ kJ mol}^{-1} \text{ (at 298 K)}$$

Looking at the equation, you would expect an **increase** in the entropy of the system because two solids are combining to produce a solid, a liquid and a gas — that's an **increase** in disorder.
Calculating ΔS_{system} using standard entropies confirms this:

$S^{\ominus}[Ba(OH)_2.8H_2O_{(s)}] = +427.0 \text{ J K}^{-1} \text{ mol}^{-1}$, $S^{\ominus}[NH_4Cl_{(s)}] = +94.6 \text{ J K}^{-1} \text{ mol}^{-1}$, $S^{\ominus}[BaCl_{2(s)}] = +123.7 \text{ J K}^{-1} \text{ mol}^{-1}$,
$S^{\ominus}[H_2O_{(l)}] = +69.9 \text{ J K}^{-1} \text{ mol}^{-1}$, $S^{\ominus}[NH_{3(g)}] = +192.3 \text{ J K}^{-1} \text{ mol}^{-1}$

$S_{reactants} = 427.0 + (2 \times 94.6) = +616.2 \text{ J K}^{-1} \text{ mol}^{-1}$
$S_{products} = 123.7 + (10 \times 69.9) + (2 \times 192.3) = +1207.3 \text{ J K}^{-1} \text{ mol}^{-1}$

$\Delta S_{system} = S_{products} - S_{reactants} = 1207.3 - 616.2 = +591.1 \text{ J K}^{-1} \text{ mol}^{-1}$

> The formula for barium hydroxide crystals is $Ba(OH)_2.8H_2O$. The $.8H_2O$ part of the formula tells you that there is water within the crystalline structure.

The reaction is **endothermic**, so the entropy change of the surroundings must be **negative**.

$\Delta S_{surroundings} = -\Delta H/T = -164\,000 \div 298 = -550.3 \text{ J K}^{-1} \text{ mol}^{-1}$

Once you know $\Delta S_{surroundings}$ and ΔS_{system} you can calculate the **total entropy change** for the reaction.

$\Delta S_{total} = \Delta S_{system} + \Delta S_{surroundings} = 591.1 - 550.3 = \mathbf{+40.8 \text{ J K}^{-1} \text{ mol}^{-1}}$

Practice Questions

Q1 What is the formula for calculating the total entropy change of a reaction?

Q2 What is the formula for calculating $\Delta S_{surroundings}$?

Q3 What sign will the entropy of surroundings be for an endothermic reaction?

Exam Questions

Q1 When a small amount of ammonium carbonate solid is added to 10 cm³ of 1.0 mol dm⁻³ ethanoic acid, carbon dioxide gas is evolved. This is an endothermic reaction, so the temperature of the reaction mixture drops.

$$(NH_4)_2CO_{3(s)} + 2CH_3CO_2H_{(aq)} \rightarrow 2CH_3CO_2NH_{4(aq)} + H_2O_{(l)} + CO_{2(g)} \qquad \Delta H^{\ominus} > 0$$

a) Looking at the equation, what would you expect to happen to the entropy of the system during this reaction? Explain your answer. [3 marks]

b) Explain how this reaction can be both endothermic and have a positive ΔS_{total}. [2 marks]

Q2 Thin ribbons of magnesium burn brightly in oxygen to leave a solid, white residue of magnesium oxide. The equation for this reaction is:

$$2Mg_{(s)} + O_{2(g)} \rightarrow 2MgO_{(s)} \qquad \Delta H = -1204 \text{ kJ mol}^{-1} \text{ (at 298 K)}$$

$S^{\ominus}[Mg_{(s)}] = +32.7 \text{ J K}^{-1} \text{ mol}^{-1}$, $S^{\ominus}[O_{2(g)}] = +205 \text{ J K}^{-1} \text{ mol}^{-1}$, $S^{\ominus}[MgO_{(s)}] = +26.9 \text{ J K}^{-1} \text{ mol}^{-1}$

a) Using the data given, calculate ΔS_{system} at 298 K. [3 marks]

b) Calculate ΔS_{total} for the reaction. [4 marks]

The entropy of my surrounds is always increasing, take a look at my kitchen...

Still awake? Great stuff. Let me be the first to congratulate you on making it to the end of this page — I nearly didn't. As a reward I suggest ten minutes of looking at clips of talented cats online. It'll cheer you up no end and you can think of all those lovely calculations while watching Mr Smudge walks on his hind legs. Ahh... the Internet.

Free Energy

Free energy — I could do with a bit of that. My gas bill is astronomical.

For Feasible Reactions ΔG must be **Negative** or **Zero**

1) The tendency of a process to take place is dependent on three things — the **entropy**, ΔS, the **enthalpy**, ΔH, and the **temperature**, T. When you put all these things **together** you get the **free energy change**, ΔG. ΔG tells you if a reaction is **feasible** or not — the more negative the value of ΔG, the more feasible the reaction.

   Of course, there's a formula for it:

   The units of ΔG are often J mol^{-1}.

   $$\Delta G = \Delta H - T\Delta S_{system}$$

   ΔH = enthalpy change (in J mol^{-1})
   T = temperature (in K)
   ΔS_{system} = entropy change of the system (in J K^{-1} mol^{-1})

   Example: Calculate the free energy change for the following reaction at 298 K.

   $MgCO_{3(g)} \rightarrow MgO_{(s)} + CO_{2(g)}$ $\Delta H^{\ominus} = +117\,000$ J mol^{-1}, $\Delta S_{system} = +175$ J K^{-1} mol^{-1}

   $\Delta G = \Delta H - T\Delta S_{system} = +117\,000 - (298 \times (+175)) = \mathbf{+64\,900}$ **J mol^{-1}** (3 s.f.)

   ΔG is positive — so the reaction isn't feasible at this temperature.

2) When $\Delta G = 0$, the reaction is **just feasible**. So the temperature at which the reaction becomes feasible can be calculated by rearranging the equation like this:

   $\Delta H - T\Delta S_{system} = 0$, so $\boxed{T = \dfrac{\Delta H}{\Delta S_{system}}}$

   Example: At what temperature does the reaction $MgCO_{3(g)} \rightarrow MgO_{(s)} + CO_{2(g)}$ become feasible?

   $$T = \frac{\Delta H}{\Delta S_{system}} = \frac{+117\,000}{+175} = \mathbf{669\ K}$$

3) You can use ΔG to **predict** whether or not a reaction is **feasible**. By looking at the equation $\Delta G = \Delta H - T\Delta S$, you can see that:

   Temperature is measured in Kelvin so will always have a positive value.

   > When ΔH is **negative** and ΔS is **positive**, ΔG will always be **negative** and the reaction is **feasible**.
   > When ΔH is **positive** and ΔS is **negative**, ΔG will always be **positive** and the reaction is **not feasible**.

   In other situations, the feasibility of the reaction is dependent on the temperature.

Feasible **Reversible** Reactions have **Large Equilibrium Constants**

1) An equilibrium constant is a measure of the ratio of the concentration of products to reactants at equilibria for a reversible reaction at a specific temperature.

2) Reactions with **negative** ΔG, and so are theoretically **feasible**, have large values for their equilibrium constants — **greater** than 1.

3) Reactions with **positive** ΔG, and so **not** theoretically feasible, have small values for their equilibrium constants — **smaller** than 1.

   If you need a recap of equilibrium constants have a look at your Year 1 notes, or at pages 2-3.

4) This relationship is represented by the equation:

   Don't worry about learning this equation. If you need it, you'll be given it in the exam.

   $$\Delta G = -RT \ln K$$

   R = gas constant, 8.31 J K^{-1} mol^{-1}
   T = temperature (in K)
   $\ln K$ = the natural log of the equilibrium constant

   Example: Ethanoic acid and ethanol were reacted together at 298 K and allowed to reach equilibrium. The equilibrium constant was calculated to be 4 at 298 K. Calculate the free energy change for the reaction.

   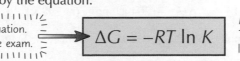

   $CH_3COOH_{(l)} + C_2H_5OH_{(l)} \rightleftharpoons CH_3COOC_2H_{5(l)} + H_2O_{(l)}$

   The equilibrium constant is **greater than 1**, so you'd **expect** ΔG to be **negative**...

   ΔG is negative — so the reaction is feasible at 298K.

   $\Delta G = -RT \ln K = -(8.31 \times 298) \times \ln(4) = \mathbf{-3430}$ **J mol^{-1}** (3 s.f.)   ...and it **is**.

Free Energy

Equilibrium Constants can be Calculated from ΔG

You may get asked to **calculate** equilibrium constants from the free energy change of a reaction.

Example: Hydrogen gas and iodine are mixed together in a sealed flask forming hydrogen iodide.
Calculate the equilibrium constant at 763 K.

$$H_{2(g)} + I_{2(g)} \rightleftharpoons 2HI_{(g)} \quad \Delta G = -24287 \text{ J mol}^{-1}$$

Firstly, you need to rearrange the equation,
$\Delta G = -RT \ln K$, to find $\ln K$:

$$\ln K = \frac{\Delta G}{-RT} = \frac{-24287}{-(8.31 \times 763)} = 3.8304$$

To find the value of K, you need to find the inverse of the log.
To do this, use the exponential function for your value of $\ln K$:

$$\ln K = 3.8304 \text{ so } K = e^{3.8304} = 46$$

Finally, you need to calculate the units of K:

$$K = \frac{(mol\,dm^{-3})(mol\,dm^{-3})}{(mol\,dm^{-3})(mol\,dm^{-3})} = \textbf{no units}$$

So $K = \textbf{46}$ (2 s.f.)

If you want a reminder of how to calculate the units for equilibrium constants, have a look at page 2.

Negative ΔG doesn't Guarantee a Reaction

The value of the free energy change doesn't tell you anything about the reaction's **rate**.
Even if ΔG shows that a reaction is theoretically feasible, it might have a really **high activation energy** or happen so slowly that you wouldn't notice it happening at all. For example:

$$H_{2(g)} + \tfrac{1}{2}O_{2(g)} \rightarrow H_2O_{(g)} \quad \Delta H^{\ominus} = -242\,000 \text{ J mol}^{-1}, \quad \Delta S^{\ominus} = -44.4 \text{ J K}^{-1}\text{mol}^{-1}$$

At 298 K, $\Delta G = -242\,000 - (298 \times (-44.4)) = \textbf{-229\,000 J mol}^{-1}$ (3 s.f.)

But this reaction **doesn't occur** at 298 K — it needs a spark to start it off due to its **high activation energy**.

Practice Questions

Q1 What are the three things that determine the value of ΔG?

Q2 If the free energy change of a reaction is positive, what can you conclude about the reaction?

Q3 What is the relationship between the free energy change and equilibrium constants?

Q4 Why might a reaction with a negative ΔG value not always be feasible?

Exam Questions

Q1 a) Use the equation below and the table on the right
to calculate the free energy change for the
complete combustion of methane at 298 K.   [2 marks]

$$CH_{4(g)} + 2O_{2(g)} \rightarrow CO_{2(g)} + 2H_2O_{(l)} \quad \Delta H^{\ominus} = -730 \text{ kJ mol}^{-1}$$

b) Explain whether the reaction is feasible at 298 K.   [1 mark]

c) What is the maximum temperature
at which the reaction is feasible?   [1 mark]

Substance	$S^{\ominus}$ (J K^{-1} mol^{-1})
$CH_{4(g)}$	186
$O_{2(g)}$	205
$CO_{2(g)}$	214
$H_2O_{(l)}$	69.9
$C_3H_7OH_{(l)}$	193

Q2 At 723 K, the equilibrium constant for the exothermic reaction $H_{2(g)} + Cl_{2(g)} \rightleftharpoons 2HCl_{(g)}$ is 60.
ΔS for the reaction is negative.

a) Calculate the free energy change for this reaction.   [1 mark]

b) Describe the effect of increasing the temperature of the reaction on the free energy change.   [2 marks]

ΔG for chemistry revision definitely has a positive value...

Okay, so ΔG won't tell you for definite whether a reaction will happen, but it will tell you if the reaction is at least theoretically feasible. Make sure you know the formulae for ΔG, how to rearrange them and how to work out the numbers to plonk in it. And don't forget to check your units, check your units, check your units.

Electrochemical Cells

On these pages there are electrons to-ing and fro-ing in redox reactions. And when electrons move, you get electricity.

If Electrons are Transferred, it's a Redox Reaction

1) A **loss** of electrons is called **oxidation**.
   When an element is **oxidised**, its **oxidation number** will **increase**.

2) A **gain** of electrons is called **reduction**. When an element is **reduced**, its **oxidation number** will **decrease**.

3) Reduction and oxidation happen **simultaneously** — hence the term "**redox**" reaction.

Look back at your Year 1 notes for more about redox reactions.

- **s-block metals** tend to react by being **oxidised** — they **lose electrons** to form **positive ions** with charges the same as their group number (i.e. **Group 1** metals form **1+ ions** and **Group 2** metals form **2+ ions**).

- **p-block metals** can react by **losing electrons** (like the s-block elements), but the **non-metals** in the **p-block** react by **gaining electrons** to form **negative ions** with charges the same as their **group number minus 8**.
  p-block elements often react to form covalent species, where electrons are shared (rather than lost or gained) — see your Year 1 notes.

- **d-block metals** form ions with **variable oxidation states** (see page 49) so predicting how these elements react can be tricky. But, they tend to form **positive ions** with **positive oxidation numbers**.

Electrochemical Cells Make Electricity

1) Electrochemical cells can be made from **two different metals** dipped in salt solutions of their **own ions** and connected by a wire (the **external circuit**). There are always **two** reactions within an electrochemical cell. One's an oxidation and one's a reduction — so it's a **redox process**.

2) Oxidation always happens at the **anode** (the positive electrode) and reduction always happens at the **cathode** (the negative electrode). Electrons flow **from** the **anode** to the **cathode**.

3) **Reactive metals** form ions **more readily** than **unreactive metals**. The **more reactive metal** gives up its electrons and is **oxidised** (it becomes the **anode**, where **electrons flow** from). The **less reactive metal** becomes the **cathode**.

Here's what happens in the **zinc/copper** electrochemical cell on the right:

- Zinc **loses electrons** more easily than copper. So in the left-hand half-cell, zinc (from the zinc electrode) is **OXIDISED** to form $Zn^{2+}_{(aq)}$ ions.

  $$Zn_{(s)} \rightarrow Zn^{2+}_{(aq)} + 2e^-$$

  This releases electrons into the external circuit.

- In the other half-cell, the **same number of electrons** are taken from the external circuit, **REDUCING** the Cu^{2+} ions to copper atoms.

  $$Cu^{2+}_{(aq)} + 2e^- \rightarrow Cu_{(s)}$$

4) **Electrons** flow through the wire from the most reactive metal to the least.

5) A voltmeter in the external circuit shows the **voltage** between the two half-cells. This is the **cell potential** or **EMF**, E_{cell}. Voltmeters also measure the direction of the flow of electrons (see page 36).

The solutions are connected by a salt bridge made from filter paper soaked in a salt solution, e.g. $KNO_{3(aq)}$. The salt ions flow through the salt bridge to complete the cell, and balance out the charges in the beakers.

You can also have half-cells involving **solutions of two aqueous ions of the same element**, such as $Fe^{2+}_{(aq)}/Fe^{3+}_{(aq)}$.

The conversion from Fe^{2+} to Fe^{3+}, or vice versa, happens on the surface of the **electrode**.

$$Fe^{2+}_{(aq)} \rightarrow Fe^{3+}_{(aq)} + e^- \qquad Fe^{3+}_{(aq)} + e^- \rightarrow Fe^{2+}_{(aq)}$$

Because neither the reactants nor the products are solids, you need something else for the **electrode**.
It needs to **conduct electricity** and be very **inert**, so that it won't react with anything in the half-cell. **Platinum** is an excellent choice, but is very **expensive**, so **graphite** is often used instead.

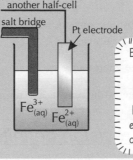

Electrochemical cells can also be made from non-metals. For systems involving a gas (e.g. chlorine), the gas can be bubbled over a platinum electrode sitting in a solution of its aqueous ions (e.g. Cl^-).

6) When drawing electrochemical cells, the half-cell where **oxidation** happens (the **anode**) should always be drawn on the **left**, and the half-cell where **reduction** happens (the **cathode**) should be drawn on the **right**.

Electrochemical Cells

The *Reactions* at Each *Electrode* are *Reversible*

1) The **reactions** that occur at each electrode in the **zinc/copper** cell on the last page are: $\Longrightarrow$ $\quad Zn^{2+}_{(aq)} + 2e^- \rightleftharpoons Zn_{(s)} \qquad Cu^{2+}_{(aq)} + 2e^- \rightleftharpoons Cu_{(s)}$

2) The **reversible arrows** show that both reactions can go in **either direction**. **Which direction** each reaction goes in depends on **how easily** each metal **loses electrons** (i.e. how easily it's **oxidised**).

3) These reactions are called **half-reactions** and, even though they're reversible, they're always written with the **reduction reaction** going in the **forward** direction, with the **electrons being added** on the **left-hand side**.

You Need to Know How to *Set Up* an *Electrochemical Cell*

You can set up an electrochemical cell and use it to take measurements of **voltage**.
Here's a method you can use to construct an **electrochemical cell** involving **two metals**.

1) Get a strip of each of the **metals** you're investigating. These are your electrodes. **Clean** the **surfaces** of the metals using a piece of **emery paper** (or **sandpaper**).

2) Clean any **grease** or **oil** from the electrodes using some **propanone**. From this point on, be careful **not to touch** the surfaces of the metals with your hands — you could transfer **grease** back onto the strips.

3) Place each electrode into a **beaker** filled with a solution containing **ions** of that metal. For example, if you had an electrode made of **zinc** metal, you could place it in a beaker of $ZnSO_4 {}_{(aq)}$. If you had an electrode made of **copper**, you could use a solution of $CuSO_4 {}_{(aq)}$. If one of the half-cells contains an oxidising agent that contains oxygen (e.g. MnO_4^-), you'll have to add acid too.

4) Create a **salt bridge** to link the two solutions together. You can do this by simply soaking a piece of filter paper in **salt solution**, e.g. $KCl_{(aq)}$ or $KNO_3 {}_{(aq)}$, and draping it between the two beakers. The ends of the filter paper should be **immersed** in the solutions.

5) Connect the electrodes to a **voltmeter** using **crocodile clips** and **wires**. If you've set up your circuit correctly, you'll get a **reading** on your voltmeter.

If your electrochemical cell is made up of half-cells where neither the oxidised or reduced species are solid (e.g. they're both aqueous ions), your method will be slightly different. For example, you'll need to use an inert electrode (e.g. platinum).

Practice Questions

Q1 Do s-block metals tend to react by losing or gaining electrons?

Q2 Does oxidation happen at the cathode or the anode?

Q3 How would you set up a half-cell cell between two ions of the same element in different oxidation states?

Exam Questions

Q1 A cell is made up of an iron and a zinc electrode. The half-equations for the two electrodes are:

$$Fe^{2+}_{(aq)} + 2e^- \rightleftharpoons Fe_{(s)} \qquad\qquad Zn^{2+}_{(aq)} + 2e^- \rightleftharpoons Zn_{(s)}$$

a) Describe how you would set up an electrochemical cell using an iron and a zinc half-cell. [4 marks]

b) Given that zinc is more easily oxidised than iron, draw a diagram to show this cell. Show the direction of the flow of electrons around the cell [4 marks]

Q2 A student sets up an electrochemical cell by placing strips of copper and silver metal in solutions containing copper and silver salts respectively. He connects the strips of metal to a voltmeter with wires, and connects the salt solutions together with a salt bridge.

a) What is the role of the salt bridge? [2 marks]

b) Suggest how the student could make the salt bridge. [1 mark]

c) Given that copper is a more reactive metal than silver, which metal strip will form the cathode? [1 mark]

Cells aren't just for biologists, you know...

You'll probably have to do an experiment involving electrochemical cells in your class, so make sure you read that method above really carefully so you can set up any electrochemical cell even with your eyes closed (though this is not advised...). You could be asked about this practical in your exam too, so even more reason to know it inside out...

Electrode Potentials

Time for some more electrochemical cell fun. Bet you can't wait — these pages have real potential...

Each **Half-Cell** has an **Electrode Potential**

1) Each **half-cell** in an electrochemical cell has its own **electrode potential** — this is a measure of how easily the substance in the half-cell is oxidised (i.e. loses electrons).

2) As the substances in the half-cells are oxidised or reduced, a **potential difference** builds up, due to the difference in charge between the electrode and the ions in solution. E.g., in the **zinc half-cell**, the **Zn electrode** is **negatively charged** (due to the electrons left behind when Zn^{2+} ions form) and the **Zn^{2+} ions** in solution are **positively charged**.

3) The half-reaction with the more **positive** electrode potential ($E^\ominus$) value goes **forwards**. The half-reaction with the more **negative** $E^\ominus$ value goes **backwards**.

4) The table on the right shows the electrode potentials for the copper and zinc half-cells. The **zinc half-cell** has a **more negative** electrode potential, so **zinc is oxidised** (the reaction goes **backwards**), while **copper is reduced** (the reaction goes **forwards**). The little $\ominus$ symbol next to the E shows they're **standard electrode potentials** (see below).

Half-cell	Electrode potential $E^\ominus$ (V)
$Zn^{2+}_{(aq)} + 2e^- \rightarrow Zn_{(s)}$	−0.76
$Cu^{2+}_{(aq)} + 2e^- \rightarrow Cu_{(s)}$	+0.34

$$Cu^{2+}_{(aq)} + Zn_{(s)} \rightleftharpoons Cu_{(s)} + Zn^{2+}_{(aq)}$$

5) In this example, zinc is being oxidised and copper is being reduced, so **zinc** is acting as a **reducing agent** and **copper** is acting as an **oxidising agent**.

Electrode Potentials are Measured Against **Standard Hydrogen Electrodes**

You measure the electrode potential of a half-cell against a **standard hydrogen electrode**.

> The **standard electrode potential**, $E^\ominus$, of a half-cell is the **voltage measured** under **standard conditions** when the **half-cell** is connected to a **standard hydrogen electrode**.

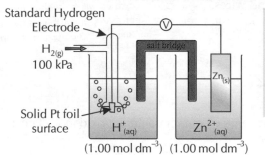

Standard Hydrogen Electrode
$H_{2(g)}$
100 kPa
salt bridge
$Zn_{(s)}$
Solid Pt foil surface
$H^+_{(aq)}$ $Zn^{2+}_{(aq)}$
(1.00 mol dm⁻³) (1.00 mol dm⁻³)

Standard conditions are:

1) The solutions of the ions you're interested in must have a concentration of **1.00 mol dm⁻³**.

2) The temperature must be **298 K (25 °C)**.

3) The pressure must be **100 kPa**.

The equation for the reaction at the hydrogen electrode is:

$$2H^+_{(aq)} + 2e^- \rightleftharpoons H_{2(g)}$$

The **standard hydrogen electrode** is always shown on the **left** — it doesn't matter whether or not the other half-cell is where oxidation happens.

The standard hydrogen electrode is a **reference electrode**, and allows scientists to work out and compare the electrode potentials of whatever half-cell the hydrogen electrode's connected to. The hydrogen half-cell has a value of **0.00 V**. This means the **voltage reading** will be equal to $E^\ominus$ of the other half-cell (as $E^\ominus$ for the standard hydrogen electrode is 0.00 V).

This reading could be positive or negative, depending which way the electrons flow.

Work Out E_{cell} From **Standard Electrode Potentials**

1) You can use standard electrode potentials to **calculate** the **cell potential**, $E^\ominus_{cell}$, of an electrochemical cell. You'll need to use this formula:

$$E^\ominus_{cell} = \left(E^\ominus_{reduction} - E^\ominus_{oxidation}\right)$$

2) The cell potential will always be a **positive voltage**, because the more negative $E^\ominus$ value is being subtracted from the more positive $E^\ominus$ value.

> **Example:** Calculate the cell potential of a magnesium-bromine electrochemical cell: $Br_2 + Mg \rightarrow Mg^{2+} + 2Br^-$
>
> $Mg^{2+}_{(aq)} + 2e^- \rightleftharpoons Mg_{(s)}$ $E^\ominus = -2.37$ V $\frac{1}{2}Br_{2(aq)} + e^- \rightleftharpoons Br^-_{(aq)}$ $E^\ominus = +1.09$ V
>
> All you have to do is substitute the standard electrode potentials of Mg/Mg^{2+} and $\frac{1}{2}Br_2/Br^-$ into the equation:
>
> $E^\ominus_{cell} = \left(E^\ominus_{reduction} - E^\ominus_{oxidation}\right)$ ⟶ $E^\ominus_{cell} = +1.09 - (-2.37) = \mathbf{+3.46}$ **V**

Electrode Potentials

Conditions Affect the Value of the Electrode Potential

Just like any other reversible reaction, the **equilibrium position** in a
half-cell is affected by changes in **temperature**, **pressure** and **concentration**.
Changing the equilibrium position changes the **cell potential**.
To get around this, **standard conditions** are used to measure electrode
potentials — using these conditions means you always get the **same value**
for the electrode potential and you can **compare values** for different cells.

*Caroline showed great potential
from a young age.*

There's a Convention for Drawing Electrochemical Cells

It's a bit of a faff drawing pictures of electrochemical cells.
There's a **shorthand** way of representing them though. This is known as the
conventional representation— for example, the **Zn/Cu cell** is shown on the right.

There are a couple of important **conventions** when drawing cells:

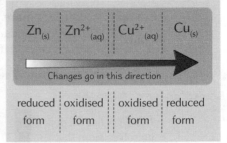

1) The **half-cell** with the **more negative** potential goes on the **left**.

2) The **oxidised forms** go in the **centre** of the cell diagram
   and **reduced** forms go on the **outside**.

3) **Double** vertical lines show the **salt bridge**, and **single**
   vertical lines separate species in **different physical states**.

4) **Commas** separate species that are in the same half-cell and in the **same physical state**.

5) In conventional representations of electrochemical cells involving the
   standard hydrogen electrode, the standard hydrogen half-cell should always go on the **left**.

6) If either of the half-cells use platinum, lead or other **inert electrodes**, show these on the outside of the diagram.

> **Example:** Draw the conventional representation of the
> electrochemical cell formed between
> magnesium and the standard hydrogen half-cell.
>
> $$Pt \mid H_{2(g)} \mid 2H^+_{(aq)} \parallel Mg^{2+}_{(aq)} \mid Mg_{(s)}$$

Practice Questions

Q1 What's the definition of standard electrode potential?

Q2 What is the voltage of the standard hydrogen electrode half-cell?

Q3 State the equation you could use to work out E_{cell}.

Exam Questions

Q1 A cell is made up of a lead and an iron plate, dipped in solutions of lead(II) nitrate and iron(II) nitrate
respectively and connected by a salt bridge. The electrode potentials for the two electrodes are:

$$Fe^{2+}_{(aq)} + 2e^- \rightleftharpoons Fe_{(s)} \quad E^{\ominus} = -0.44 \text{ V} \qquad\qquad Pb^{2+}_{(aq)} + 2e^- \rightleftharpoons Pb_{(s)} \quad E^{\ominus} = -0.13 \text{ V}$$

a) Which metal becomes oxidised in the cell? Explain your answer. [2 marks]

b) Find the standard cell potential of this cell. [1 mark]

Q2 An electrochemical cell containing a zinc half-cell and a silver half-cell was set up using
a potassium nitrate salt bridge. The cell potential at 25 °C was measured to be 1.40 V.

$$Zn^{2+}_{(aq)} + 2e^- \rightleftharpoons Zn_{(s)} \qquad E^{\ominus} = -0.76 \text{ V} \qquad\qquad Ag^+_{(aq)} + e^- \rightleftharpoons Ag_{(s)} \qquad E^{\ominus} = +0.80 \text{ V}$$

a) Use the standard electrode potentials given to calculate the standard cell potential for a zinc-silver cell. [1 mark]

b) Suggest two possible reasons why the actual cell potential
was different from the value calculated in part (a). [2 marks]

This is potentially the best page I've ever read...

*Standard electrode potentials are measured under standard conditions — the name kind of gives it away doesn't it?
Make sure you remember what those conditions are though. Since I'm nice, I'll remind you. They're a temperature of
298 K, a pressure of 100 kPa, and all the reacting ions have to have concentrations of 1.00 mol dm⁻³. Got it? I hope so...*

The Electrochemical Series

The electrochemical series is like a pop chart of the most reactive metals — but without the pop. So it's really just a chart.

The **Electrochemical Series** Shows You What's **Reactive** and What's Not

1) The **more reactive** a **metal** is, the **more** easily it **loses electrons** to form a **positive ion**. **More reactive metals** have **more negative standard electrode potentials**.

> **Example:** Magnesium is **more reactive** than zinc — so it forms 2+ ions more easily than zinc. The list of standard electrode potentials shows that Mg^{2+}/Mg has a **more negative** value than Zn^{2+}/Zn. In terms of oxidation and reduction, magnesium would **reduce** Zn^{2+} (or Zn^{2+} would **oxidise** Mg).

2) The more reactive a **non-metal** is, the **more** easily it **gains electrons** to form a **negative ion**. **More reactive non-metals** have **more positive standard electrode potentials**.

> **Example:** Chlorine is **more reactive** than bromine — so it forms a negative ion more easily than bromine does. The list of standard electrode potentials shows that $\frac{1}{2}Cl_2/Cl^-$ is **more positive** than $\frac{1}{2}Br_2/Br^-$. In terms of oxidation and reduction, chlorine would **oxidise** Br^- (or Br^- would **reduce** Cl_2).

3) Here's an **electrochemical series** showing some standard electrode potentials:

More positive electrode potentials mean that:
1. The left-hand substances are more easily reduced.
2. The right-hand substances are more stable.

Half-reaction	$E^{\ominus}/V$
$Mg^{2+}_{(aq)} + 2e^- \rightleftharpoons Mg_{(s)}$	−2.37
$Zn^{2+}_{(aq)} + 2e^- \rightleftharpoons Zn_{(s)}$	−0.76
$H^+_{(aq)} + e^- \rightleftharpoons \frac{1}{2}H_{2(g)}$	0.00
$Cu^{2+}_{(aq)} + 2e^- \rightleftharpoons Cu_{(s)}$	+0.34
$\frac{1}{2}Br_{2(aq)} + e^- \rightleftharpoons Br^-_{(aq)}$	+1.09

More negative electrode potentials mean that:
1. The right-hand substances are more easily oxidised.
2. The left-hand substances are more stable.

Use **Electrode Potentials** to **Predict** Whether a Reaction Will Happen

To figure out if a metal will react with the aqueous ions of another metal, you can use their $E^{\ominus}$ values. If a reaction is **thermodynamically feasible**, the overall potential will be **positive**. A reaction isn't feasible if $E^{\ominus}$ is negative.

> **Example:** Predict whether zinc metal reacts with aqueous copper ions.
>
> First write the two **half-equations** down as reduction reactions:
>
> $Zn^{2+}_{(aq)} + 2e^- \rightleftharpoons Zn_{(s)}$ $\quad E^{\ominus} = -0.76\,V$ $\qquad\qquad Cu^{2+}_{(aq)} + 2e^- \rightleftharpoons Cu_{(s)}$ $\quad E^{\ominus} = +0.34\,V$
>
> Then combine them to create the reaction described in the question (in this case, you'll have to swap the direction of the zinc one, since the question is talking about the reaction of zinc metal).
>
> The two half-equations combine to give: $Zn_{(s)} + Cu^{2+}_{(aq)} \rightarrow Zn^{2+}_{(aq)} + Cu_{(s)}$
>
> *Zinc loses electrons so is oxidised. Copper gains electrons so is reduced.*
>
> Then, use the equation $E^{\ominus}_{cell} = \left(E^{\ominus}_{reduction} - E^{\ominus}_{oxidation}\right)$ to work out the overall potential of this reaction. $\Longrightarrow E^{\ominus}_{cell} = 0.34 - (-0.76) = \mathbf{+1.10\,V}$
>
> The overall cell potential is **positive**, so zinc **will** react with aqueous copper ions.

Electrode Potentials can Predict Whether **Disproportionation** Reactions will Happen

During a **disproportionation** reaction, an element is simultaneously oxidised and reduced. You can use electrode potentials to show why these sorts of reactions happen.

> **Example:** Use the following equations to predict whether or not Ag^+ ions will disproportionate in solution.
> $Ag^+_{(aq)} + e^- \rightarrow Ag_{(s)}$ $\quad E^{\ominus} = +0.80\,V$ $\qquad\qquad Ag^{2+}_{(aq)} + e^- \rightarrow Ag^+_{(aq)}$ $\quad E^{\ominus} = +2.00\,V$
>
> First combine the half-equations to create the equation for the disproportionation of Ag^+: $2Ag^+_{(aq)} \rightarrow Ag_{(s)} + Ag^{2+}_{(aq)}$
>
> Then, use the equation $E^{\ominus}_{cell} = \left(E^{\ominus}_{reduction} - E^{\ominus}_{oxidation}\right)$ to work out the overall potential of this reaction. $\Longrightarrow E^{\ominus}_{cell} = 0.80 - (2.00) = \mathbf{-1.20\,V}$
>
> The overall cell potential is **negative**, so silver **will not disproportionate** in solution.

The Electrochemical Series

Sometimes the Prediction is Wrong

A **prediction** using E° only states if a reaction is **possible** under **standard conditions**. The prediction might be **wrong if...**

...the conditions are not standard.

1) Changing the **concentration** (or temperature) of the solution can cause the electrode potential to **change**.

2) For example the zinc/copper cell has these half equations in equilibrium:

$$Zn_{(s)} \rightleftharpoons Zn^{2+}_{(aq)} + 2e^- \quad E^\circ = -0.76\,V$$
$$Cu^{2+}_{(aq)} + 2e^- \rightleftharpoons Cu_{(s)} \quad E^\circ = +0.34\,V$$

$$Zn_{(s)} + Cu^{2+}_{(aq)} \rightleftharpoons Zn^{2+}_{(aq)} + Cu_{(s)} \quad E_{cell} = +1.10\,V$$

3) If you **increase** the concentration of Zn^{2+}, the **equilibrium** will shift to the **left**, **reducing** the ease of **electron loss** of Zn. The electrode potential of Zn/Zn^{2+} becomes **less negative** and the whole cell potential will be lower.

4) If you **increase** the concentration of Cu^{2+}, the **equilibrium** will shift to the **right**, **increasing** the ease of **electron gain** of Cu^{2+}. The electrode potential of Cu^{2+}/Cu becomes **more positive** and the whole cell potential is higher.

...the reaction kinetics are not favourable.

1) The **rate of a reaction** may be so **slow** that the reaction might **not appear** to happen.

2) If a reaction has a **high activation energy**, this may stop it happening.

Cell Potential is Related to Entropy and the Equilibrium Constant

The bigger the **cell potential**, the bigger the **total entropy change** taking place during the reaction in the cell. This gives the following equations:

∝ means 'directly proportional'

$$E^\ominus \propto \Delta S_{total}$$

ΔS_{total} = total entropy change

$$E^\ominus \propto \ln K$$

This one comes from the fact that entropy and the equilibrium constant, K, are linked — see page 32.

Practice Questions

Q1 Use electrode potentials to show that zinc metal will react with Cu^{2+} ions.

Q2 How are cell potential and the total entropy change during a reaction related?

Exam Questions

Q1 Use the $E^\ominus$ values in the table on the right and on the previous page to determine the outcome of mixing the following solutions. If there is a reaction, determine the $E^\ominus$ value and write the equation. If there isn't a reaction, state this and explain why.

a) Zinc metal and Ni^{2+} ions. [2 marks]

b) Acidified MnO_4^- ions and Sn^{2+} ions. [2 marks]

c) $Br_{2(aq)}$ and acidified $Cr_2O_7^{2-}$ ions. [2 marks]

Half-reaction	$E^\ominus$/V
$MnO_4^-{}_{(aq)} + 8H^+{}_{(aq)} + 5e^- \rightleftharpoons Mn^{2+}{}_{(aq)} + 4H_2O_{(l)}$	+1.51
$Cr_2O_7^{2-}{}_{(aq)} + 14H^+{}_{(aq)} + 6e^- \rightleftharpoons 2Cr^{3+}{}_{(aq)} + 7H_2O_{(l)}$	+1.33
$Sn^{4+}{}_{(aq)} + 2e^- \rightleftharpoons Sn^{2+}{}_{(aq)}$	+0.14
$Ni^{2+}{}_{(aq)} + 2e^- \rightleftharpoons Ni_{(s)}$	−0.25

Q2 Potassium manganate(VII), $KMnO_4$, and potassium dichromate, $K_2Cr_2O_7$, are both used as oxidising agents. From their electrode potentials (given in the table above), which would you predict is the stronger oxidising agent? Explain why. [2 marks]

Q3 A cell is set up with copper and nickel electrodes in $1\,mol\,dm^{-3}$ solutions of their ions, Cu^{2+} and Ni^{2+}, connected by a salt bridge.

a) What is the overall equation for this reaction? [1 mark]

b) How would the voltage of the cell change if a more dilute copper solution was used? [1 mark]

My Gran's in a rock band — they call themselves the electrochemical dearies...

All these positive and negative electrode potentials get me in a spin. Fortunately, you'll be given all the electrode potential data you need in the data booklet in your exam, so you don't need to memorise it — you just need to know how to use it.

Storage and Fuel Cells

More electrochemical reactions on these pages. It's like Christmas come early (if electrochemistry is your sort of thing)...

Energy Storage Cells are Like Electrochemical Cells

Energy storage cells (fancy name for a battery) have been around for ages and modern ones **work** just like an **electrochemical cell**. For example the nickel-iron cell was developed way back at the start of the 1900s and is often used as a back-up power supply because it can be repeatedly charged and is very robust. You can work out the **voltage** produced by these **cells** by using the **electrode potentials** of the substances used in the cell.

There are **lots** of different cells and you **won't** be asked to remember the E° for the reactions, but you might be **asked** to work out the **cell potential** or **cell voltage** for a given cell... so here's an example I prepared earlier.

Example: The nickel-iron cell has a nickel oxide hydroxide (NiO(OH)) cathode and an iron (Fe) anode
with potassium hydroxide as the electrolyte. Using the half equations given:
a) write out the full equation for the reaction.
b) calculate the cell voltage produced by the nickel-iron cell.

$$Fe(OH)_2 + 2e^- \rightleftharpoons Fe + 2OH^- \qquad E^\circ = -0.89\,V$$
$$NiO(OH) + H_2O + e^- \rightleftharpoons Ni(OH)_2 + OH^- \qquad E^\circ = +0.49\,V$$

You have to double everything in the second equation so that the electrons balance those in the first equation.

For the first part you have to **combine** the two half-equations together in the feasible direction (when E° is positive). This involves switching the reaction with the less positive electrode potential around. The e^- and the OH^- are not shown because they get cancelled out.

The **overall** reaction is...
$$2NiO(OH) + 2H_2O + Fe \rightarrow 2Ni(OH)_2 + Fe(OH)_2$$

To calculate the **cell voltage** you use the **same** formula for working out the **cell potential** (page 36).

So the **cell voltage** $= E^\circ_{\text{reduction}} - E^\circ_{\text{oxidation}}$
$$= +0.49 - (-0.89) = \mathbf{1.38\ V}$$

Fuel Cells can Generate Electricity From Hydrogen and Oxygen

In most cells the **chemicals** that generate the electricity are contained in the **electrodes** and the **electrolyte** that form the cell. In a **fuel cell** the chemicals are **stored separately** outside the cell and fed in when electricity is required. One example of this is the **alkaline hydrogen-oxygen fuel cell**, which can be used to **power electric vehicles**. **Hydrogen** and **oxygen gases** are fed into two separate platinum-containing electrodes. The electrodes are separated by an **anion-exchange membrane** that **allows anions** (OH^-) and water to pass through it, but **not** hydrogen and oxygen gas. The **electrolyte** is an aqueous alkaline (KOH) solution.

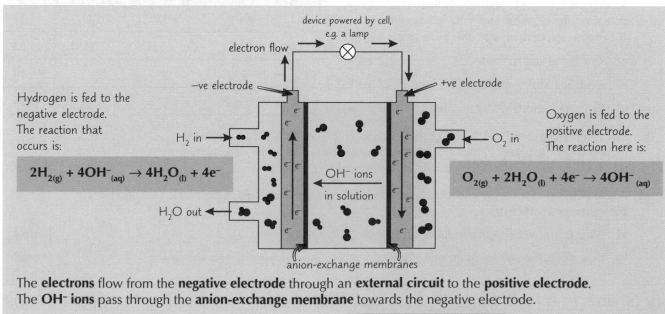

device powered by cell, e.g. a lamp

electron flow

−ve electrode

+ve electrode

Hydrogen is fed to the negative electrode. The reaction that occurs is:

H_2 in

$$2H_{2(g)} + 4OH^-_{(aq)} \rightarrow 4H_2O_{(l)} + 4e^-$$

H_2O out

OH^- ions in solution

Oxygen is fed to the positive electrode. The reaction here is:

O_2 in

$$O_{2(g)} + 2H_2O_{(l)} + 4e^- \rightarrow 4OH^-_{(aq)}$$

anion-exchange membranes

The **electrons** flow from the **negative electrode** through an **external circuit** to the **positive electrode**. The **OH⁻ ions** pass through the **anion-exchange membrane** towards the negative electrode.

The **overall effect** is that H_2 and O_2 react to make **water**: $2H_{2(g)} + O_{2(g)} \rightarrow 2H_2O_{(l)}$

Storage and Fuel Cells

Hydrogen-Oxygen Fuel Cells Work in Acidic Conditions Too

1) At the **anode** the platinum catalyst **splits** the H_2 into protons and electrons.

2) The **polymer electrolyte membrane** (PEM) **only** allows the H^+ across and this **forces** the e^- to travel **around** the circuit to get to the cathode.

3) An **electric current** is created in the circuit, which is used to **power** something like a car or a bike or a dancing Santa.

4) At the **cathode**, O_2 **combines** with the H^+ from the anode and the e^- from the circuit to make H_2O. This is the only waste product.

$2e^-$

Fuel (H_2) in →

→ Unused fuel out

Anode
$H_2 \rightarrow 2H^+ + 2e^-$

Polymer electrolyte membrane $\downarrow H^+$ ions

Cathode
$\frac{1}{2}O_2 + 2H^+ + 2e^- \rightarrow H_2O$

Oxidant (O_2) in →

→ H_2O out

$2e^-$

Fuel Cells Don't Just Use Hydrogen

Scientists in the car industry are developing fuel cells that use **hydrogen-rich fuels** — these have a high percentage of hydrogen in their molecules and can be converted into H_2 in the car by a **reformer**. Such fuels include the two simplest alcohols, **methanol** and **ethanol**. There is also a **new generation** of fuel cells that can use alcohols **directly** without having to reform them to produce hydrogen.

A rowdy, ethanol-fuelled brawl had broken out in Hastings.

In these new fuel cells, the alcohol is **oxidised** at the **anode** in the presence of **water**. ⟶ E.g. $CH_3OH + H_2O \rightarrow CO_2 + 6e^- + 6H^+$

The H^+ **ions** pass through the electrolyte and are **oxidised** themselves to water. ⟶ $6H^+ + 6e^- + \frac{3}{2}O_2 \rightarrow 3H_2O$

Practice Questions

Q1 Name a metal that is used in the electrodes of an alkaline hydrogen-oxygen fuel cell.

Q2 What electrolyte is used in an alkaline hydrogen-oxygen fuel cell?

Exam Questions

Q1 The diagram on the right shows the structure of an alkaline hydrogen-oxygen fuel cell.

a) i) Label the site of oxidation and the site of reduction on the diagram. [1 mark]

ii) Draw an arrow to show the direction of the flow of electrons. [1 mark]

b) Write a half-equation for the reaction at each electrode. [2 marks]

c) Explain the purpose of the anion-exchange membrane in the fuel cell. [1 mark]

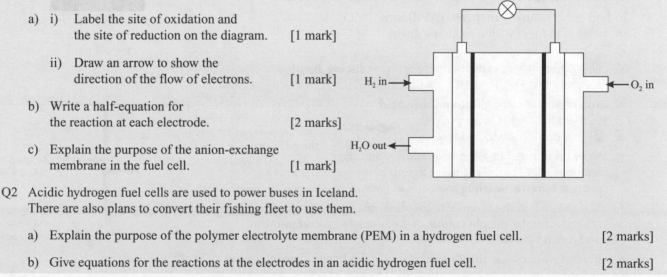

H_2 in →

← O_2 in

H_2O out ←

Q2 Acidic hydrogen fuel cells are used to power buses in Iceland. There are also plans to convert their fishing fleet to use them.

a) Explain the purpose of the polymer electrolyte membrane (PEM) in a hydrogen fuel cell. [2 marks]

b) Give equations for the reactions at the electrodes in an acidic hydrogen fuel cell. [2 marks]

Fuel sells — £1.15 per litre of petrol, £1.20 per litre of diesel...

These fuel cells are pretty nifty aren't they? Make sure you can draw the hydrogen-oxygen fuel cells in both acidic and alkaline conditions. Make sure you know the equations happening at the anode and cathode in each one too.

Redox Titrations

Better check your Year 1 notes and brush up on acid-base titrations. Redox titrations work like acid-base titrations but they're used to find out how much oxidising agent is needed to exactly react with a quantity of reducing agent (or vice versa).

Acid-Base Titrations — How Much Acid is Needed to Neutralise a Base

1) You met titrations back in Year 1. They allow you to find out **exactly** how much acid is needed to **neutralise** a quantity of alkali (or vice versa).

2) A known volume of an alkali with an **unknown concentration** is titrated with an acid of known concentration. The **volume** of acid needed to neutralise the acid can then be used to calculate the **concentration** of the alkali.

3) To carry out a titration, you'll need to apparatus a bit like this:

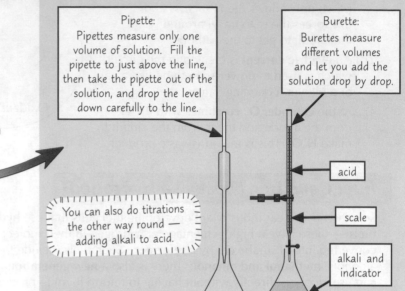

Pipette:
Pipettes measure only one volume of solution. Fill the pipette to just above the line, then take the pipette out of the solution, and drop the level down carefully to the line.

Burette:
Burettes measure different volumes and let you add the solution drop by drop.

acid

scale

alkali and indicator

You can also do titrations the other way round — adding alkali to acid.

Titrations Using Transition Element Ions are Redox Titrations

1) An **oxidising agent** accepts electrons and gets reduced. A **reducing agent** donates electrons and gets oxidised.

2) Transition (d-block) elements are good at changing **oxidation number** (see page 49). This makes them useful as oxidising and reducing agents as they'll readily **give out** or **receive** electrons.

3) To work out the **concentration** of a reducing agent, you just need to titrate a **known volume** of it against an oxidising agent of **known concentration**. This allows you to work out how much oxidising agent is needed to **exactly react** with your sample of reducing agent.

4) To find out how many **manganate(VII) ions** (MnO_4^-) are needed to react with a reducing agent:

Fred's celebration dance was a good indicator of the end point.

- First you measure out a quantity of the **reducing agent**, e.g. aqueous Fe^{2+} ions, using a pipette, and put it in a conical flask.

- You then add some **dilute sulfuric acid** to the flask — this is an excess, so you don't have to be too exact. ← The acid is added to make sure there are plenty of H^+ ions to allow the oxidising agent to be reduced.

- Now do a rough titration — gradually add the aqueous MnO_4^- (the **oxidising agent**) to the reducing agent using a **burette**, **swirling** the conical flask as you do so.

- You stop when the mixture in the flask **just** becomes tainted with the **purple colour** of the MnO_4^- (the **end point**) and record the volume of the oxidising agent added.

- Run a few accurate **titrations** and then calculate the **mean volume** of MnO_4^-.

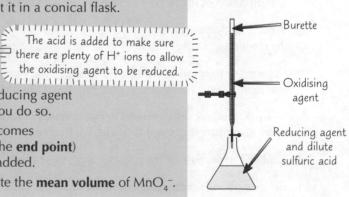

Burette

Oxidising agent

Reducing agent and dilute sulfuric acid

5) You can also do titrations the **other way round** — adding the reducing agent to the oxidising agent. The rule tends to be that you add the substance of **known** concentration to the substance of **unknown** concentration.

You can also work out the concentration of an oxidising agent by titrating it with a reducing agent of known concentration.

Redox Titrations

You Don't Always Need an Indicator During Redox Titrations

1) As transition metals change oxidation state they often also change **colour**, so it's easy to spot when the reaction is finished. Here are a couple of examples:

Acidified **potassium manganate(VII)** solution, $KMnO_{4(aq)}$, is used as an **oxidising agent**. It contains **manganate(VII) ions** (MnO_4^-), in which manganese has an oxidation number of **+7**. They can be reduced to Mn^{2+} ions during a **redox reaction**.

Example: The oxidation of Fe^{2+} to Fe^{3+} by manganate(VII) ions in solution.

Half-equations:
$$MnO_4^- + 8H^+ + 5e^- \rightarrow Mn^{2+} + 4H_2O \quad \text{Manganese is reduced}$$
$$5Fe^{2+} \rightarrow 5Fe^{3+} + 5e^- \quad \text{Iron is oxidised}$$
$$\overline{MnO_4^- + 8H^+ + 5Fe^{2+} \rightarrow Mn^{2+} + 4H_2O + 5Fe^{3+}}$$

$MnO_4^-{}_{(aq)}$ is purple. $Mn^{2+}{}_{(aq)}$ is colourless. During this reaction, you'll see a colour change from purple to colourless.

Acidified **potassium dichromate** solution, $K_2Cr_2O_{7(aq)}$, is another **oxidising agent**. It contains **dichromate(VI) ions** ($Cr_2O_7^{2-}$) in which chromium has an oxidation number of **+6**. They can be reduced to Cr^{3+} ions during a **redox reaction**.

Example: The oxidation of Zn to Zn^{2+} by dichromate(VI) ions in solution.

Half-equations:
$$Cr_2O_7^{2-} + 14H^+ + 6e^- \rightarrow 2Cr^{3+} + 7H_2O \quad \text{Chromium is reduced}$$
$$3Zn \rightarrow 3Zn^{2+} + 6e^- \quad \text{Zinc is oxidised}$$
$$\overline{Cr_2O_7^{2-} + 14H^+ + 3Zn \rightarrow 2Cr^{3+} + 7H_2O + 3Zn^{2+}}$$

$Cr_2O_7^{2-}{}_{(aq)}$ is orange. $Cr^{3+}{}_{(aq)}$ is violet, but usually looks green. During this reaction, you'll see a colour change from orange to green.

2) So, when you're carrying out redox titrations, you need to watch out for a **sharp colour change**.

3) When you're adding an oxidising agent to a reducing agent, they start reacting. This reaction will continue until **all** of the reducing agent is used up. The **very next drop** into the flask will give the mixture the **colour of the oxidising agent**. The trick is to spot **exactly** when this happens. (You could use a coloured reducing agent and a colourless oxidising agent instead — then you'd be watching for the moment that the colour in the flask disappears.)

4) Doing the reaction in front of a **white surface** can make colour changes easier to spot.

You Can Calculate the Concentration of a Reagent from the Titration Results

It wouldn't be a titration without some horrid calculations...

Example: 27.5 cm^3 of $0.0200 \text{ mol dm}^{-3}$ aqueous potassium manganate(VII) reacted with 25.0 cm^3 of acidified iron(II) sulfate solution. Calculate the concentration of Fe^{2+} ions in the solution.

$$MnO_4^-{}_{(aq)} + 8H^+{}_{(aq)} + 5Fe^{2+}{}_{(aq)} \rightarrow Mn^{2+}{}_{(aq)} + 4H_2O_{(l)} + 5Fe^{3+}{}_{(aq)}$$

1) Work out the number of **moles of MnO_4^- ions** added to the flask.

$$\text{Number of moles } MnO_4^- \text{ added} = \frac{\text{concentration} \times \text{volume}}{1000} = \frac{0.0200 \times 27.5}{1000} = 5.50 \times 10^{-4} \text{ moles}$$

2) Look at the balanced equation to find how many moles of **Fe^{2+}** react with **one mole** of MnO_4^-. Then you can work out the **number of moles of Fe^{2+}** in the flask.

5 moles of Fe^{2+} react with 1 mole of MnO_4^-. So moles of $Fe^{2+} = 5.50 \times 10^{-4} \times 5 = 2.75 \times 10^{-3}$ moles.

3) Work out the **number of moles of Fe^{2+}** that would be in 1000 cm^3 (1 dm^3) of solution — this is the **concentration**.

25.0 cm^3 of solution contained 2.75×10^{-3} moles of Fe^{2+}.

1000 cm^3 of solution would contain $\frac{(2.75 \times 10^{-3}) \times 1000}{25.0} = 0.110$ moles of Fe^{2+}.

So the concentration of Fe^{2+} is **$0.110 \text{ mol dm}^{-3}$**.

Redox Titrations

You Can Also Estimate the *Percentage of Iron* in *Iron Tablets*

This titration can be used to find out the percentage of iron in the iron tablets that are used to treat people with the blood disorder anaemia. The iron is usually in the form of iron(II) sulfate.

Example: A 2.56 g iron tablet was dissolved in dilute sulfuric acid to give 250 cm³ of solution. 25.0 cm³ of this solution was found to react with 12.5 cm³ of 0.0250 mol dm⁻³ potassium manganate(VII) solution. Calculate the percentage of iron in the tablet.

$$MnO_4^-{}_{(aq)} + 8H^+{}_{(aq)} + 5Fe^{2+}{}_{(aq)} \rightarrow Mn^{2+}{}_{(aq)} + 4H_2O_{(l)} + 5Fe^{3+}{}_{(aq)}$$

The first two steps are the same as the example on the previous page.

1) Work out the number of moles of **manganate(VII) ions** which took part in the reaction:

$$\text{Number of moles of } MnO_4^- = \frac{\text{concentration} \times \text{volume}}{1000} = \frac{0.0250 \times 12.5}{1000} = \textbf{3.125} \times \textbf{10}^{-4} \textbf{ moles}$$

2) From the equation, you can see that **5 moles** of iron(II) ions react with **1 mole** of manganate(VII) ions.

So in 25.0 cm³ of the iron solution there must be: $5 \times 3.125 \times 10^{-4}$ = **1.5625 ×10⁻³ moles of iron(II) ions**.

3) Now you can work out the number of moles of iron in **250 cm³** of the solution — this will be the number of moles of iron in the **whole tablet**:

$$\text{Number of moles of } Fe^{2+} = 1.5625 \times 10^{-3} \times 10 = \textbf{1.5625} \times \textbf{10}^{-2} \textbf{ moles}$$

4) From this, you can work out the **mass** of iron in the tablet:

1 mole of iron weighs **55.8 g**, so 1 tablet contains: $1.5625 \times 10^{-2} \times 55.8 = 0.871...$ g of iron

5) Finally, you can calculate the percentage of iron in the tablet. The total weight of the tablet is **2.56 g**.

So, the percentage of iron = $(0.871... \div 2.56) \times 100 = \textbf{34.1\%}$

Practice Questions

Q1 Write a half equation to show manganate(VII) ions acting as an oxidising agent.

Q2 Why is dilute acid added to the reaction mixture in redox titrations involving MnO_4^- ions?

Exam Questions

Q1 A 3.20 g iron tablet was dissolved in dilute sulfuric acid and made up to 250 cm³ with deionised water. 25.0 cm³ of this solution was found to react with 15.0 cm³ of 0.00900 mol dm⁻³ potassium manganate(VII) solution.

    a) Calculate the number of moles of iron in 25.0 cm³ of the solution.   [2 marks]

    b) Calculate the number of moles of iron in the tablet.   [1 mark]

    c) What percentage, by mass, of the tablet is iron?   [2 marks]

Q2 A 10.0 cm³ sample of 0.500 mol dm⁻³ SnCl₂ solution was titrated with acidified potassium manganate(VII) solution. Exactly 20.0 cm³ of 0.100 mol dm⁻³ potassium manganate(VII) solution was needed to fully oxidise the tin(II) chloride.

    a) What type of reaction is this?   [1 mark]

    b) How many moles of tin(II) chloride were present in the 10.0 cm³ sample?   [2 marks]

    c) How many moles of potassium manganate(VII) were needed to fully oxidise the tin(II) chloride?   [2 marks]

The half-equation for acidified MnO_4^- acting as an oxidising agent is: $MnO_4^- + 8H^+ + 5e^- \rightarrow Mn^{2+} + 4H_2O$

    d) Find the oxidation number of the oxidised tin ions present in the solution at the end of the titration.   [4 marks]

And how many moles does it take to change a light bulb...

...two, one to change the bulb, and another to ask "Why do we need light bulbs? We're moles — most of the time that we're underground, we keep our eyes shut. And the electricity costs a packet. We haven't thought this through..."

More on Redox Titrations

This is another example of a redox titration — it's a nifty little reaction that you can use to find the concentration of an oxidising agent. And since it's a titration, that also means a few more calculations to get to grips with...

Iodine-Sodium Thiosulfate Titrations are Dead Handy

Iodine-sodium thiosulfate titrations are a way of finding the concentration of an **oxidising agent**.

The **more concentrated** an oxidising agent is, the **more ions will be oxidised** by a certain volume of it.
So here's how you can find out the concentration of a solution of the oxidising agent **potassium iodate(V)**:

STAGE 1: Use a sample of oxidising agent to oxidise as much iodide as possible.

1) Measure out a certain volume of **potassium iodate(V)** solution (**KIO_3**) (the oxidising agent) — say **25.0 cm³**.

2) Add this to an excess of acidified **potassium iodide** solution (**KI**).
   The iodate(V) ions in the potassium iodate(V) solution
   oxidise some of the **iodide ions** to **iodine**. $\Longrightarrow$ $IO_3^-{}_{(aq)} + 5I^-{}_{(aq)} + 6H^+{}_{(aq)} \rightarrow 3I_{2(aq)} + 3H_2O_{(l)}$

STAGE 2: Find out how many moles of iodine have been produced.

You do this by **titrating** the resulting solution with **sodium thiosulfate** ($Na_2S_2O_3$).
(You need to know the concentration of the sodium thiosulfate solution.)

The iodine in the solution reacts
with **thiosulfate ions** like this: $\Longrightarrow$ $I_{2\ (aq)} + 2S_2O_3^{2-}{}_{(aq)} \rightarrow 2I^-{}_{(aq)} + S_4O_6^{2-}{}_{(aq)}$

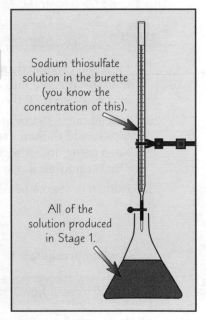

Sodium thiosulfate
solution in the burette
(you know the
concentration of this).

All of the
solution produced
in Stage 1.

Titration of Iodine with Sodium Thiosulfate

1) Take the flask containing the solution that was produced in Stage 1.

2) From a burette, add sodium thiosulfate solution to the flask **drop by drop**.

3) It's hard to see the end point, so when the iodine colour fades to a
   pale yellow (this is close to the end point), add 2 cm³ of **starch solution**
   (to detect the presence of iodine). The solution in the conical flask will go
   dark blue, showing there's still some iodine there.

4) Add sodium thiosulfate **one drop at a time** until the blue colour disappears.

5) When this happens, it means all the iodine has **just** been reacted.

6) Now you can **calculate** the number of moles of iodine in the solution.

Here's how you'd do the titration calculation to find
the **number of moles of iodine** produced in Stage 1.

> **Example:** The iodine in the solution produced in Stage 1 reacted fully with 11.0 cm³ of 0.120 mol dm⁻³
> thiosulfate solution. Work out the number of moles of iodine present in the starting solution.
>
> $$I_2 + 2S_2O_3^{2-} \rightarrow 2I^- + S_4O_6^{2-}$$
> **11.0 cm³**
> **0.120 mol dm⁻³**
>
> **Number of moles of thiosulfate** = $\dfrac{\text{concentration} \times \text{volume (cm}^3)}{1000} = \dfrac{0.120 \times 11.0}{1000} = $ **1.32 × 10⁻³ moles**
>
> **1 mole** of iodine reacts with **2 moles** of thiosulfate.
>
> So number of **moles of iodine** in the solution = 1.32 × 10⁻³ ÷ 2 = **6.60 × 10⁻⁴ moles**

More on Redox Titrations

STAGE 3: Calculate the concentration of the oxidising agent.

1) Now look back at your original equation: $IO_3^-{}_{(aq)} + 5I^-{}_{(aq)} + 6H^+{}_{(aq)} \rightarrow 3I_{2(aq)} + 3H_2O_{(l)}$

2) 25.0 cm³ of potassium iodate(V) solution produced **6.60 × 10⁻⁴ moles of iodine**.
The equation shows that **one mole** of iodate(V) ions will produce **three moles** of iodine.

3) That means there must have been **6.60 × 10⁻⁴ ÷ 3 = 2.20 × 10⁻⁴ moles of iodate(V) ions** in the original solution.
So now it's straightforward to find the **concentration** of the potassium iodate(V) solution, which is what you're after:

$$\text{number of moles} = \frac{\text{concentration} \times \text{volume}\,(\text{cm}^3)}{1000} \qquad 2.20 \times 10^{-4} = \frac{\text{concentration} \times 25.0}{1000}$$

$$\Rightarrow \text{concentration of potassium iodate(V) solution} = \textbf{0.00880 mol dm}^{-3}$$

You Can Use the *Titration* to Find the *Percentage of Copper* in an *Alloy*

Copper(II) ions will **oxidise** iodide ions to **iodine**.
This can be used to find the percentage of copper in an alloy, e.g. brass...

STAGE 1: Use a sample of oxidising agent to oxidise as much iodide as possible.

1) Dissolve a **weighed amount** of the alloy in some **concentrated nitric acid**.
Pour this mixture into a **250 cm³** volumetric flask
and make up to 250 cm³ with **deionised water**.

2) Pipette out a **25 cm³** portion of the diluted solution and transfer to a flask.
Slowly add **sodium carbonate solution** to neutralise any remaining nitric acid.
Keep going until a slight precipitate forms.
This is removed if you add a few drops of **ethanoic acid**.

3) Add an excess of **potassium iodide solution** which reacts with the copper ions:

$$2Cu^{2+}{}_{(aq)} + 4I^-{}_{(aq)} \rightarrow 2CuI_{(s)} + I_{2(aq)}$$

King Henry was 30% steel,
20% velvet and 50% bravery.

4) A **white precipitate** of **copper(I) iodide** forms. The copper(II) ions have been reduced to copper(I).

STAGE 2: Find out how many moles of iodine have been produced.

Titrate the **product mixture** against **sodium thiosulfate solution** to
find the number of moles of **iodine** present.

STAGE 3: Calculate the concentration of the oxidising agent.

1) Now you can work out the **number of moles of copper** present in both the 25 cm³ and 250 cm³ solutions
(from the equation above, you can see that **2 moles** of copper ions produce **1 mole** of iodine).

2) From this you can calculate the **mass of copper** in the whole piece of brass.

3) Finally, you can work out the **percentage** of copper in the alloy.

There are a Few *Sources of Error* in These Titrations...

1) The **starch indicator** for the sodium thiosulfate titration needs to be added at the right point,
when most of the iodine has **reacted**, or else the blue colour will be very **slow to disappear**.

2) The starch solution needs to be **freshly made** or else it won't behave as expected.

3) The **precipitate of copper(I) iodide** makes seeing the **colour of the solution** quite hard.

4) The **iodine** produced in the reaction can **evaporate** from the solution, giving a **false titration reading**.
The final figure for the percentage of copper would be **too low** as a result. It helps if the solution is kept **cool**.

More on Redox Titrations

Q1 How can an iodine-sodium thiosulfate titration help you to work out the concentration of an oxidising agent?

Q2 How many moles of thiosulfate ions react with one mole of iodine molecules?

Q3 What is added during an iodine-sodium thiosulfate titration to make the end point easier to see?

Q4 Describe the colour change at the end point of the iodine-sodium thiosulfate titration.

Exam Questions

Q1 $10.0 \ cm^3$ of potassium iodate(V) solution was reacted with excess acidified potassium iodide solution. All of the resulting solution was titrated with $0.150 \ mol \, dm^{-3}$ sodium thiosulfate solution. It fully reacted with $24.0 \ cm^3$ of the sodium thiosulfate solution.

   a) Write an equation showing how iodine is formed in the reaction between iodate(V) ions and iodide ions in acidic solution. [1 mark]

   b) How many moles of thiosulfate ions were there in $24.0 \ cm^3$ of the sodium thiosulfate solution? [1 mark]

   c) In the titration, iodine reacted with sodium thiosulfate according to this equation:

   $$I_{2(aq)} + 2Na_2S_2O_{3(aq)} \rightarrow 2NaI_{(aq)} + Na_2S_4O_{6(aq)}$$

   Calculate the number of moles of iodine that reacted with the sodium thiosulfate solution. [1 mark]

   d) How many moles of iodate(V) ions produce 1 mole of iodine from potassium iodide? [1 mark]

   e) What was the concentration of the potassium iodate(V) solution? [2 marks]

Q2 An $18.0 \ cm^3$ sample of potassium manganate(VII) solution was reacted with an excess of acidified potassium iodide solution. The resulting solution was titrated with $0.300 \ mol \, dm^{-3}$ sodium thiosulfate solution. $12.5 \ cm^3$ of sodium thiosulfate solution were needed to fully react with the iodine.

   When they were mixed, the manganate(VII) ions reacted with the iodide ions according to this equation:

   $$2MnO_4^{-}{}_{(aq)} + 10I^{-}{}_{(aq)} + 16H^+ \rightarrow 5I_{2(aq)} + 8H_2O_{(aq)} + 2Mn^{2+}{}_{(aq)}$$

   During the titration, the iodine reacted with sodium thiosulfate according to this equation:

   $$I_{2(aq)} + 2Na_2S_2O_{3(aq)} \rightarrow 2NaI_{(aq)} + Na_2S_4O_{6(aq)}$$

   Calculate the concentration of the potassium manganate(VII) solution. [4 marks]

Q3 A $4.20 \ g$ coin, made of a copper alloy, was dissolved in acid and the solution made up to $250 \ cm^3$ with distilled water. $25.0 \ cm^3$ of this solution was added to excess potassium iodide solution. The following reaction occurred:

   $$2Cu^{2+}{}_{(aq)} + 4I^{-}{}_{(aq)} \rightarrow 2CuI_{(s)} + I_{2(aq)}$$

   The resulting solution was neutralised and then titrated with $0.150 \ mol \, dm^{-3}$ sodium thiosulfate. The iodine and thiosulfate reacted according to this equation:

   $$I_{2(aq)} + 2S_2O_3^{2-}{}_{(aq)} \rightarrow 2I^{-}{}_{(aq)} + S_4O_6^{2-}{}_{(aq)}$$

   The average titration result was $19.3 \ cm^3$.

   a) How many moles of iodine were present in the solution used in the titration? [2 marks]

   b) How many moles of copper ions must have been in the $25.0 \ cm^3$ of solution used for the titration? [2 marks]

   c) What percentage of the coin, by mass, was copper? [3 marks]

Two vowels went out for dinner — they had an iodate...

This might seem like quite a faff — you do a redox reaction to release iodine, titrate the iodine solution, do a sum to find the iodine concentration, write an equation, then do another sum to work out the concentration of something else. The thing is, it does work, and you do have to know how. If you're rusty on the calculations, look back at pages 45-46.

Transition Metals

The d-block can be found slap bang in the middle of the periodic table. It's here you'll find the transition metals. You'll also find the most precious metals in the world here. That's got to make it worth a look...

Transition Metals are Found in the d-Block

The **d-block** is the block of elements in the middle of the periodic table. Most of the elements in the d-block are **transition metals** (or transition elements).

You mainly need to know about the ones in the first row of the d-block. These are the elements from **titanium** to **copper**.

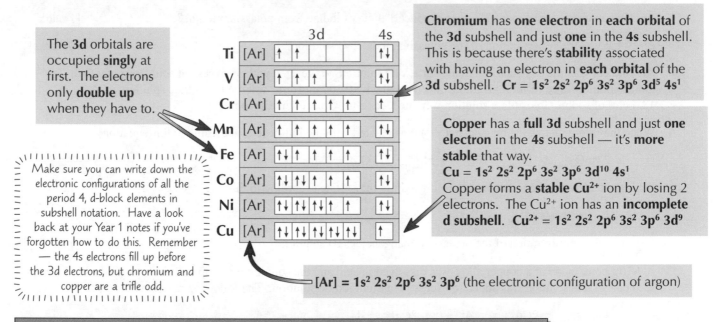

s-block   d-block   p-block

You Need to Know the Electronic Configurations of the Transition Metals

Transition metals are d-block elements that can form **one** or **more stable ions** with **incompletely filled d-orbitals**.

A d subshell has **5 orbitals** so can hold **10** electrons. So transition metals can form **at least one ion** that has **between 1 and 9 electrons** in its d-orbitals. All the period 4 d-block elements are transition metals apart from **scandium** and **zinc** (see below). The diagram below shows the 3d and 4s subshells of the period 4 transition metals:

The **3d** orbitals are occupied **singly** at first. The electrons only **double up** when they have to.

Make sure you can write down the electronic configurations of all the period 4, d-block elements in subshell notation. Have a look back at your Year 1 notes if you've forgotten how to do this. Remember — the 4s electrons fill up before the 3d electrons, but chromium and copper are a trifle odd.

Chromium has **one electron** in **each orbital** of the **3d** subshell and just **one** in the **4s** subshell. This is because there's **stability** associated with having an electron in **each orbital** of the 3d subshell. $Cr = 1s^2\ 2s^2\ 2p^6\ 3s^2\ 3p^6\ 3d^5\ 4s^1$

Copper has a **full 3d** subshell and just **one electron** in the **4s** subshell — it's **more stable** that way. $Cu = 1s^2\ 2s^2\ 2p^6\ 3s^2\ 3p^6\ 3d^{10}\ 4s^1$
Copper forms a **stable** Cu^{2+} ion by losing 2 electrons. The Cu^{2+} ion has an **incomplete d subshell**. $Cu^{2+} = 1s^2\ 2s^2\ 2p^6\ 3s^2\ 3p^6\ 3d^9$

$[Ar] = 1s^2\ 2s^2\ 2p^6\ 3s^2\ 3p^6$ (the electronic configuration of argon)

When Ions are Formed, the s Electrons are Removed First

When transition metals form **positive** ions, outer **s electrons** are removed **first**, then the d electrons.

Example: Titanium can form Ti^{2+} ions and Ti^{3+} ions. Give the electronic configurations for these two ions.

When titanium forms 2+ ions, it loses **both its 4s electrons**.
$Ti = 1s^2\ 2s^2\ 2p^6\ 3s^2\ 3p^6\ 3d^2\ 4s^2 \rightarrow Ti^{2+} = 1s^2\ 2s^2\ 2p^6\ 3s^2\ 3p^6\ 3d^2$

To form 3+ ions, it loses both its 4s electrons, and then a **3d electron** as well.
$Ti^{2+} = 1s^2\ 2s^2\ 2p^6\ 3s^2\ 3p^6\ 3d^2 \rightarrow Ti^{3+} = 1s^2\ 2s^2\ 2p^6\ 3s^2\ 3p^6\ 3d^1$

Titanium can also form 4+ ions, with the electronic configuration [Ar].

Sc and Zn Aren't Transition Metals

1) **Scandium** only forms one ion, Sc^{3+}, which has an **empty d subshell**. Scandium has the electronic configuration $[Ar]3d^1\ 4s^2$, so when it loses three electrons to form Sc^{3+}, it ends up with the electronic configuration [Ar].

2) **Zinc** only forms one ion, Zn^{2+}, which has a **full d subshell**. Zinc has the electronic configuration $[Ar]3d^{10}\ 4s^2$. When it forms Zn^{2+} it loses 2 electrons, both from the 4s subshell. This means it keeps its full 3d subshell.

Transition Metals

Transition Metals have *Variable Oxidation Numbers*

1) Most transition metals can form multiple **stable ions**.
In each ion, the transition metal is present with a different oxidation number.
For example, **vanadium** has **four** stable oxidation numbers:
vanadium(II) V^{2+}, vanadium(III) V^{3+}, vanadyl(IV) VO^{2+} and vanadate(V) VO_2^+.

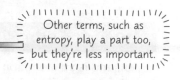
Oxidation numbers tell you how many electrons an atom has gained or lost in an ion or a compound.

2) To form a **compound** or a **complex** (see page 50) containing an ion
with a certain oxidation number, the energy given out when the ion
forms a compound or a complex needs to be greater than the energy
taken to remove the outer electrons and form the ion (the **ionisation energy**). ⬅

Other terms, such as entropy, play a part too, but they're less important.

3) **Transition metals** form ions by losing electrons from both their **4s** and **3d subshells**.
The **4s** and **3d** subshells are at **similar energy levels**, so it takes a similar amount of
energy to remove an electron from the 4s subshell as it does to remove an electron
from the 3d subshell. There is not a large increase between the ionisation energies
of removing successive electrons either, so multiple electrons can be removed
from these subshells, to form ions with different oxidation numbers.

4) The energy released when ions form a complex or compound increases
with the **ionic charge** (see page 22). Therefore, the increase in the energy required
to remove outer electrons to form transition metal ions with higher oxidation
numbers is usually **counteracted** by the increase in the energy released.

Priesh had many stable irons.

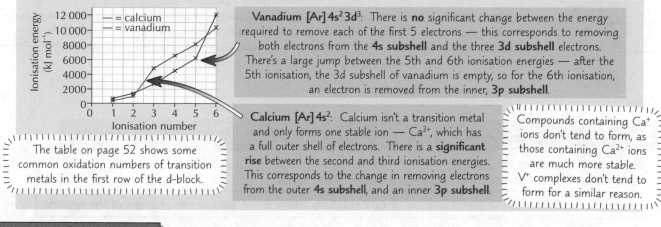

Vanadium $[Ar]\,4s^2\,3d^3$: There is **no** significant change between the energy required to remove each of the first 5 electrons — this corresponds to removing both electrons from the **4s subshell** and the three **3d subshell** electrons. There's a large jump between the 5th and 6th ionisation energies — after the 5th ionisation, the 3d subshell of vanadium is empty, so for the 6th ionisation, an electron is removed from the inner, **3p subshell**.

The table on page 52 shows some common oxidation numbers of transition metals in the first row of the d-block.

Calcium $[Ar]\,4s^2$: Calcium isn't a transition metal and only forms one stable ion — Ca^{2+}, which has a full outer shell of electrons. There is a **significant rise** between the second and third ionisation energies. This corresponds to the change in removing electrons from the outer **4s subshell**, and an inner **3p subshell**.

Compounds containing Ca^+ ions don't tend to form, as those containing Ca^{2+} ions are much more stable. V^+ complexes don't tend to form for a similar reason.

Practice Questions

Q1 What is the definition of a transition metal?

Q2 Why doesn't chromium have 2 electrons in its 4s subshell?

Q3 When vanadium forms an ion, which subshell does it lose its electrons from first?

Q4 Why is zinc not counted as a transition metal?

Exam Questions

Q1 Manganese is a transition metal. It forms stable manganese(II) ions, Mn^{2+},
and stable permanganate(VII) ions, MnO_4^-. With reference to the electronic configurations
of these ions, explain why manganese shows variable oxidation numbers. [3 marks]

Q2 Iron and copper are two common transition metals.

a) Write the electronic configuration of an iron atom and a copper atom. [2 marks]

b) Explain what is unusual about the electronic configuration of
copper among transition metals, and explain why this feature occurs. [2 marks]

c) Explain, in terms of iron's orbital and electronic configuration,
what happens when Fe^{2+} and Fe^{3+} ions are formed. [2 marks]

Scram Sc and Zn — we don't take kindly to your types round these parts...

As long as you're up to speed with your electronic confiugration rules, these pages are a bit of a breeze. Chromium and copper do throw a couple of spanners in the works (those banterous scamps), so make sure you don't get complacent.

Complex Ions

Transition metals are always forming complex ions. These aren't as complicated as they sound, though. Honest.

Complex Ions are Metal Ions Surrounded by Ligands

Transition metals can form **complex ions**. E.g. iron forms a **complex ion with water** — $[Fe(H_2O)_6]^{2+}$.

> A **complex ion** is a **metal ion** surrounded by **dative covalently** (**coordinately**) **bonded ligands**.

> A dative covalent bond is a covalent bond in which both electrons in the shared pair come from the same atom.

Ligands Form Bonds Using Lone Pairs of Electrons

A **ligand** is an atom, ion or molecule that **donates a pair of electrons** to a central metal atom or ion. A ligand must have **at least one lone pair of electrons**, otherwise it won't have anything to form a **dative covalent bond** with.

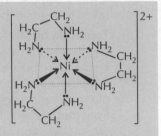

1) Ligands with **one lone pair** are called **monodentate** — e.g. $H_2O:$, $:NH_3$, $:Cl^-$, $:OH^-$.

2) Ligands with **two lone pairs** are called **bidentate** — e.g. 1,2-diaminoethane. Bidentate ligands can each form **two dative covalent bonds** with a metal ion.

3) Ligands with **more than two lone pairs** are called **multidentate** — e.g. $EDTA^{4-}$ has six lone pairs (so it's **hexadentate**). It can form **six dative bonds** with a metal ion.

In this complex, the nickel ion is bonded to three bidentate 1,2-diaminoethane ($NH_2CH_2CH_2NH_2$) ligands.

> 1,2-diaminoethane is also called ethylenediamine and can be abbreviated to 'en'.

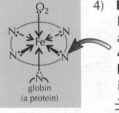

globin (a protein)

4) **Haemoglobin** is used to transport **oxygen** around the body. It's an iron(II) complex containing a **multidentate ligand** called a **haem** group. The haem group is made up of a **ring** containing **4 nitrogen atoms**. This means it's able to form **four dative covalent bonds** to the iron(II) ion. There are two other ligands bonded to the iron(II) ion — a protein called globin and either oxygen or water.

> There's more on haemoglobin on page 56.

Complex Ions Have an Overall Charge or Total Oxidation Number

The **overall charge** on the complex ion is its **oxidation number**. It's put **outside** the **square** brackets. You can use this to work out the **oxidation number of the metal**:

> **oxidation number of the metal ion = total oxidation number − sum of the charges of the ligands**

E.g. $[Fe(CN)_6]^{4-}_{(aq)}$: The total oxidation number is **−4** and each CN^- ligand has a charge of **−1**. So in this complex, iron's oxidation number = $-4 - (6 \times -1) = +2$.

Complex Ions Can Have Different Numbers of Ligands

1) The **coordination number** is the **number** of **dative covalent** (**coordinate**) **bonds** formed with the central metal ion.

2) The usual coordination numbers are **6** and **4**. If the ligands are **small**, like H_2O or NH_3, **6** can fit around the central metal ion. But if the ligands are **larger**, like Cl^-, only **4** can fit around the central metal ion.

3) The bonding electrons in the dative covalent bonds of a complex **repel** each other. This means that, in general, the ligands are positioned **as far away** from each other as possible. This causes complexes with different **coordination numbers** to have **distinctive shapes**.

> There's more about the shapes of molecules in your Year 1 notes.

Complexes with Six-Fold Coordination

Six-fold coordination means an **octahedral shape**. In octahedral complexes, the **bond angles** are all **90°**.

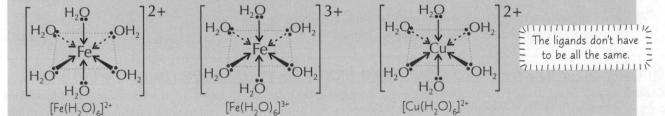

$[Fe(H_2O)_6]^{2+}$ $[Fe(H_2O)_6]^{3+}$ $[Cu(H_2O)_6]^{2+}$

> The ligands don't have to be all the same.

Complex Ions

Complexes With *Four-Fold Coordination*

Four-fold coordination usually means a **tetrahedral shape**.
E.g. the $[CuCl_4]^{2-}$ complex, which is yellow, and the $[Co(Cl)_4]^{2-}$ complex ion, which is deep blue.

The **bond angles** are **109.5°**.

Make sure you learn the shapes of these complexes. The d subshells mean you can't always use electron pair repulsion theory (see your Year 1 notes) to predict the shapes.

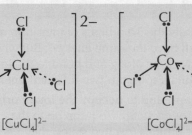

$[CuCl_4]^{2-}$ $[CoCl_4]^{2-}$

Occasionally, **four-fold coordination** results in a **square planar shape**. E.g. cis-platin (shown on the right). The **bond angles** are **90°**.

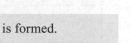

The Leow family were proud of their colour coordination.

Complex Ions Can Show *Cis/Trans Isomerism*

Cis/trans isomerism is a special case of **E/Z isomerism** (see your Year 1 notes).

Square planar and **octahedral** complex ions that have at least **two pairs** of identical ligands show **cis/trans isomerism**. **Cis** isomers have the **same groups** on the **same side**, **trans** have the **same groups opposite** each other. For example:

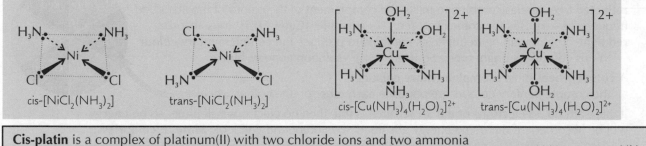

cis-$[NiCl_2(NH_3)_2]$ trans-$[NiCl_2(NH_3)_2]$ cis-$[Cu(NH_3)_4(H_2O)_2]^{2+}$ trans-$[Cu(NH_3)_4(H_2O)_2]^{2+}$

Cis-platin is a complex of platinum(II) with two chloride ions and two ammonia molecules in a square planar shape. It is used as an **anti-cancer** drug.

The two chloride ions are **next to each other**, so this complex is **cis-platin**. If they were **opposite** each other you would have **trans-platin**, which is toxic. It's therefore important that only the **cis** form of the complex is given to patients being treated for cancer.

Practice Questions

Q1 What is meant by the term 'complex ion'?

Q2 Describe how a ligand, such as ammonia, bonds to a central metal ion.

Q3 Draw the shape of the complex ion $[Cu(H_2O)_6]^{2+}$. Name the shape and state the size(s) of the bond angles.

Exam Question

Q1 When concentrated hydrochloric acid is added to an aqueous solution of $Cu^{2+}_{(aq)}$ a yellow solution is formed.

 a) State the coordination number and shape of the $Cu^{2+}_{(aq)}$ complex ion in the initial solution.   [2 marks]

 b) State the coordination number, shape, bond angles and formula of the complex ion responsible for the yellow solution.   [4 marks]

 c) Explain why the coordination number is different in the yellow solution than in the starting aqueous copper solution.   [2 marks]

Put your hands up — we've got you surrounded...

You'll never get transition element ions floating around by themselves in a solution — they'll always be surrounded by other molecules. It's kind of like what'd happen if you put a dish of sweets in a room of eight (or eighteen) year-olds.

Complex Ions and Colour

One property of transition metals is that they form coloured complexes. You're about to find out why...

Ligands **Split** the 3d Subshell into **Two Energy Levels**

1) Normally the 3d orbitals of transition metal ions **all** have the **same energy**. But when **ligands** come along and bond to the ions, the 3d orbitals split into **two different energy levels**.

2) Electrons tend to **occupy the lower orbitals** (the ground state). To jump up to the higher orbitals (excited states) they need **energy** equal to the energy gap, ΔE. They get this energy from **visible light**.

3) The larger the energy gap, the higher the frequency of light that is absorbed.

4) The amount of energy (and so the frequency of the light) needed to make electrons jump depends upon the **central metal ion**, its **oxidation number**, the **ligands** and the **coordination number** — these affect the **size of the energy gap** (ΔE).

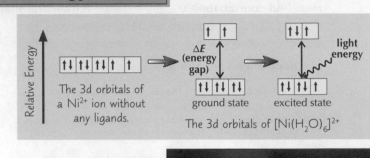

frequency increases ⟹

The **Colours** of Compounds are the **Complement** of Those That are **Absorbed**

1) As you saw above, the splitting of the d-orbitals in transition metals by ligands causes some frequencies of light to be absorbed by the complexes.

2) The rest of the frequencies of light are **transmitted** (or **reflected**). These **transmitted** or **reflected** frequencies combine to make the **complement** of the colour of the absorbed frequencies — this is the **colour** you see. For example, $[Cu(H_2O)_6]^{2+}$ ions absorb **red light**. The remaining frequencies **combine** to produce the **complementary colour** — in this case that's bright blue. So $[Cu(H_2O)_6]^{2+}$ solution appears **blue**.

3) A **colour wheel** shows **complementary colours** — the complementary colours are opposite each other on the colour wheel.

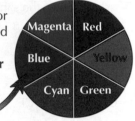

4) If there are **no** 3d electrons or the 3d subshell is **full**, then no electrons will jump, so **no energy** will be absorbed. If there's no energy absorbed, the compound will look **white** or **colourless**.

The **Colours** of Aqueous Complexes Can Help to **Identify** Transition Metal Ions

When a solid containing a **transition metal ion** is dissolved in **water**, the transition metal ion will form an **aqueous complex** in solution (the metal ion will be surrounded by water ligands). The **colour** of this aqueous solution can help to identify the transition metal ion that is present.

Oxidation No.	+7	+6	+5	+4	+3	+2
Titanium					Ti^{3+} (purple)	Ti^{2+} (violet)
Vanadium			VO_2^+ (yellow)	VO^{2+} (blue)	V^{3+} (green)	V^{2+} (violet)
Chromium		$Cr_2O_7^{2-}$ (orange)			Cr^{3+} (green)	
Manganese	MnO_4^- (purple)	MnO_4^{2-} (green)				Mn^{2+} (pale pink)
Iron					Fe^{3+} (yellow)	Fe^{2+} (pale green)
Cobalt						Co^{2+} (pink)
Nickel						Ni^{2+} (green)
Copper						Cu^{2+} (pale blue)

You don't need to learn the colours of aqueous titanium, manganese or nickel complexes.

Complex Ions and Colour

Vanadium Forms *Stable Ions* with Different *Oxidation Numbers*

1) You learnt on page 49 that one of the properties of transition metals is that they can exist in variable oxidation numbers. For example, vanadium can exist in **four oxidation numbers** in solution — +2, +3, +4 and +5. You can tell them apart by their colours, which are shown on the previous page.

2) When you switch between oxidation numbers, it's a **redox reaction** — ions are either oxidised (they lose electrons and their oxidation number increases) or reduced (they gain electrons and their oxidation number decreases).

3) You can write ionic half-equations to show the reduction of ions or atoms. Each reaction also has its own **reduction potential**. Here are the ionic half-equations for the reduction reactions of the different vanadium ions:

Oxidation Number of Vanadium	Reduction Half-Equation	Reduction Potential ($E^{\ominus}$)
+5	$VO_2^+{}_{(aq)} + 2H^+{}_{(aq)} + e^- \rightleftharpoons VO^{2+}{}_{(aq)} + H_2O_{(l)}$	+1.00 V
+4	$VO^{2+}{}_{(aq)} + 2H^+{}_{(aq)} + e^- \rightleftharpoons V^{3+}{}_{(aq)} + H_2O_{(l)}$	+0.34 V
+3	$V^{3+}{}_{(aq)} + e^- \rightleftharpoons V^{2+}{}_{(aq)}$	−0.26 V
+2	$V^{2+}{}_{(aq)} + 2e^- \rightleftharpoons V_{(s)}$	−1.18 V

4) You can use the **reduction potentials** to work out whether redox reactions involving transition metals are likely to happen. The method for this is the same as the one on page 38.

Reduction potentials is just another name for electrode potentials.

Example: Use the table above to determine the colour change(s) observed when zinc metal is added to an acidified solution containing $VO^{2+}{}_{(aq)}$ ions. $Zn^{2+}{}_{(aq)} + 2e^- \rightleftharpoons Zn_{(s)}$ $E^{\ominus} = -0.76$ V

First work out the **cell potential** for each of the reduction reactions of the vanadium ions by zinc:

$2VO_2^+{}_{(aq)} + 4H^+{}_{(aq)} + Zn_{(s)} \rightleftharpoons 2VO^{2+}{}_{(aq)} + 2H_2O_{(l)} + Zn^{2+}{}_{(aq)}$ $E^{\ominus} = +1.76$ V

$2VO^{2+}{}_{(aq)} + 4H^+{}_{(aq)} + Zn_{(s)} \rightleftharpoons 2V^{3+}{}_{(aq)} + 2H_2O_{(l)} + Zn^{2+}{}_{(aq)}$ $E^{\ominus} = +1.10$ V

$2V^{3+}{}_{(aq)} + Zn_{(s)} \rightleftharpoons 2V^{2+}{}_{(aq)} + Zn^{2+}{}_{(aq)}$ $E^{\ominus} = +0.50$ V

$V^{2+}{}_{(aq)} + Zn_{(s)} \rightleftharpoons V_{(s)} + Zn^{2+}{}_{(aq)}$ $E^{\ominus} = -0.42$ V

Redox reactions are only feasible if $E^{\ominus}$ is positive.

$E^{\ominus}$ for the first three reactions is **positive**, so zinc metal is able to reduce **vanadium(V)** to **vanadium(IV)**, which will then be reduced to **vanadium(III)**, which in turn will be reduced to **vanadium(II)**. The reduction potential for the reaction of vanadium(II) with zinc is **negative**. So under standard conditions, vanadium(II) **won't** be reduced by zinc to vanadium metal.

So the solution will change from **yellow** to **blue** to **green** to **violet**.

The mixture of yellow $VO_2^+{}_{(aq)}$ ions and blue $VO^{2+}{}_{(aq)}$ ions might make the solution look green.

Practice Questions

Q1 Which subshell is split by the presence of ligands?

Q2 State three factors that can affect the frequency of light absorbed by a transition metal complex.

Q3 What colour are VO^{2+} ions in solution?

Exam Questions

Q1 a) Using a noble gas core, [Ar], complete the electron arrangements for the following ions:

   i) Cu^+ ii) Cu^{2+} [2 marks]

  b) Which one of the above ions has coloured compounds? Explain your answer.   [1 mark]

Q2* Transition metal ions form a wide range of different colours when bonded to ligands. Using your knowledge of 3d orbitals, explain how ligands cause transition metals to be coloured. [6 marks]

Blue's not my complementary colour — it clashes with my hair...

Finally, some real Chemistry, with pretty colours and everything. It only took you 53 pages to get there. Make sure you understand how the colours are made — there have to be electrons in the d-orbitals that are able to jump up from the lower energy d-orbitals to the higher energy d-orbitals. Otherwise you'll just have a colourless solution. Yawn.

* The quality of your extended response will be assessed for this question.

TOPIC 15 — TRANSITION METALS

Chromium

Can't get enough of transition metals? Well, you're in luck, because it's time for the chemistry of chromium...

Chromium Ions *Usually Exist in the* **+2**, **+3** *or* **+6** *Oxidation Numbers*

1) Chromium exists in compounds in many oxidation numbers. The +3 state is the most stable, followed by the +6 and then +2.

2) Chromium forms **two ions** with oxygen in the +6 oxidation number — **chromate(VI) ions**, CrO_4^{2-}, and **dichromate(VI) ions**, $Cr_2O_7^{2-}$. These ions are **good oxidising agents** because they are easily reduced to Cr^{3+}.

3) When **Cr^{3+} ions** are surrounded by 6 water ligands they're **violet**. But the water ligands are usually **substituted** with impurities in the water, e.g. Cl^-. This makes the solution look green.

Oxidation number	Formula of ion	Colour of ion in water
+6	$Cr_2O_7^{2-}{}_{(aq)}$	Orange
+6	$CrO_4^{2-}{}_{(aq)}$	Yellow
+3	$Cr^{3+}{}_{(aq)}$	Green (Violet)
+2	$Cr^{2+}{}_{(aq)}$	Blue

Chromium Ions can be *Oxidised* and *Reduced*

Chromium has lots of different oxidation numbers and can take part in lots of redox reactions.

1) Dichromate(VI) ions can be **reduced** using a reducing agent such as **zinc** and **dilute acid**.

Oxidation no: +6   O   +2   +3
$$Cr_2O_7^{2-}{}_{(aq)} + 14H^+{}_{(aq)} + 3Zn_{(s)} \rightarrow 3Zn^{2+}{}_{(aq)} + 2Cr^{3+}{}_{(aq)} + 7H_2O_{(l)} \quad E^{\ominus} = +2.09\,V$$

2) Zinc will **reduce** Cr^{3+} further to Cr^{2+}. You'll need to use an inert atmosphere — Cr^{2+} is so **unstable** that it oxidises straight back to Cr^{3+} in air.

Oxidation no: +3   O   +2   +2
$$2Cr^{3+}{}_{(aq)} + Zn_{(s)} \rightarrow Zn^{2+}{}_{(aq)} + 2Cr^{2+}{}_{(aq)} \quad E^{\ominus} = +0.35\,V$$

3) You can oxidise Cr^{3+} to chromate(VI) ions with **hydrogen peroxide** in an **alkaline** solution.

Oxidation no: +3   +6
$$2Cr^{3+}{}_{(aq)} + 10OH^-{}_{(aq)} + 3H_2O_{2(aq)} \rightarrow 2CrO_4^{2-}{}_{(aq)} + 8H_2O_{(l)} \quad E^{\ominus} = +1.08\,V$$

Adding acid shifts the equilibrium to the right. Adding alkali shifts it to the left.

4) If you add some **acid** to this yellow solution, you form an **orange solution** that contains **dichromate(VI) ions**. This is a reversible reaction, so an equilibrium exists between **chromate(VI)** and **dichromate(VI) ions**.

Oxidation no: +6   +6
$$2CrO_4^{2-}{}_{(aq)} + 2H^+{}_{(aq)} \rightleftharpoons Cr_2O_7^{2-}{}_{(aq)} + H_2O_{(l)}$$

Chromium Hydroxide is *Amphoteric*

1) When you mix an aqueous solution of **chromium(III) ions** with aqueous **sodium hydroxide** (NaOH) or aqueous **ammonia** (NH_3) you get a **chromium hydroxide precipitate** — $Cr(OH)_3(H_2O)_{3(s)}$.

$$[Cr(H_2O)_6]^{3+}{}_{(aq)} + 3OH^-{}_{(aq)} \rightarrow [Cr(OH)_3(H_2O)_3]_{(s)} + 3H_2O_{(l)}$$
green solution   grey-green precipitate

$$[Cr(H_2O)_6]^{3+}{}_{(aq)} + 3NH_{3(aq)} \rightarrow [Cr(OH)_3(H_2O)_3]_{(s)} + 3NH_4^+{}_{(aq)}$$
green solution   grey-green precipitate

2) Chromium hydroxide $[Cr(H_2O)_3(OH)_3]$ is **amphoteric**. This means it can react with **both** acids and bases.

$$[Cr(H_2O)_6]^{3+}{}_{(aq)} \xleftarrow{+3H^+{}_{(aq)}} [Cr(OH)_3(H_2O)_3]_{(s)} \xrightarrow{+3OH^-{}_{(aq)}} [Cr(OH)_6]^{3-}{}_{(aq)} + 3H_2O_{(l)}$$
With acid   With base

3) So if you add **excess sodium hydroxide** to a chromium hydroxide precipitate, the H_2O ligands **deprotonate**, and a solution containing $[Cr(OH)_6]^{3-}{}_{(aq)}$ forms.

$$[Cr(OH)_3(H_2O)_3]_{(s)} + 3OH^-{}_{(aq)} \rightarrow [Cr(OH)_6]^{3-}{}_{(aq)} + 3H_2O_{(l)}$$
grey-green precipitate   dark green solution

4) If you add **acid** to the chromium hydroxide precipitate, the OH^- ligands **protonate** and a solution containing $[Cr(H_2O)_6]^{3+}{}_{(aq)}$ forms.

$$[Cr(OH)_3(H_2O)_3]_{(s)} + 3H^+{}_{(aq)} \rightarrow [Cr(H_2O)_6]^{3+}{}_{(aq)}$$
grey-green precipitate   green solution

5) The **reactions** above are **NOT** ligand exchanges (see page 56). Instead, they're acid-base reactions — the ligands are **chemically modified** by the acid or the alkali (by the addition or removal of an H^+ ion).

6) But, if you add **excess ammonia** to the chromium hydroxide precipitate, a **ligand exchange reaction** occurs.

$$[Cr(OH)_3(H_2O)_3]_{(s)} + 6NH_{3(aq)} \rightarrow [Cr(NH_3)_6]^{3+}{}_{(aq)} + 3OH^-{}_{(aq)} + 3H_2O_{(l)}$$
grey-green precipitate   purple solution

Chromium

You Can **Prepare** Transition Metal Complexes

Making transition metal complexes can be as simple as adding a solution or solid containing your **transition metal ion** to a solution containing your **ligand** and giving it a mix. This is how you would prepare the complexes on page 57.

It's not always that easy, however. Take the **chromium** complex **chromium(II) ethanoate**, $Cr_2(CH_3COO)_4(H_2O)_2$, for instance. To make it, you start off with sodium dichromate(VI) solution. The reaction happens in **two parts**.

1) **Orange** sodium dichromate(VI) is **reduced** with zinc in acid solution to first form a **green** solution containing Cr^{3+} ions, and then to give a **blue** solution of Cr^{2+} ions (like you saw on the previous page).

$$Cr_2O_7^{2-}{}_{(aq)} + 14H^+{}_{(aq)} + 3Zn_{(s)} \rightarrow 3Zn^{2+}{}_{(aq)} + 2Cr^{3+}{}_{(aq)} + 7H_2O_{(l)} \qquad 2Cr^{3+}{}_{(aq)} + Zn_{(s)} \rightarrow 2Cr^{2+}{}_{(aq)} + Zn^{2+}{}_{(aq)}$$

2) **Sodium ethanoate** is mixed with this solution and a **red precipitate** of **chromium(II) ethanoate** forms.

$$2Cr^{2+}{}_{(aq)} + 4CH_3COO^-{}_{(aq)} + 2H_2O_{(l)} \rightarrow [Cr_2(CH_3COO)_4(H_2O)_2]_{(s)}$$

3) Unfortunately it's not that simple as Cr^{2+} ions are **very easily oxidised**. You have to do the whole experiment in an **inert atmosphere** (such as nitrogen) to keep the air out and remove the oxygen from all the liquids in your experiment before using them (e.g. by bubbling nitrogen though them).

- Slowly add **hydrochloric acid** to a flask containing sodium dichromate(VI) solution and zinc mesh. As well as reducing the dichromate(VI) ions, some of the zinc metal will react with the acid to produce **hydrogen gas**, which can escape through a rubber tube into a beaker of water.

- As soon as you see the solution turn a **clear blue** colour, **pinch the rubber tube shut** so hydrogen can **no longer escape** from the flask.

- The build up of **pressure** in the flask will force the Cr^{2+} solution through the open glass tube and into a flask of **sodium ethanoate**.

- As soon as the blue solution reacts with the sodium ethanoate, a **red precipitate** forms. Ta-da, you've made **chromium(II) ethanoate**.

- **Filter** off the precipitate and **wash** it using **water**, then **ethanol**, then **ether** (while still keeping the chromium(II) ethanoate in an inert atmosphere to stop it getting oxidised).

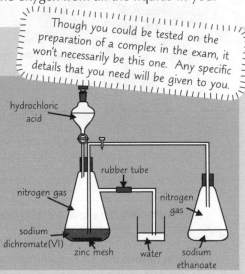

Though you could be tested on the preparation of a complex in the exam, it won't necessarily be this one. Any specific details that you need will be given to you.

Practice Questions

Q1 What colours are the +3 and +2 chromium aqua-ions?

Q2 Write an equation for the reaction between chromium(III) ions and hydrogen peroxide in an alkaline solution.

Exam Questions

Q1 Potassium dichromate(VI) $(K_2Cr_2O_7)$ is a powerful oxidising agent in acidic solution.
When potassium dichromate(VI) is acidified and mixed with zinc powder in air, a colour change is seen.

    a) Describe the colour change seen in the solution.   [1 mark]

    b) Give the changes in oxidation number for Cr and Zn and write an ionic equation for the reaction.   [3 marks]

    c) If the reaction is carried out in an inert atmosphere, a different result will occur.
       State how the result will differ and explain why.   [3 marks]

Q2 Chromium hydroxide, $Cr(OH)_3(H_2O)_3$, is an amphoteric complex.

    a) Explain what is meant by the term 'amphoteric', and give equations that demonstrate
       the amphoteric behaviour of the chromium hydroxide complex.   [3 marks]

    b) Write an equation for the reaction between chromium hydroxide and excess ammonia.
       Include any observations you would expect to see.   [2 marks]

What do you call a bird's mother? Crow-mum...

Sorry, all these equations seem to be getting to my head a bit. Time for an emergency biscuit. First, have another look at the reactions of chromium hydroxide and make sure you know whether the ligands are being exchanged or modified.

Reactions of Ligands

There are more substitutions on this page than the number of elephants you can fit in a mini.

Ligands can Exchange Places with One Another

One ligand can be **swapped** for another ligand — this is **ligand exchange**. It usually causes a **colour change**.

1) If the ligands are of **similar size**, e.g. H_2O, NH_3, CN^- or OH^-, then the **coordination number** of the complex ion **doesn't change**, and neither does the **shape**.

$$[Cr(H_2O)_6]^{3+}{}_{(aq)} + 6NH_{3(aq)} \rightleftharpoons [Cr(NH_3)_6]^{3+}{}_{(aq)} + 6H_2O_{(l)}$$
octahedral   octahedral
dark green   purple

Like ligands, a large, charged rugby player can also lead to a change in coordination.

2) If a **small**, **uncharged** ligand (e.g. H_2O) is substituted for a **large**, **charged** ligand (e.g. Cl^-), or vice versa, there's a **change of coordination number** and a **change of shape**.

$$[Cu(H_2O)_6]^{2+}{}_{(aq)} + 4Cl^-{}_{(aq)} \rightleftharpoons [CuCl_4]^{2-}{}_{(aq)} + 6H_2O_{(l)}$$
octahedral   tetrahedral
pale blue   yellow

$$[Co(H_2O)_6]^{2+}{}_{(aq)} + 4Cl^-{}_{(aq)} \rightleftharpoons [CoCl_4]^{2-}{}_{(aq)} + 6H_2O_{(l)}$$
octahedral   tetrahedral
pale pink   blue

3) Sometimes the substitution is only **partial**.

$$[Cu(H_2O)_6]^{2+}{}_{(aq)} + 4NH_{3(aq)} \rightleftharpoons [Cu(NH_3)_4(H_2O)_2]^{2+}{}_{(aq)} + 4H_2O_{(l)}$$
octahedral   octahedral
pale blue   deep blue

As it's in solution and contains ligands that aren't water, you need to include all the water ligands when writing the formula of a complex like $[Cu(NH_3)_4(H_2O)_2]^{2+}$. But if you're writing out the formula of a precipitate, such as $[Cu(H_2O)_4(OH)_2]$, you can leave out the water ligands and just write $Cu(OH)_2$.

This reaction only happens when you add an excess of ammonia — if you just add a bit, you get a blue precipitate of $[Cu(OH)_2(H_2O)_4]$ instead (see the next page).

Carbon Monoxide Poisoning Happens Because of Ligand Exchange

The oxygen or water molecule in **haemoglobin** (see page 50) can be replaced in a ligand exchange reaction by **carbon monoxide (CO)**, forming **carboxyhaemoglobin**. This is bad news because carbon monoxide forms **strong** dative covalent bonds (see your Year 1 notes) with the **iron** ion and **doesn't** readily exchange with oxygen or water ligands, meaning the haemoglobin **can't transport oxygen** any more. This leads to **carbon monoxide poisoning**.

A Positive Entropy Change Makes a More Stable Complex

1) When a **ligand exchange reaction** occurs, dative bonds are **broken** and **formed**. The **strength** of the bonds being broken is often very **similar** to the strength of the new bonds being made. So the **enthalpy change** for a ligand exchange reaction is usually very **small**. For example, the reaction substituting ammonia with ethane-1,2-diamine in a nickel complex has a very **small** enthalpy change of reaction:

$$[Ni(NH_3)_6]^{2+} + 3NH_2CH_2CH_2NH_2 \rightarrow [Ni(NH_2CH_2CH_2NH_2)_3]^{2+} + 6NH_3 \quad \Delta H = -13 \text{ kJ mol}^{-1}$$

Break 6 coordinate bonds between Ni and N.   Form 6 coordinate bonds between Ni and N.

2) This is actually a **reversible** reaction, but the equilibrium lies so **far to the right** that it is thought of as being irreversible — $[Ni(NH_2CH_2CH_2NH_2)_3]^{2+}$ is **much more stable** than $[Ni(NH_3)_6]^{2+}$. This isn't accounted for by an enthalpy change. Instead, it's to do with the **entropy change** of the reaction:

> When monodentate ligands are substituted with bidentate or multidentate ligands, the number of particles in solution increases — the **more particles**, the **greater the entropy**. Reactions that result in an increase in entropy are **more likely** to occur.

3) When the **hexadentate ligand EDTA⁴⁻** replaces monodentate or bidentate ligands, the complex formed is **a lot more stable**.

$$[Cr(NH_3)_6]^{3+} + EDTA^{4-} \rightarrow [Cr(EDTA)]^- + 6NH_3 \quad \textbf{2 particles} \rightarrow \textbf{7 particles}$$

The enthalpy change for this reaction is almost zero and the entropy change is big and positive. This makes the free energy change ($\Delta G = \Delta H - T\Delta S$) negative, so the reaction is feasible (see page 32).

Reactions of Ligands

Transition Element *Hydroxides* are *Brightly Coloured Precipitates*

1) When you mix an aqueous solution of **transition element ions** with aqueous **sodium hydroxide** (NaOH) or aqueous **ammonia** (NH₃), the water ligands are **deprotonated** in an acid-base reaction and you get a **coloured hydroxide precipitate**.

2) You can reverse these reactions by adding an **acid** to the **hydroxide precipitate** — the hydroxide ligands will **protonate** and the precipitate will dissolve as the soluble **metal-aqua ions** are reformed.

3) In **aqueous solutions**, transition elements take the form $[M(H_2O)_6]^{n+}$. They can also be written as $M^{n+}_{(aq)}$, as long as the metal ion is **only** bonded to **water**. If it's bonded to anything else you need to write out the whole formula.

4) You need to know the **equations** for the following reactions, and the **colours** of the hydroxide precipitates:

> *A metal-aqua ion is a metal ion complex that only contains water ligands.*

copper(II): $[Cu(H_2O)_6]^{2+}_{(aq)} + 2OH^-_{(aq)} \rightarrow [Cu(OH)_2(H_2O)_4]_{(s)} + 2H_2O_{(l)}$

this can also be written as: $Cu^{2+}_{(aq)} + 2OH^-_{(aq)} \rightarrow Cu(OH)_{2(s)}$

$[Cu(H_2O)_6]^{2+}_{(aq)} + 2NH_{3(aq)} \rightarrow [Cu(OH)_2(H_2O)_4]_{(s)} + 2NH_4^+_{(aq)}$

This goes from a pale blue solution to a blue precipitate.

In excess ammonia, copper(II) hydroxide undergoes a **ligand exchange reaction**:

$[Cu(OH)_2(H_2O)_4]_{(s)} + 4NH_{3(aq)} \rightarrow [Co(NH_3)_4(H_2O)_2]^{2+}_{(aq)} + 2OH^-_{(aq)}\ 4H_2O_{(l)}$

This goes from a blue precipitate to a deep blue solution.

iron(II): $[Fe(H_2O)_6]^{2+}_{(aq)} + 2OH^-_{(aq)} \rightarrow [Fe(OH)_2(H_2O)_4]_{(s)} + 2H_2O_{(l)}$

$[Fe(H_2O)_6]^{2+}_{(aq)} + 2NH_{3(aq)} \rightarrow [Fe(OH)_2(H_2O)_4]_{(s)} + 2NH_4^+_{(aq)}$

This goes from a pale green solution to a green precipitate, which darkens on standing (as the precipitate is oxidised by water and oxygen in the air to form iron(III) hydroxide).

iron(III): $[Fe(H_2O)_6]^{3+}_{(aq)} + 3OH^-_{(aq)} \rightarrow [Fe(OH)_3(H_2O)_3]_{(s)} + 3H_2O_{(l)}$

$[Fe(H_2O)_6]^{3+}_{(aq)} + 3NH_{3(aq)} \rightarrow [Fe(OH)_3(H_2O)_3]_{(s)} + 3NH_4^+_{(aq)}$

This goes from a yellow solution to an orange precipitate, which darkens on standing.

cobalt(II): $[Co(H_2O)_6]^{2+}_{(aq)} + 2OH^-_{(aq)} \rightarrow [Co(OH)_2(H_2O)_4]_{(s)} + 2H_2O_{(l)}$

$[Co(H_2O)_6]^{2+}_{(aq)} + 2NH_{3(aq)} \rightarrow [Co(OH)_2(H_2O)_4]_{(s)} + 2NH_4^+_{(aq)}$

This goes from a pale pink solution to a blue precipitate, which turns brown on standing.

In excess ammonia, cobalt(II) hydroxide undergoes a **ligand exchange reaction**:

$[Co(OH)_2(H_2O)_4]_{(s)} + 6NH_{3(aq)} \rightarrow [Co(NH_3)_6]^{2+}_{(aq)} + 2OH^-_{(aq)}\ 4H_2O_{(l)}$

On standing, this is **oxidised** to form a brown solution containing $[Co(NH_3)_6]^{3+}_{(aq)}$ ions.

The blue (or pink) precipitate dissolves to form a yellow-brown solution.

> *Have a look at page 54 to see how chromium(II) reacts with sodium hydroxide and ammonia.*

Practice Questions

Q1 Give an example of a ligand substitution reaction that involves a change of coordination number.

Q2 What do you see when ammonia solution is slowly added to a copper(II) sulfate solution until it's in excess?

Q3 Why does adding excess NH₃ give different results from adding excess NaOH to copper(II) sulfate solution?

Exam Questions

Q1 When a solution of EDTA⁴⁻ ions is added to an aqueous solution of $[Fe(H_2O)_6]^{3+}$ ions, a ligand substitution reaction occurs.

   a) Write an equation for the reaction that takes place. [1 mark]

   b) The new complex that is formed is more stable than $[Fe(H_2O)_6]^{3+}$. Explain why. [1 mark]

Q2 Ammonia solution is added to a pale pink solution containing a hydrated transition metal complex. Initially, a blue precipitate is formed. When an excess of ammonia is added, the precipitate dissolves to form a yellow-brown solution.

   a) Identify the transition metal complex present in the initial pale pink solution. [1 mark]

   b) Write equations for both reactions, and state the type of reaction taking place each time. [4 marks]

Where do transition metals sell their shares? On the ligand exchange...

Ligands generally don't mind swapping with other ligands, so long as they're not too tightly attached to the central metal ion. They also won't fancy changing if it means forming fewer molecules and having less entropy. Fussy things...

Transition Metals and Catalysis

As if you haven't seen enough evidence for the greatness of transition metals, here's more. They're darn good catalysts...

Transition Metals and their Compounds make **Good Catalysts**

Transition metals and their compounds make **good catalysts** because they can **change oxidation number** by gaining or losing electrons within their **d-orbitals**. This means they can **transfer electrons** to **speed up** reactions.

Example: In the Contact Process, SO_2 is oxidised to SO_3: $SO_2 + \frac{1}{2}O_2 \rightarrow SO_3$.
Vanadium(V) oxide is used as a catalyst as it can be reduced to vanadium(IV) oxide and oxidise SO_2.
It's then oxidised back to vanadium(V) oxide by oxygen ready to start all over again.

This example uses a heterogeneous catalyst (see the next page), but the principle also applies to homogeneous catalysts.

Vanadium oxidises SO_2 to SO_3 and is reduced itself.

$$V_2O_5 + SO_2 \rightarrow V_2O_4 + SO_3$$
vanadium(V) $\rightarrow$ vanadium(IV)

The reduced catalyst is then oxidised by oxygen gas back to its original state.

$$V_2O_4 + \tfrac{1}{2}O_2 \rightarrow V_2O_5$$
vanadium(IV) $\rightarrow$ vanadium(V)

Transition Metal Compounds are Good **Homogeneous Catalysts**

1) **Homogeneous catalysts** are in the **same physical state** as the reactants.
   Usually a **homogeneous** catalyst is an **aqueous catalyst** for a reaction between two **aqueous solutions**.

2) Homogeneous catalysts work by combining with the reactants to form an **intermediate species** which then reacts to form the **products** and **reform the catalyst**.

3) The activation energy needed to form the **intermediates** (and to form the products from the intermediates) is **lower** than that needed to make the products directly from the reactants.

4) The catalyst is always **reformed** so it can carry on catalysing the reaction.

Example: Peroxodisulfate ions oxidising iodide ions.

The **redox** reaction between iodide ions and peroxodisulfate ($S_2O_8^{2-}$) ions takes place **annoyingly slowly** because both ions are **negatively charged**. The ions **repel** each other, so it's unlikely they'll **collide** and **react**.

$$S_2O_8{}^{2-}{}_{(aq)} + 2I^-{}_{(aq)} \rightarrow I_{2(aq)} + 2SO_4{}^{2-}{}_{(aq)}$$

But if **Fe²⁺ ions** are added, things really **speed up** because each stage of the reaction involves a **positive and a negative ion**, so there's **no repulsion**.

1) First, the Fe^{2+} ions are **oxidised** to Fe^{3+} ions by the $S_2O_8^{2-}$ ions.

$$S_2O_8{}^{2-}{}_{(aq)} + 2Fe^{2+}{}_{(aq)} \rightarrow 2Fe^{3+}{}_{(aq)} + 2SO_4{}^{2-}{}_{(aq)}$$

2) The newly formed intermediate Fe^{3+} ions now **easily oxidise** the I^- ions to iodine, and the **catalyst is regenerated**.

$$2Fe^{3+}{}_{(aq)} + 2I^-{}_{(aq)} \rightarrow I_{2(aq)} + 2Fe^{2+}{}_{(aq)}$$

The Fe^{2+} is a homogeneous catalyst — it's in the same phase as the reactants.

Autocatalysis is when a **Product** Catalyses the Reaction

Another example of a **homogeneous catalyst** is Mn^{2+} in the reaction between $C_2O_4^{2-}$ and MnO_4^-.
It's an **autocatalysis reaction** because Mn^{2+} is a **product** of the reaction and **acts as a catalyst** for the reaction.
This means that as the reaction progresses and the **amount** of the **product increases**, the reaction **speeds up**.

The reactant ions are both negatively charged so repel each other and cause the rate of the uncatalysed reaction to be very slow.

$$2MnO_4{}^-{}_{(aq)} + 16H^+{}_{(aq)} + 5C_2O_4{}^{2-}{}_{(aq)} \rightarrow 2Mn^{2+}{}_{(aq)} + 8H_2O_{(l)} + 10CO_{2(g)}$$

1) Mn^{2+} catalyses the reaction by first reacting with MnO_4^- to form **Mn³⁺ ions**:

$$MnO_4{}^-{}_{(aq)} + 4Mn^{2+}{}_{(aq)} + 8H^+{}_{(aq)} \rightarrow 5Mn^{3+}{}_{(aq)} + 4H_2O_{(l)}$$

2) The newly formed **Mn³⁺** ions then react with $C_2O_4^{2-}$ ions to form carbon dioxide and **re-form** the Mn^{2+} catalyst ions:

$$2Mn^{3+}{}_{(aq)} + C_2O_4{}^{2-}{}_{(aq)} \rightarrow 2Mn^{2+}{}_{(aq)} + 2CO_{2(g)}$$

Transition Metals and Catalysis

Transition Metals and Their Compounds can be **Heterogeneous Catalysts**

A **heterogeneous catalyst** is in a **different phase** from the reactants. Usually the reactants are gases or in solution and the catalyst is a solid — the reaction occurs on the surface of the catalyst. Transition metals make good heterogeneous catalysts because they can use their partially filled **d-orbitals** to make weak **bonds** with the reactant molecules.

Catalytic converters are used in cars to reduce emissions of **nitrogen monoxide** and **carbon monoxide** produced by internal combustion engines. They use a **platinum** or **rhodium** catalyst to convert these gases into nitrogen and carbon dioxide.

$$2NO_{(g)} + 2CO_{(g)} \rightarrow N_{2(g)} + 2CO_{2(g)}$$

Have a look at your Year 1 notes to see why carbon monoxide and nitrogen monoxide emissions can be a problem.

Here's how it works —

1) The **reactant** molecules are **attracted** to the surface of the solid catalyst and stick to it — this is called **adsorption**.

2) The surface of the catalyst **activates** the molecules so they react more easily. In the reaction between nitrogen monoxide and carbon dioxide, the bonds between the **reactants'** atoms are **weakened** making them **easier** to **break** and reform as the products.

3) The **product** molecules **leave** the surface of the catalyst making way for fresh reactants to take their place. This is called **desorption**.

Practice Questions

Q1 What property of transition metals makes them good catalysts?

Q2 Why is the rate of the uncatalysed reaction between iodide and peroxodisulfate ions so slow?

Q3 What term describes the process when a product catalyses a reaction?

Q4 Which two transition metals are used in catalytic converters?

Exam Questions

Q1 Transition metal compounds are used as both heterogeneous and homogeneous catalysts.

a) Explain the meaning of the terms 'heterogeneous' and 'homogeneous'. [1 mark]

b) How does the fact that a transition metal has partially filled d-orbitals help it act as a heterogeneous catalyst? [1 mark]

c) How does the fact that transition metals have variable oxidation numbers allow them to act as homogeneous catalysts? [2 marks]

Q2 A student is measuring the rate of the reaction between MnO_4^- ions and $C_2O_4^{2-}$ over time. She predicts that the rate will decrease with time, but discovers instead that the rate of reaction over the first five minutes increases. Explain the student's results with use of appropriate equations. [5 marks]

Q3 Catalytic converters use a platinum or rhodium catalyst to reduce emissions of carbon monoxide and nitrogen monoxide from internal combustion engines.

a) The first step in the catalysis reaction is the adsorption of nitrogen monoxide and carbon monoxide onto the surface of the catalyst. What is meant by the term 'adsorption'? [1 mark]

b) Explain how adsorption helps to catalyse the reaction. [2 marks]

Burmese cats are top of my cat list...

Transition metals are able to do so many different things. And it's all down to those d-orbital electron thingies. Unfortunately that means there's a lot for you to remember. It's not even as if there's only one sort of catalyst to remember. There are two — homogeneous catalysts and heterogeneous catalysts... And you need to know both.

Reaction Rates

Welcome, one and all to Kinetics. Your emergency exits are located here, here and here. Thank you.

The **Reaction Rate** Tells You How Fast **Reactants** are Converted to **Products**

The **reaction rate** is the **change in the amount** of reactants or products **per unit time** (normally per second).

There are **Loads** of Ways to **Follow the Rate** of a **Reaction**

Although there are a lot of ways to follow reactions, not every method works for every reaction. You've got to pick a property that changes as the reaction goes on. The following methods are all **continuous monitoring** methods of following the rate of reaction — continuous monitoring means measurements are taken over the duration of the reaction.

Gas volume

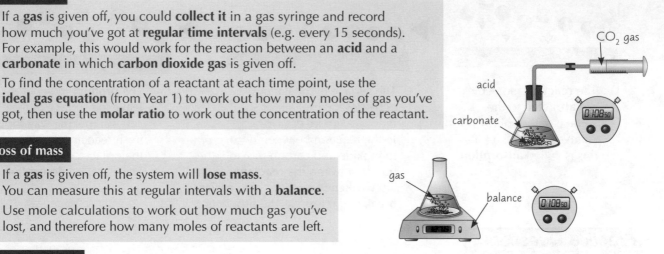

If a **gas** is given off, you could **collect it** in a gas syringe and record how much you've got at **regular time intervals** (e.g. every 15 seconds). For example, this would work for the reaction between an **acid** and a **carbonate** in which **carbon dioxide gas** is given off.

To find the concentration of a reactant at each time point, use the **ideal gas equation** (from Year 1) to work out how many moles of gas you've got, then use the **molar ratio** to work out the concentration of the reactant.

Loss of mass

If a **gas** is given off, the system will **lose mass**.
You can measure this at regular intervals with a **balance**.

Use mole calculations to work out how much gas you've lost, and therefore how many moles of reactants are left.

Colour change

You can sometimes track the colour change of a reaction using a gadget called a **colorimeter**. A colorimeter measures **absorbance** (the amount of light absorbed by the solution). The **more concentrated** the **colour** of the solution, the **higher** the **absorbance** is.

For example, in the reaction between propanone and iodine, the **brown** colour fades. So the absorbance of the solution will **decrease**.

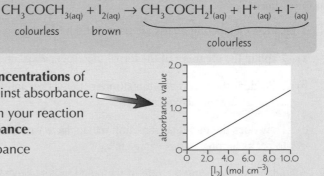

$$CH_3COCH_{3(aq)} + I_{2(aq)} \rightarrow CH_3COCH_2I_{(aq)} + H^+_{(aq)} + I^-_{(aq)}$$

colourless   brown   colourless

You measure the change in absorbance like this:

1) Plot a **calibration curve** — a graph of **known concentrations** of the coloured solution (in this case I_2) plotted against absorbance.

2) During the experiment, take a **small sample** from your reaction solution at **regular intervals** and read the **absorbance**.

3) Use your calibration curve to **convert** the absorbance at each time point into a **concentration**.

Change in pH

If the reaction produces or uses up H^+ ions, the pH of the solution will change. So you could measure the **pH** of the solution at **regular intervals** and calculate the **concentration of H^+**.

See page 10 for more about working out $[H^+]$ using pH.

Titration

You can take small samples of a reaction at **regular time intervals** and titrate them using a **standard solution**. The rate can be found from measuring the change in concentration of the products or reactant over time.

There's more about titrations on pages 42-47.

Electrical conductivity

If the **number of ions** changes, so will the **electrical conductivity**.

Reaction Rates

Work Out Reaction Rate from a Concentration-Time Graph

1) By repeatedly taking **measurements** during a reaction (continuous monitoring) you can draw a graph of the **amount of reactant** or **product** (on the y-axis) against **time** (on the x-axis).

2) The rate at any point in the reaction is given by the **gradient** (slope) at that point on the graph.

3) If the graph is a curve, you'll have to draw a **tangent** to the curve and find the gradient of that.

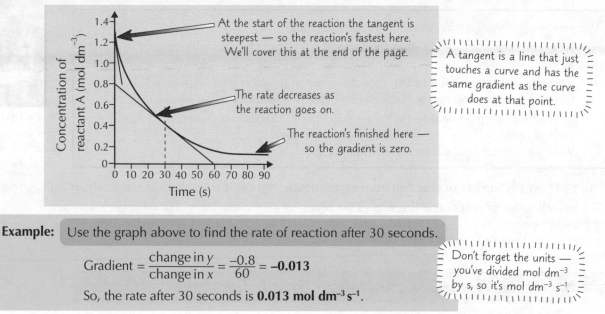

At the start of the reaction the tangent is steepest — so the reaction's fastest here. We'll cover this at the end of the page.

The rate decreases as the reaction goes on.

The reaction's finished here — so the gradient is zero.

A tangent is a line that just touches a curve and has the same gradient as the curve does at that point.

Example: Use the graph above to find the rate of reaction after 30 seconds.

$$\text{Gradient} = \frac{\text{change in } y}{\text{change in } x} = \frac{-0.8}{60} = -0.013$$

So, the rate after 30 seconds is **0.013 mol dm^{-3} s^{-1}**.

Don't forget the units — you've divided mol dm^{-3} by s, so it's mol dm^{-3} s^{-1}.

4) The **sign** of the gradient doesn't really matter — it's a **negative** gradient when you're measuring **reactant concentration** because the reactant decreases. If you measured the **product concentration**, it'd be a **positive** gradient.

Practice Questions

Q1 What is the definition of reaction rate?

Q2 Give an example of a reaction where gas volume can be measured to follow reaction rate.

Q3 For a straight line graph of concentration of reactants against time, how do you work out reaction rate?

Exam Question

Q1 The reaction between iodine and propanone in acidic conditions was investigated.

$$I_{2(aq)} + CH_3COCH_{3(aq)} \xrightarrow{H^+_{(aq)}} CH_3COCH_2I_{(aq)} + H^+_{(aq)} + I^-_{(aq)}$$

a) Apart from colorimetry, suggest, with a reason, one method that could be used to follow the reaction rate. [1 mark]

b) Outline how the rate of reaction with respect to propanone, at any particular time, could be determined. [2 marks]

The following data was collected at 25 °C.

Time (s)	0	10	20	30	40
Concentration of CH$_3$COCH$_3$ (mol dm^{-3})	0.2	0.07	0.025	0.0098	0.0031

c) Plot a graph, using the data provided. From the graph, determine the rate of reaction at 25 °C after 15 seconds. [3 marks]

My concentration-time graph for chemistry revision has a negative gradient...

This kinetics topic really comes at you at a fast rate... I can't promise the jokes are going to get a whole lot better throughout the topic but I can promise it's gonna cover a lot of different stuff to do with reaction rates. So it's worth making sure you understand the gradient = rate thing now, as well as how to find the gradient of different graphs.

Orders of Reactions

You might think the rate of a reaction will change if you change the concentration of the reactants. But this isn't always the case... Read on for some juicy information about the orders of reactions. Speaking of orders... can I order a pizza?

Orders *Tell You How a Reactant's* Concentration *Affects the* Rate

1) The **order of reaction** with respect to a particular reactant tells you how the **reactant's concentration** affects the **rate**.

> Where [X] is the concentration of a particular reactant:
> - If [X] changes and the rate **stays the same**, the order of reaction with respect to X is **0**. So if [X] doubles, the rate will stay the same. If [X] triples, the rate will stay the same.
> - If the rate is **proportional to [X]**, then the order of reaction with respect to X is **1**. So if [X] doubles, the rate will double. If [X] triples, the rate will triple.
> - If the rate is **proportional to [X]²**, then the order of reaction with respect to X is **2**. So if [X] doubles, the rate will be $2^2 = 4$ times faster. If [X] triples, the rate will be $3^2 = 9$ times faster.

No matter how hard Jane concentrated, she couldn't increase the rate of the meeting.

2) You can only find **orders of reaction** from **experiments**. You **can't** work them out from chemical equations.

3) The **overall order of reaction** is the **sum** of the orders of all the reactants. For example, if the reaction, $A + B + C \rightarrow D$ is **first order** with respect to A and B and **zero order** with respect to C, then the **overall order** of reaction is **2**.

The Shape *of a* Rate-Concentration Graph *Tells You the* Order

You can use data from a **concentration-time graph** to construct a **rate-concentration graph**, which can tell you the **reaction order**. Here's how...

1) Find the **gradient** at various points on the graph. This will give you the **rate** at that particular **concentration**. With a **straight-line graph**, this is easy, but if it's a **curve**, you need to draw **tangents** and find their gradients.

2) Now plot each point on a new graph with the axes **rate** and **concentration**. Then draw a smooth line or curve through the points. The shape of the line will tell you the order of the reaction with respect to that reactant.

The notation [X] means the concentration of reactant X.

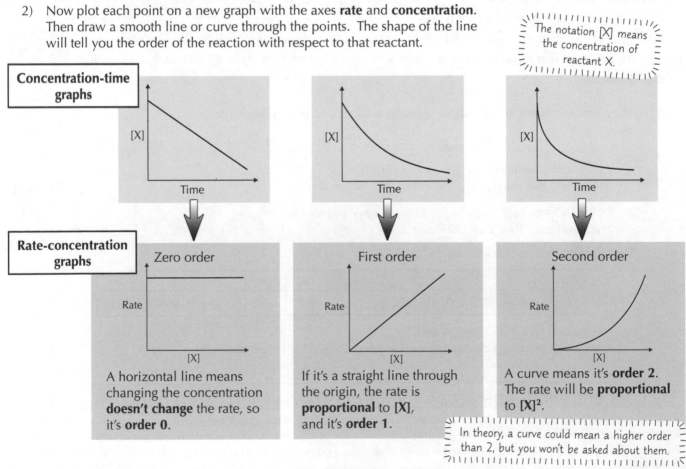

Concentration-time graphs

Rate-concentration graphs

Zero order — A horizontal line means changing the concentration **doesn't change** the rate, so it's **order 0**.

First order — If it's a straight line through the origin, the rate is **proportional** to **[X]**, and it's **order 1**.

Second order — A curve means it's **order 2**. The rate will be **proportional** to **[X]²**.

In theory, a curve could mean a higher order than 2, but you won't be asked about them.

Orders of Reactions

The **Half-Life** is the **Time** it takes for **Half** of the **Reactant** to be **Used Up**

To work out the **half-life** ($t_{1/2}$) of a reaction, plot a **concentration–time graph**. Then **draw lines** across from the y-axis at points where the concentration has **halved** and read off the time taken.

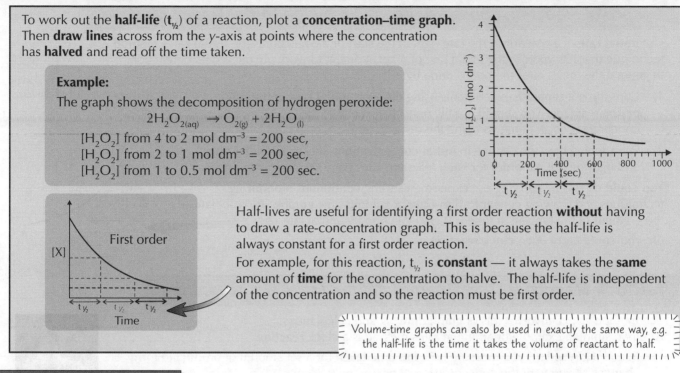

Example:

The graph shows the decomposition of hydrogen peroxide:
$$2H_2O_{2(aq)} \rightarrow O_{2(g)} + 2H_2O_{(l)}$$
$[H_2O_2]$ from 4 to 2 mol dm^{-3} = 200 sec,
$[H_2O_2]$ from 2 to 1 mol dm^{-3} = 200 sec,
$[H_2O_2]$ from 1 to 0.5 mol dm^{-3} = 200 sec.

Half-lives are useful for identifying a first order reaction **without** having to draw a rate-concentration graph. This is because the half-life is always constant for a first order reaction.

For example, for this reaction, $t_{1/2}$ is **constant** — it always takes the **same** amount of **time** for the concentration to halve. The half-life is independent of the concentration and so the reaction must be first order.

Volume-time graphs can also be used in exactly the same way, e.g. the half-life is the time it takes the volume of reactant to half.

Practice Questions

Q1 Sketch rate-concentration graphs for zero, first and second order reactions.

Q2 How does the half-life change with time in a first order reaction?

Exam Questions

Q1 The table shows the results of an experiment on the decomposition of nitrogen(V) oxide at constant temperature.
$$2N_2O_5 \rightarrow 4NO_2 + O_2$$

Time (s)	0	50	100	150	200	250	300
$[N_2O_2]$ (mol dm^{-3})	2.5	1.66	1.14	0.76	0.5	0.33	0.22

a) Plot a graph of these results. [2 marks]

b) From the graph, find the times for the concentration of N_2O_5 to decrease:

i) to half its original concentration, [1 mark]

ii) from 2.0 mol dm^{-3} to 1.0 mol dm^{-3}. [1 mark]

c) Giving a reason, deduce the order of this reaction. [1 mark]

Q2 A student measures the rate for the following reaction.
$$A + B \rightarrow C$$

The rate of reaction is found to be first order with respect to A and second order with respect to B.

a) What would be the change in the rate if the concentration of B was doubled and the concentration of A was halved? [1 mark]

b) What is the overall order for the reaction? [1 mark]

Describe the link between concentration and rate, soldier — that's an order...

There's quite a lot on this page, graphically speaking. And graphs are always great, easy marks. Just remember — labelled axes, accurately plotted points and a smoooooth curve or a smoooooth line of best fit. If you do these things then all the other calculations will become a lot easier. And remember smoooooth — like a freshly licked lollipop.

The Initial Rates Method

The initial rate is just what it sounds like — the rate of reaction right at the start of the reaction. They're not very imaginative these chemists, but they do love using experiments to calculate the orders of reactions, as you'll soon see...

Orders of Reaction can be Worked Out by the Initial Rates Method

The **initial rate** of a reaction is the rate right at the **start** of the reaction. The **initial rates method** is a technique that lets you use the initial rate of an experiment to work out the orders of reaction. In general the initial rates method is done by:

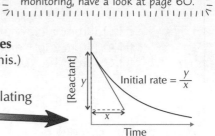
For different techniques for continuous monitoring, have a look at page 60.

1) Carrying out **separate** experiments using **different initial concentrations** of **one** reactant. You should usually only change **one** of the concentrations at a time, keeping the rest constant.

2) Then seeing how the change in **initial concentrations** affects the **initial rates** and figuring out the **order** for each reactant. (See page 66 for how to do this.)

You **could** do this by carrying out experiments using **continuous monitoring** techniques and drawing **concentration-time** or **volume-time graphs**. By calculating the **gradient** of the tangent at time = 0, you can find the initial rate.

Or, you could carry out a **clock reaction**...

Initial rate = $\frac{y}{x}$

(Graph: [Reactant] vs Time)

A Clock Reaction is an Example of the Initial Rates Method

The method above involves lots of graph drawing and calculations. Another, simpler, example of an initial rates method is a **clock reaction**.

1) In a clock reaction, you measure how the **time taken** for a set amount of product to form **changes** as you **vary the concentration** of one of the reactants.

2) As part of a clock reaction, there will be a **sudden increase** in the concentration of a certain product as a **limiting reactant** is used up.

3) There's usually an **easily observable end point**, such as a colour change, to tell you when the desired amount of product has formed.

4) The **quicker** the clock reaction finishes, the **faster** the initial rate of the reaction.

A tanned gent.

5) When carrying out a clock reaction you need to make the following assumptions:

- The **concentration** of each reactant **doesn't change** significantly over the time period of your clock reaction.
- The **temperature** stays **constant**.
- When the end point is seen, the reaction has not proceeded **too far**.

The Iodine Clock Reaction is a Well-Known Clock Reaction

In an iodine clock reaction, the reaction you're monitoring is:

The iodine clock is also known as the Harcourt-Esson Reaction.

$$H_2O_{2(aq)} + 2I^-_{(aq)} + 2H^+_{(aq)} \rightarrow 2H_2O_{(l)} + I_{2(aq)}$$

1) A **small amount of sodium thiosulfate** solution and starch are added to an **excess of hydrogen peroxide** and iodide ions in acid solution. (Starch is used as an indicator — it turns blue-black in the presence of iodine.)

2) The sodium thiosulfate that is added to the reaction mixture reacts **instantaneously** with any iodine that forms:

$$2S_2O_3^{2-}_{(aq)} + I_{2(aq)} \rightarrow 2I^-_{(aq)} + S_4O_6^{2-}_{(aq)}$$

3) To begin with, all the iodine that forms in the first reaction is **used up straight away** in the **second reaction**. But once all the sodium thiosulfate is **used up**, any more iodine that forms will **stay in solution**, so the starch indicator will suddenly turn the solution **blue-black**. This is the end of the clock reaction.

4) Varying the iodide or hydrogen peroxide concentration, while keeping the others constant, will give **different times** for the colour change.

5) The **time it takes** for the reaction to occur along with the **concentration** of reactants allows you to calculate the **initial rate** with respect to iodide or hydrogen peroxide.

The Initial Rates Method

Here's How to Carry Out the Iodine Clock Reaction in the Lab...

To find the order with respect to **potassium iodide**:

1) Rinse a **clean** pipette with **sulfuric acid**. Then, use this pipette to transfer a small amount of sulfuric acid, of **known concentration** (e.g. 0.25 mol dm^{-3}), to a clean beaker. This beaker is your reaction vessel.

2) Using a clean pipette or measuring cylinder, add **distilled water** to the beaker containing the sulfuric acid.

3) Using a dropping pipette, add a few drops of **starch solution** to the same beaker.

4) Measure a known amount of **potassium iodide solution** of a known concentration, using either a pipette or a burette, rinsed with potassium iodide solution. Transfer this volume to the reaction vessel.

5) Next, using a pipette rinsed with **sodium thiosulfate solution**, or a clean measuring cylinder, add sodium thiosulfate to the reaction vessel. Swirl the contents of the beaker so all the solutions are evenly mixed.

6) Finally, rinse a pipette with **hydrogen peroxide solution**. Then, use the pipette to transfer hydrogen peroxide solution to the reaction vessel while stirring the contents and simultaneously **start a stop watch**.

7) Continue to stir, and stop the stop watch when the contents of the beaker turn from **colourless to blue-black**, this marks the **end point**. Record this time in a results table, along with the quantities of sulfuric acid, water, potassium iodide and sodium thiosulfate solutions you used in that experiment.

8) **Repeat** the experiment varying the volume of potassium iodide solution. Keep the volume of sulfuric acid, sodium thiosulfate and hydrogen peroxide **constant** and use **varying** amounts of **distilled water** in each experiment so the **overall volume** of the reaction mixture remains **constant**.

An example of how to work out orders of reaction from initial rates data is on page 66.

An **approximation** of the initial rate at each concentration can be found from the **time** it took to reach the end point. By **comparing** these initial rates you can find the reaction order with **respect to** potassium iodide.

The Initial Rate of the Iodination of Propanone can be Found by Titrating

The rate of reaction for the iodine-propanone reaction can be followed by a **continuous monitoring** titrimetric method.

$$CH_3COCH_{3(aq)} + I_{2(aq)} \xrightarrow{H^+_{(aq)}} CH_3COCH_2I_{(aq)} + H^+_{(aq)} + I^-_{(aq)}$$

A titrimetric method uses titrations to find out information about a reaction.

You can monitor the reaction by **taking samples** at regular intervals. You first need to **stop** the reaction in each sample by adding **sodium hydrogencarbonate** to neutralise the acid. Then **titrate** each sample against sodium thiosulfate and starch to work out the **concentration** of the **iodine**. You'll need to carry out the experiment several times and in each experiment change the concentration of just **one reactant**.

Practice Questions

Q1 How do you find the initial rate of reaction from a concentration-time graph?

Q2 Why is sodium hydrogencarbonate added to samples from the reaction between propanone and iodine?

Exam Questions

Q1 A student carried out an iodine clock reaction:

$$H_2O_{2(aq)} + 2I^-_{(aq)} + 2H^+_{(aq)} \rightarrow 2H_2O_{(l)} + I_{2(aq)}$$
$$2S_2O_3^{2-}_{(aq)} + I_{2(aq)} \rightarrow 2I^-_{(aq)} + S_4O_6^{2-}_{(aq)}$$

a) After some time, the starch indicator in solution turns blue-black. State why this change occurs. [1 mark]

b) The amount of sodium thiosulfate added to the reaction mixture was increased. Explain what change this would have on the time it takes for the colour change to occur. [1 mark]

Q2 Propanone can be reacted with iodine to form iodopropanone via an acid-catalysed reaction. Describe how you could use titration to investigate how the rate of reaction changes as the concentration of iodine varies. [3 marks]

The alarm clock reaction — the end point is a broken bedside table...

I know experiments like these might not seem the most exciting in the world. But you've got to learn them. Besides, once upon a time they were thrilling. People would go crazy for a chemical colour change. Honest...

Rate Equations

This is when it all gets a bit mathsy. You've just got to take a deep breath and dive in...

The Rate Equation links Reaction Rate to Reactant Concentrations

Rate equations look ghastly, but all they really do is tell you how the **rate** is affected by the **concentrations of reactants**. For a general reaction: **A + B → C + D**, the **rate equation** is:

$$Rate = k[A]^m[B]^n$$

The units of rate are normally mol dm^{-3} s^{-1}.

1) k is the **rate constant** — the **bigger** it is, the **faster** the reaction.
2) **m** and **n** are the **orders of the reaction** with respect to reactant A and reactant B.
   m tells you how the **concentration of reactant A** affects the **rate** and **n** tells you the same for **reactant B**.
3) The overall order of the reaction is **m + n**.

Example: The chemical equation below shows the acid-catalysed reaction between propanone and iodine.

$$CH_3COCH_{3(aq)} + I_{2(aq)} \xrightarrow{H^+_{(aq)}} CH_3COCH_2I_{(aq)} + H^+_{(aq)} + I^-_{(aq)}$$

This reaction is first order with respect to propanone and H$^+_{(aq)}$ and zero order with respect to iodine. Write down the rate equation.

Even though H$^+_{(aq)}$ is a catalyst, rather than a reactant, it can still appear in the rate equation.

The **rate equation** is: rate = $k[CH_3COCH_{3(aq)}]^1[H^+_{(aq)}]^1[I_{2(aq)}]^0$

But [X]^1 is usually written as **[X]**, and [X]^0 equals **1** so is usually **left out** of the rate equation.

So you can **simplify** the rate equation to: **rate = $k[CH_3COCH_{3(aq)}][H^+_{(aq)}]$**

Think about the powers laws from maths.

Spectator ions (ions that don't take part in the chemical reaction) are normally not included in rate equations.

You can use the Initial Rates Method to Work Out Orders of Reaction

1) By using the **initial rates method** (see pages 64-65) to collect data about the initial rate of a reaction.
2) By comparing the initial rate of a reaction with varying concentrations of reactants, you can find the **orders of reaction** for reactants in a reaction.
3) Once you know the chemical **equation** for a reaction, along with the orders of reaction, you can **write the rate equation**.

Example:
The table on the right shows the results of a series of initial rate experiments for the reaction:

$$NO_{(g)} + CO_{(g)} + O_{2(g)} \rightarrow NO_{2(g)} + CO_{2(g)}$$

The experiments were carried out at a constant temperature.
Write down the rate equation for the reaction.

Experiment number	[NO] (mol dm^{-3})	[CO] (mol dm^{-3})	[O$_2$] (mol dm^{-3})	Initial rate (mol dm^{-3} s^{-1})
1	2.0×10^{-2}	1.0×10^{-2}	1.0×10^{-2}	0.17
2	6.0×10^{-2}	1.0×10^{-2}	1.0×10^{-2}	1.53
3	2.0×10^{-2}	2.0×10^{-2}	1.0×10^{-2}	0.17
4	4.0×10^{-2}	1.0×10^{-2}	2.0×10^{-2}	0.68

1) Look at experiments 1 and 2 — when **[NO] triples** (and all the other concentrations stay constant) the rate is **nine times** faster, and 9 = 3^2. So the reaction is **second order** with respect to NO.
2) Look at experiments 1 and 3 — when **[CO]** doubles (but all the other concentrations stay constant), the rate **stays the same**. So the reaction is **zero order** with respect to CO.
3) Look at experiments 1 and 4 — the rate of experiment 4 is **four times faster** than experiment 1. The reaction is **second order** with respect to **[NO]**, so the rate will **quadruple** when you **double** [NO]. But in experiment 4, **[O$_2$]** has also been **doubled**. As doubling [O$_2$] hasn't had any additional effect on the rate, the reaction must be **zero order** with respect to O$_2$.
4) Now that you know the order with respect to each reactant you can write the rate equation: **rate = $k[NO]^2$**.

Rate Equations

You can Calculate the Rate Constant from the Orders and Rate of Reaction

Once the rate and the orders of the reaction have been found by experiment, you can work out the **rate constant**, *k*. The rate constant is always the **same** for a certain reaction at a **particular temperature** — but if you **increase** the temperature, the rate constant's going to **rise** too. The units **vary**, so you have to work them out. The example below shows you how.

Example: The reaction below was found to be second order with respect to NO and zero order with respect to CO and O_2. The rate is 1.76×10^{-3} mol dm^{-3} s^{-1} when $[NO_{(g)}] = [CO_{(g)}] = [O_{2(g)}] = 2.00 \times 10^{-3}$ mol dm^{-3}.

$$NO_{(g)} + CO_{(g)} + O_{2(g)} \rightarrow NO_{2(g)} + CO_{2(g)}$$

Find the value of the rate constant.

First write out the **rate equation**: $\quad$ Rate $= k[NO_{(g)}]^2[CO_{(g)}]^0[O_{2(g)}]^0 = k[NO_{(g)}]^2$

Next insert the **concentration** and the **rate**. **Rearrange** the equation and calculate the value of *k*:

$$\text{Rate} = k[NO_{(g)}]^2, \text{ so } 1.76 \times 10^{-3} = k \times (2.00 \times 10^{-3})^2 \longrightarrow k = \frac{1.76 \times 10^{-3}}{(2.00 \times 10^{-3})^2} = 440$$

Find the **units for *k*** by putting the other units in the rate equation:

$$\text{Rate} = k[NO_{(g)}]^2, \text{ so mol dm}^{-3}\text{ s}^{-1} = k \times (\text{mol dm}^{-3})^2 \longrightarrow k = \frac{\text{mol dm}^{-3}\text{ s}^{-1}}{(\text{mol dm}^{-3})^2} = \frac{\text{s}^{-1}}{\text{mol dm}^{-3}} = \text{dm}^3\text{ mol}^{-1}\text{ s}^{-1}$$

So the answer is: $\quad$ **$k = 440$ dm^3 mol^{-1} s^{-1}**

Practice Questions

Q1 What does the size of the rate constant tell you about the reaction rate?

Q2 How do you find the overall order for a reaction?

Q3 How does the rate constant change with an increase in temperature?

Exam Questions

Q1 The following reaction is second order with respect to NO and first order with respect to H$_2$.

$$2NO_{(g)} + 2H_{2(g)} \rightarrow 2H_2O_{(g)} + N_{2(g)}$$

a) Write a rate equation for the reaction and state the overall order of the reaction. [2 marks]

b) The rate of the reaction at 800 °C was determined to be 0.0027 mol dm^{-3} s^{-1} when $[H_2] = 0.0020$ mol dm^{-3} and $[NO] = 0.0040$ mol dm^{-3}.

  i) Calculate a value for the rate constant at 800 °C, including units. [2 marks]

  ii) Predict the effect on the rate constant of decreasing the temperature of the reaction to 600 °C. [1 mark]

Q2 An experiment is carried out with reactants X, Y, Z. The initial rates method is used to find the orders of reaction with respect to each reactant. The table to the right shows the results obtained.

a) Give the order with respect to X, Y and Z.
Explain your reasoning [3 marks]

b) Give the initial rate if Experiment 2 was repeated, but the concentration of Z was tripled. [1 mark]

c) Write the rate equation for the reaction investigated. [1 mark]

Experiment	[X]	[Y]	[Z]	Initial rate (mol dm^{-3} s^{-1})
1	0.25	0.1	0.4	1.30×10^{-3}
2	0.5	0.1	0.4	1.30×10^{-3}
3	0.25	0.2	0.4	5.20×10^{-3}
4	0.25	0.2	0.8	0.0104

This kinetics joke is so good — it's a gag of the first order...

Working with rate equations is actually pretty fun when you get the hang of it. No, really. And speaking of things that are fun can I recommend to you flying kites, peeling bananas, making models of your friends out of apples, the literary works of Jan Pieńkowski, counting spots on the carpet, the 1980s, goats, eating all the pies, darts... All fantastic fun.

The Rate-Determining Step

You know when you're trying to get out of a room to go to lunch, but it takes ages because not everyone can get through the door at the same time? Well getting through that door is the rate determining step. Talking about lunch...

The **Rate-Determining Step** is the **Slowest Step** in a Multi-Step Reaction

Reaction mechanisms can have **one step** or a **series of steps**.
In a series of steps, each step can have a **different rate**.
The **overall rate** is decided by the step with the **slowest** rate — the **rate-determining step**.

Otherwise known as the rate-limiting step.

Reactants in the **Rate Equation** Affect the **Rate**

The rate equation is handy for helping you work out the **mechanism** of a chemical reaction.
You need to be able to pick out which reactants from the chemical equation are involved in the **rate-determining step**.
Here are the **rules** for doing this:

- If a reactant appears in the **rate equation**, it must affect the **rate**.
  So this reactant, or something derived from it, must be in the **rate-determining step**.

- If a reactant **doesn't** appear in the **rate equation**, then it **isn't** involved
  in the **rate-determining step** (and neither is anything derived from it).

Catalysts can appear in rate equations, so they can be in rate-determining steps too.

Some **important points** to remember about rate-determining steps and mechanisms are:

1) The rate-determining step **doesn't** have to be the first step in a mechanism.
2) The reaction mechanism **can't** usually be predicted from **just** the chemical equation.

You Can Predict the **Rate Equation** from the **Rate-Determining Step**...

The **order of a reaction** with respect to a reactant shows the **number of molecules** of that reactant which are involved **in** or **before** the **rate-determining step**.

So, if a reaction's second order with respect to X, there'll be two molecules of X in the rate-determining step.

Example: The mechanism for the reaction between **chlorine free radicals** and **ozone**, O_3, consists of **two steps**:

$$Cl\bullet_{(g)} + O_{3(g)} \rightarrow ClO\bullet_{(g)} + O_{2(g)} \text{ — } \textbf{slow (rate-determining step)}$$
$$ClO\bullet_{(g)} + O_{(g)} \rightarrow Cl\bullet_{(g)} + O_{2(g)} \text{ — } \textbf{fast}$$

Predict the rate equation for this reaction.

$Cl\bullet$ and O_3 must both be in the rate equation, so the rate equation is of the form: **rate = $k[Cl\bullet]^m[O_3]^n$**.
There's only **one** $Cl\bullet$ radical and **one** O_3 molecule in the rate-determining step,
so the **orders**, m and n, are both **1**. So the rate equation is **rate = $k[Cl\bullet][O_3]$**.

...And You Can Predict the **Mechanism** from the **Rate Equation**

Knowing exactly which reactants are in the **rate-determining step** gives you an idea of the reaction **mechanism**.

For example, here are two possible mechanisms for the reaction: $(CH_3)_3CBr + OH^- \rightarrow (CH_3)_3COH + Br^-$.

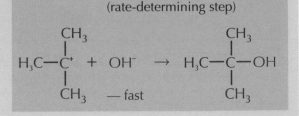

The actual **rate equation** was worked out by rate experiments:
rate = $k[(CH_3)_3CBr]$
OH^- isn't in the **rate equation**, so it **can't** be involved in the
reaction until **after** the rate-determining step. So, **mechanism 2**
is most likely to be correct — there is **1 molecule** of **$(CH_3)_3CBr$**
(and **no molecules of OH^-**) in the **rate determining step**.
This agrees with the **rate equation**.

The Rate-Determining Step

You've seen it before and it's back again. The reaction between **propanone** and **iodine**, catalysed by hydrogen ions.
The full equation for this reaction is...

$$CH_3COCH_{3(aq)} + I_{2(aq)} \xrightarrow{\ H^+_{(aq)}\ } CH_3COCH_2I_{(aq)} + H^+_{(aq)} + I^-_{(aq)}$$

And the rate equation for the reaction is...

$$Rate = k[CH_3COCH_3][H^+]$$

So, using the rules from the previous page, here's what you can say about the reaction —

1) Propanone and H^+ are **in the rate equation** — so they, or something **derived**
   from them, must be **in the rate-determining step**.

2) Iodine is **not in the rate equation** so it's **not** involved until **after** the **rate determining step.**

3) The **order** of reaction for both propanone and H^+ is **1** — so the rate-determining step must use **1 molecule** of each.

4) H^+ is a **catalyst** — so it must be **regenerated** in another step.

And when you put all that together you could come up with a reaction mechanism like this...

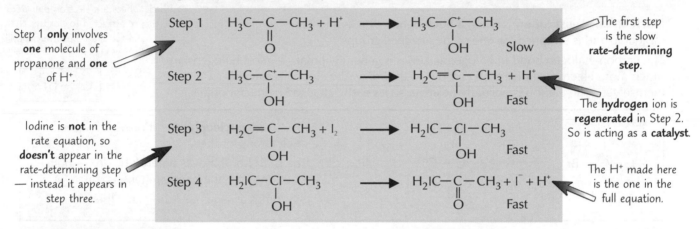

Step 1 **only** involves **one** molecule of propanone and **one** of H^+.

The first step is the slow **rate-determining step**.

The **hydrogen** ion is **regenerated** in Step 2. So is acting as a **catalyst**.

Iodine is **not** in the rate equation, so **doesn't** appear in the rate-determining step — instead it appears in step three.

The H^+ made here is the one in the full equation.

Q1 Can catalysts appear in rate equations?

Q2 Knowing the order of reaction is important for suggesting a rate-determining step. Why?

Q3 In the reaction of iodine with propanone, why doesn't iodine appear in the rate equation?

Exam Questions

Q1 For the reaction; $CH_3COOH_{(aq)} + C_2H_5OH_{(aq)} \rightarrow CH_3COOC_2H_{5(aq)} + H_2O_{(l)}$, the rate equation is:

$$rate = k[CH_3COOH][H^+]$$

What can you deduce about the role that H^+ plays in the reaction? Explain your answer. [2 marks]

Q2 Hydrogen reacts with iodine monochloride as in the equation; $H_{2(g)} + 2ICl_{(g)} \rightarrow I_{2(g)} + 2HCl_{(g)}$.
The rate equation for this reaction is: $rate = k[H_2][ICl]$.

a) The mechanism for the reaction consists of two steps.
    Identify the molecules that affect the rate-determining step. Justify your answer. [2 marks]

b) A chemist suggested the following mechanism for the reaction:

$$2ICl_{(g)} \rightarrow I_{2(g)} + Cl_{2(g)} \quad \text{slow}$$
$$H_{2(g)} + Cl_{2(g)} \rightarrow 2HCl_{(g)} \quad \text{fast}$$

Suggest, with reasons, whether this mechanism is likely to be correct. [2 marks]

I found rate-determining step aerobics a bit on the slow side...

These pages show you how rate equations, orders of reaction, and reaction mechanisms all tie together and how each actually means something in the grand scheme of A-Level Chemistry. It's all very profound. So get it all learnt, answer the questions and then you'll have plenty of time to practise the cha-cha-cha for your Strictly Come Dancing routine.

Halogenoalkanes and Reaction Mechanisms

'Lean hog on a lake' is an anagram of halogenoalkane. A good thing to know...

Halogenoalkanes can be Hydrolysed by Hydroxide Ions

There are three different types of halogenoalkane. They can all be hydrolysed (split) by heating them with sodium hydroxide — but they react using different mechanisms.

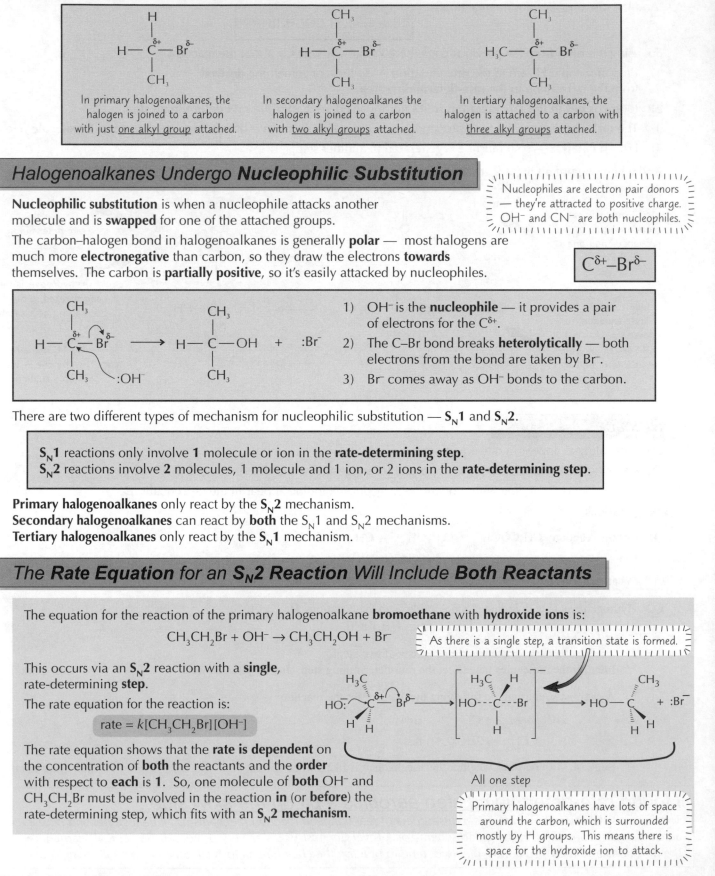

In primary halogenoalkanes, the halogen is joined to a carbon with just <u>one alkyl group</u> attached.

In secondary halogenoalkanes the halogen is joined to a carbon with <u>two alkyl groups</u> attached.

In tertiary halogenoalkanes, the halogen is attached to a carbon with <u>three alkyl groups</u> attached.

Halogenoalkanes Undergo Nucleophilic Substitution

Nucleophiles are electron pair donors — they're attracted to positive charge. OH^- and CN^- are both nucleophiles.

Nucleophilic substitution is when a nucleophile attacks another molecule and is **swapped** for one of the attached groups.

The carbon–halogen bond in halogenoalkanes is generally **polar** — most halogens are much more **electronegative** than carbon, so they draw the electrons **towards** themselves. The carbon is **partially positive**, so it's easily attacked by nucleophiles.

$$C^{\delta+}\!-\!Br^{\delta-}$$

1) OH^- is the **nucleophile** — it provides a pair of electrons for the $C^{\delta+}$.

2) The C–Br bond breaks **heterolytically** — both electrons from the bond are taken by Br^-.

3) Br^- comes away as OH^- bonds to the carbon.

There are two different types of mechanism for nucleophilic substitution — S_N1 and S_N2.

> S_N1 reactions only involve **1** molecule or ion in the **rate-determining step**.
> S_N2 reactions involve **2** molecules, 1 molecule and 1 ion, or 2 ions in the **rate-determining step**.

Primary halogenoalkanes only react by the S_N2 mechanism.
Secondary halogenoalkanes can react by **both** the S_N1 and S_N2 mechanisms.
Tertiary halogenoalkanes only react by the S_N1 mechanism.

The Rate Equation for an S_N2 Reaction Will Include Both Reactants

The equation for the reaction of the primary halogenoalkane **bromoethane** with **hydroxide ions** is:

$$CH_3CH_2Br + OH^- \rightarrow CH_3CH_2OH + Br^-$$

As there is a single step, a transition state is formed.

This occurs via an S_N2 reaction with a **single**, rate-determining **step**.

The rate equation for the reaction is:

$$\text{rate} = k[CH_3CH_2Br][OH^-]$$

The rate equation shows that the **rate is dependent** on the concentration of **both** the reactants and the **order** with respect to **each** is **1**. So, one molecule of **both** OH^- and CH_3CH_2Br must be involved in the reaction **in** (or **before**) the rate-determining step, which fits with an S_N2 **mechanism**.

All one step

Primary halogenoalkanes have lots of space around the carbon, which is surrounded mostly by H groups. This means there is space for the hydroxide ion to attack.

Halogenoalkanes and Reaction Mechanisms

The **Rate Equation** shows **Tertiary** Halogenoalkanes Use S_N1

The equation for the reaction of the tertiary halogenoalkane **2-bromo-2-methylpropane** with **hydroxide ions** looks similar to the reaction with bromoethane on the previous page:

$$(CH_3)_3CBr + OH^- \rightarrow (CH_3)_3COH + Br$$

But the rate equation for this reaction is different: $\quad \boxed{\text{rate} = k[(CH_3)_3CBr]}$

The **rate is only dependent** on the concentration of the **halogenoalkane**. So the hydroxide ion is only involved in the reaction **after** the **rate-determining** step.

The reaction happens in two steps. In the first step, the halogen leaves the halogenoalkane. The nucleophile is then able to attack in the second step.

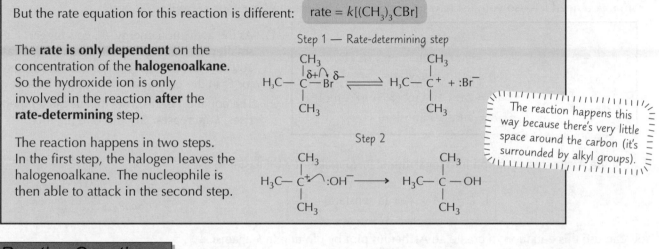

The reaction happens this way because there's very little space around the carbon (it's surrounded by alkyl groups).

Practice Questions

Q1 How many alkyl groups are attached to a tertiary halogenoalkane?

Q2 What is the role of the hydroxide ion in the hydrolysis of a halogenoalkane?

Q3 How many molecules/ions are involved in the rate determining step of an S_N2 reaction?

Q4 In which step does the nucleophile attack in an S_N2 reaction?

Exam Questions

Q1 For the reaction between sodium hydroxide and 1-chloropropane:

$$CH_3CH_2CH_2Cl + NaOH \rightarrow CH_3CH_2CH_2OH + NaCl$$

Predict which one of the following is the correct rate equation.

    A Rate = $k[OH^-]$ **B** Rate = $k[CH_3CH_2CH_2Cl]$

    C Rate = $k[CH_3CH_2CH_2Cl]_2$ **D** Rate = $k[CH_3CH_2CH_2Cl][OH^-]$ [1 mark]

Q2 The following equation shows the hydrolysis of 1-iodobutane by hydroxide ions:

$$CH_3CH_2CH_2CH_2I + OH^- \rightarrow CH_3CH_2CH_2CH_2OH + I^-$$

a) Is 1-iodobutane a primary, secondary or tertiary iodoalkane?   [1 mark]

b) Write the rate equation for this reaction.   [1 mark]

c) What type of mechanism is involved in this reaction?   [1 mark]

d) Draw the mechanism of this reaction.   [3 marks]

Q3 2-bromo-2-methylpentane is hydrolysed via a reaction with hydroxide ions.

a) Suggest a likely rate equation for the reaction.   [1 mark]

b) Draw the mechanism of this reaction and label the rate determining step.   [3 marks]

Way-hay!!! — It's the curly arrows...

Whenever I talk to someone who's studied chemistry the one thing they've remembered is curly arrows. They have no idea how they work. But they know they exist. The thing is, they don't have an exam, but you do — so make sure you understand where the arrows are coming from and going to. Check back to your Year 1 stuff if you're unsure.

Activation Energy

It's more maths on this page. But keep going, the end is in sight — even though it's over the page.

Use the **Arrhenius Equation** to Calculate the **Activation Energy**

The **Arrhenius equation** (nasty-looking thing in the blue box) links the **rate constant** (k) with **activation energy** (E_a, the minimum amount of kinetic energy particles need to react) and **temperature** (T). This is probably the **worst** equation there is in A-Level Chemistry. But the good news is, you **don't** have to learn it — you'll be given it in the exam if you need it — so you just have to understand what it's showing you. Here it is:

$$k = A\,e^{\frac{-E_a}{RT}}$$

It's an exponential relationship. This 'e' is the e^x button on your calculator.

k = rate constant
E_a = activation energy (J)
T = temperature (K)
R = gas constant (8.31 J K^{-1} mol^{-1})
A = another constant

1) As the activation energy, E_a, gets **bigger**, k gets **smaller**. So, a **large E_a** will mean a **slow rate**. You can **test** this out by trying **different numbers** for E_a in the equation... ahh go on, be a devil.

2) The equation also shows that as the temperature **rises**, k **increases**. Try this one out too.

Putting the **Arrhenius equation** into **logarithmic form** makes it a bit easier to use.

$$\ln k = \ln A - \frac{E_a}{RT} = (\text{a constant}) - \frac{E_a}{RT}$$

There's a handy 'ln' button on your calculator for this.

You can use this equation to create an **Arrhenius plot** by plotting **ln k** against $\frac{1}{T}$.
This will produce a graph with a gradient of $\frac{-E_a}{R}$. And once you know the gradient, you can find **activation energy**.

Example: The graph on the right shows an Arrhenius plot for the decomposition of hydrogen iodide. Calculate the activation energy for this reaction. $R = 8.31$ J K^{-1} mol^{-1}.

The gradient, $\dfrac{-E_a}{R} = \dfrac{-15}{0.0008} = -18\,750$

So, $E_a = -(-18\,750 \times 8.31) = 155\,812.5$ J mol^{-1} ≈ **156 kJ mol^{-1}**

To **Calculate** the **Activation Energy**, First Collect and Process the **Data...**

Here's another example of how to work out the activation energy.

$$S_2O_8{}^{2-}{}_{(aq)} + 2I^-{}_{(aq)} \rightarrow 2SO_4{}^{2-}{}_{(aq)} + I_{2(aq)}$$

You can only do this kind of mathematical trickery if all the concentrations are kept the same.

You can use the **iodine-clock reaction** to monitor when a fixed amount of I_2 has been made. The **rate of the reaction** is **inversely proportional** to the **time taken (t)** for the solution to change colour — a faster rate means a shorter time taken.

So, mathematically speaking, the rate is **proportional** to **1/time**. This means that 1/t can be used instead of k in the Arrhenius equation, which means you can calculate the activation energy. Hurrah!!

Time, t (s)	Temp, T (K)	1/t (s^{-1})	ln 1/t	1/T (K^{-1})
204	303	0.0049	-5.32	0.0033
138	308	0.0072	-4.93	0.00325
115	312	0.0087	-4.74	0.00321
75	318	0.0133	-4.32	0.00314
55	323	0.0182	-4.01	0.0031

Here's some collected data for this reaction at different temperatures. The first two columns show the raw data and the other columns show the data that's needed to draw a graph of **ln (1/t)** against **1/T** (see the next page).

Activation Energy

...Then Draw an *Arrhenius Plot* to Find E_a

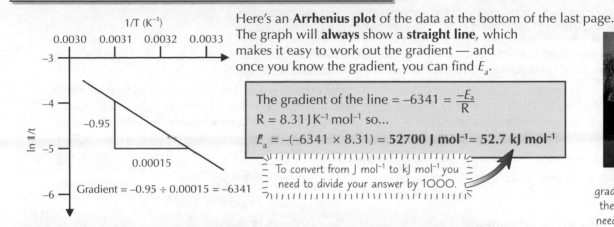

Here's an **Arrhenius plot** of the data at the bottom of the last page. The graph will **always** show a **straight line**, which makes it easy to work out the gradient — and once you know the gradient, you can find E_a.

The gradient of the line = $-6341 = \frac{-E_a}{R}$

$R = 8.31 \, J \, K^{-1} \, mol^{-1}$ so...

$E_a = -(-6341 \times 8.31) = 52700 \, J \, mol^{-1} = 52.7 \, kJ \, mol^{-1}$

To convert from $J \, mol^{-1}$ to $kJ \, mol^{-1}$ you need to divide your answer by 1000.

$1/T \, (K^{-1})$

Gradient = $-0.95 \div 0.00015 = -6341$

Looking at the gradient, Steve decided the activation energy needed to walk up the mountain was too high.

Catalysts Lower the *Activation Energy* of a Reaction

You can use **catalysts** to make chemical reactions happen **faster**. A **catalyst** increases the **rate** of a reaction by providing an **alternative reaction pathway** with a **lower activation energy**. The catalyst is **chemically unchanged** at the end of the reaction — they don't get used up. Catalysts can be classified into two different types:

1 **Homogeneous catalysts** are in the **same state** as the reactant. So for example, if the reactants are **gases**, the catalyst must be a **gas** too. An example of **homogeneous catalysis** would be the $H^+_{(aq)}$ catalysis of the iodination of propanone — all reactants are aqueous (dissolved in water).

Physical state and phase mean the same thing.

2 **Heterogeneous catalysts** are in a **different physical state** from the reactants:

- **Solid** heterogeneous catalysts provide a **surface** for the reaction to take place on. The catalyst is usually a **mesh** or a **fine powder** to increase the **surface area**. Alternatively it might be spread over an **inert support**.
- Heterogeneous catalysts can be easily **separated** from the products and leftover reactants.
- **Heterogeneous catalysts** can be poisoned though. A **poison** is a substance that clings to the catalyst's surface **more strongly** than the reactant does, **preventing** the catalyst from getting involved in the reaction it's meant to be **speeding up**. For instance, **sulfur** can poison the **iron catalyst** used in the **Haber process**.

Practice Questions

Q1 The Arrhenius equation can be written as $\ln k$ = a constant $-E_a/RT$. What do the terms k, T and R represent?

Q2 In an Arrhenius plot, where $1/T$ on the x-axis is plotted against $\ln k$ on the y-axis, what will the gradient show?

Exam Questions

Q1 The table gives values for the rate constant of the reaction between hydroxide ionsand bromoethane at different temperatures

a) Complete the table and then plot a graph of $\ln k$ (y-axis) against $1/T$ (x-axis). [4 marks]

b) Calculate the gradient of the straight line produced. [1 mark]

c) Using the Arrhenius equation, $\ln k$ = a constant $-E_a/RT$, calculate the activation energy of the reaction. ($R = 8.31 \, J \, K^{-1} mol^{-1}$) [2 marks]

T (K)	k	$1/T$ (K^{-1})	$\ln k$
305	0.181	0.00328	−1.709
313	0.468		
323	1.34		
333	3.29	0.00300	1.191
344	10.1		
353	22.7	0.00283	3.127

Q2 State the major difference between homogeneous and heterogenous catalysts. [1 mark]

Aaaaaaaaggggggggggggggghhhhhhhhhhhh...

The thing to remember here is you'll be given the Arrhenius equation in the exam if you need it. So concentrate on learning how to use it — which bits to put on an Arrhenius plot and what things to calculate to work out the E_a.

Optical Isomerism

You know you were crying out for some organic chemistry? Well here you go... This time we're looking at what the spatial arrangement of atoms can tell us about the molecule. Can you think of anything more exciting? Thought not...

Optical Isomers are Mirror Images of Each Other

1) **Optical isomerism** is a type of stereoisomerism. Stereoisomers have the **same structural formula**, but have their atoms arranged differently in **space**.

Sometimes molecules can have more than one chiral centre.

2) A **chiral** (or **asymmetric**) carbon atom (known as a **chiral centre**) is a carbon atom that has **four different groups** attached to it. It's possible to arrange the groups in two different ways around the carbon atom so that two different molecules are made — these molecules are called **enantiomers** or **optical isomers**.

3) The enantiomers are **mirror images** and no matter which way you turn them, they can't be **superimposed**.

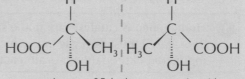

If molecules can be superimposed, they're achiral — and there's no optical isomerism.

4) You have to be able to **draw** optical isomers. But first you have to identify the chiral centre...

1) **Locating any chiral centres:**
Look for any carbon atoms with **four different groups** attached. Here it's the carbon with the four groups H, OH, COOH and CH₃ attached.

chiral centre

2-hydroxypropanoic acid

A solid wedge shows a bond coming out of the page towards you. A dotted line shows a bond going into the page away from you.

2) **Drawing isomers:**
Once you know the **chiral centre**, draw one enantiomer in a **tetrahedral shape**. Don't try to draw the full structure of each group — it gets confusing. Then draw a **mirror image** beside it. If there's more than one chiral centre, mirror each chiral centre one by one to get all the possible isomers.

$$HOOC \quad CH_3 \quad | \quad H_3C \quad COOH$$
$$OH \quad \quad OH$$

enantiomers of 2-hydroxypropanoic acid

Optical Isomers Rotate Plane-Polarised Light

1) Normal light is made up of a range of different wavelengths and vibrates in all directions. **Monochromatic, plane-polarised light** has a single wavelength and only vibrates in one direction.

2) Optical isomers are **optically active** — they **rotate** the plane of polarisation of plane-polarised monochromatic light.

3) One enantiomer rotates it in a **clockwise** direction, and the other rotates it in an **anticlockwise** direction.

Christmas is a time to embrace your choral centre.

A Racemic Mixture is a Mixture of Both Optical Isomers

A **racemic mixture** (or **racemate**) contains **equal quantities** of each enantiomer of a chiral compound.

Racemic mixtures **don't** rotate plane polarised light — the two enantiomers **cancel** each other's light-rotating effect.

Chemists often react two **achiral** things together and get a **racemic** mixture of a **chiral** product.

This is because when two molecules react there's often an **equal chance** of forming each of the enantiomers.

Look at the reaction between butane and chlorine:

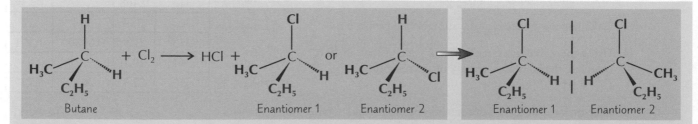

A **chlorine** atom replaces one of the **H** atoms, to give **2-chlorobutane**.

Either of the H atoms can be replaced, so the reaction produces a **mixture** of the two possible **enantiomers**.

Each hydrogen has an **equal chance** of being replaced, so the two optical isomers are formed in **equal amounts**.

Optical Isomerism

You Can Use *Optical Activity* to *Work Out* a Reaction *Mechanism*

Optical activity can give you some insight into how the **mechanism** of a reaction works. For example, **nucleophilic substitution reactions** (see your Year 1 notes) can take place by one of two mechanisms.

> Have a look at pages 70-71 for a reminder on this.

S_N1 mechanism

If it's an S_N1 mechanism and you start with a **single enantiomer** reactant, the product will be a **racemic mixture** of **two optical isomers** of each other, so won't rotate plane-polarised light.

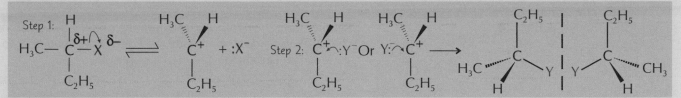

In **step 1**, a group breaks off, leaving a **planar** (flat) ion.
In **step 2**, the planar ion can be **attacked** by a nucleophile from **either side** — this results in two optical isomers.

S_N2 mechanism

In an S_N2 mechanism, a **single enantiomer** reactant produces a **single enantiomer** product.

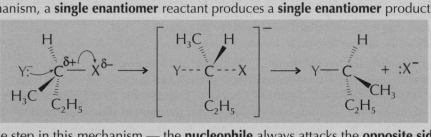

There's only one step in this mechanism — the **nucleophile** always attacks the **opposite side** to the leaving group, so only one product is produced. The product will rotate plane-polarised light **differently** to the reactant, the extent and direction of rotation occurs can be measured experimentally.

So if you know the **optical activity** of the **reactant** and **products**, you can sometimes work out the reaction **mechanism**.

Practice Questions

Q1 What is meant by a chiral carbon atom?
Q2 What is a racemic mixture?
Q3 Which nucleophilic substitution reaction mechanism produces a racemic mixture?
Q4 Which nucleophilic substitution reaction mechanism has a single enantiomer as a product?

Exam Question

Q1 The molecule 2-bromobutane displays optical isomerism.

a) Draw the structure of 2-bromobutane, and mark the chiral centre of the molecule on the diagram. [1 mark]

A sample of a single, pure optical isomer of 2-bromobutane is dissolved in an ethanol and water solvent and mixed with dilute sodium hydroxide solution. This mixture is gently heated under reflux and a substitution reaction occurs. The product of the reaction is a racemic mixture of butan-2-ol.

b) Explain why the butan-2-ol solution produced will not rotate plane-polarised light. [1 mark]

c) Has the substitution reaction proceeded via an S_N1 mechanism or an S_N2 mechanism? Explain your answer. [2 marks]

Time for some quiet reflection...

This optical isomer stuff's not all bad — you get to draw pretty little pictures of molecules. If you're having difficulty picturing them as 3D shapes, you could always make some models with matchsticks and some balls of coloured clay.

Aldehydes and Ketones

The sun is shining outside, the birds are singing, flowers are in bloom. Alas, you have to stay in and learn about the properties and reactions of organic compounds... It's tough, but that's the life you've chosen, my friend.

Aldehydes and Ketones Contain a Carbonyl Group

Aldehydes and ketones are **carbonyl compounds** — they contain the **carbonyl** functional group, **C=O**.

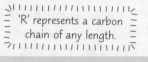
'R' represents a carbon chain of any length.

Introducing the carbonyl group — the coolest pop group in the charts.

Aldehydes have their carbonyl group at the **end** of the carbon chain. Their names end in **–al**.

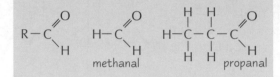
methanal   propanal

Ketones have their carbonyl group in the middle of the carbon chain. Their names end in **–one**, and often have a number to show which **carbon** the carbonyl group is on.

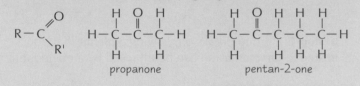
propanone   pentan-2-one

Aldehydes and Ketones Don't Hydrogen Bond with Themselves...

Aldehydes and ketones **don't** have a **polar O–H bond**, so they can't form **hydrogen bonds** with other aldehyde or ketone molecules.

Look back at your Year 1 notes if you're rusty on polarity or intermolecular forces.

This lack of hydrogen bonding means **solutions** of aldehydes and ketones have **lower boiling points** than their equivalent alcohols (which **can** form hydrogen bonds because they **do** have a polar O–H bond). However, the molecules of aldehydes and ketones still bond with each other through **London forces** and **permanent dipole-permanent dipole bonds**.

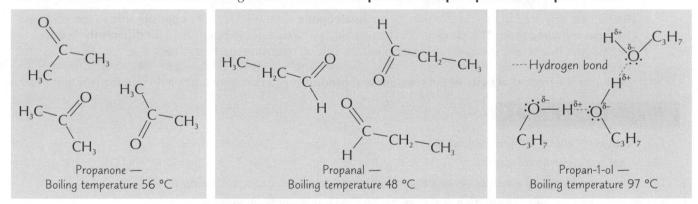

Propanone — Boiling temperature 56 °C

Propanal — Boiling temperature 48 °C

Propan-1-ol — Boiling temperature 97 °C

...But Aldehydes and Ketones can Hydrogen Bond with Water

1) Although aldehydes and ketones don't have polar -OH groups, they do have a **lone pair of electrons** on the **O** atom of the C=O group.

2) The oxygen can use its lone pairs to form **hydrogen bonds** with hydrogen atoms on **water** molecules. So **small** aldehydes and ketones will **dissolve** in water.

3) Large aldehydes and ketones have **longer** carbon chains which aren't able to form hydrogen bonds with water. When larger aldehydes or ketones are mixed with water, these hydrocarbon chains **disrupt** the hydrogen bonding between the water molecules, but **aren't able** to form hydrogen bonds themselves.

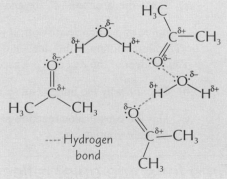
---- Hydrogen bond

4) So if an aldehyde or ketone is **large enough**, the intermolecular forces (in this case **London forces**) between the **aldehyde** or **ketone** molecules, and the hydrogen bonding between water molecules will be stronger than the hydrogen bonds that could form between the aldehyde/ketone and water. So the compound **won't dissolve**.

Aldehydes and Ketones

There are a Few Ways of Testing for *Aldehydes*

Although aldehydes and ketones have similar physical properties, there are tests that let you distinguish between them.
They all work on the idea that an **aldehyde** can be **easily oxidised** to a carboxylic acid, but a ketone can't.
As an aldehyde is oxidised, another compound is **reduced** — so a reagent is used that **changes colour** as it's reduced.

Tollens' Reagent

Tollens' reagent is a **colourless** solution of **silver nitrate** dissolved in **aqueous ammonia**.

If it's heated in a test tube with an aldehyde, a **silver mirror** forms after a few minutes.

$$Ag(NH_3)_2^+{}_{(aq)} + e^- \rightarrow Ag_{(s)} + 2NH_{3(aq)}$$
colourless   silver

> You shouldn't heat the test tube directly over a flame — most organic compounds are flammable. Use a water bath or heating mantle instead.

$$2Ag(NH_3)_2^+{}_{(aq)} + RCHO_{(aq)} + 3OH^-{}_{(aq)} \rightarrow 2Ag_{(s)} + RCOO^-{}_{(aq)} + 4NH_{3(aq)} + 2H_2O$$

Fehling's solution or Benedict's solution

Fehling's solution is a **blue** solution of complexed **copper(II) ions** dissolved in **sodium hydroxide**.

If it's heated with an aldehyde, the copper(II) ions are reduced to a **brick-red precipitate** of **copper(I) oxide**.

$$Cu^{2+}{}_{(aq)} + e^- \rightarrow Cu^+{}_{(s)}$$
blue   brick-red

$$RCHO_{(aq)} + 2Cu^{2+} + 5OH^- \rightarrow RCOO^-{}_{(aq)} + Cu_2O_{(s)} + 3H_2O_{(l)}$$

Benedict's solution is exactly the same as Fehling's solution except the copper(II) ions are dissolved in **sodium carbonate** instead. You still get a **brick-red precipitate** of copper(I) oxide though.

Acidified dichromate(VI) ions

If you **heat** an **aldehyde** with **acidified dichromate(VI) ions,** you get a carboxylic acid.

The **dichromate(VI) ions** are the oxidising agent, [O].
Potassium dichromate(VI) with dilute sulfuric acid is often used. The solution turns orange to green as the dichromate(VI) ions are reduced.

$$Cr_2O_7{}^{2-} + 14H^+ + 6e^- \rightarrow 2Cr^{3+} + 7H_2O$$
Orange   Green

Ketones won't oxidise with acidified **dichromate(VI) ions**.

Practice Questions

Q1 Why do short chain aldehydes and ketones readily dissolve in water?

Q2 Describe how you'd use Tollens' reagent to test for the presence of aldehydes.

Q3 What would you see if you heated Fehling's solution with an aldehyde?

Q4 Describe the colour change seen when an aldehyde is heated with acidified dichromate(VI) ions.

Exam Question

Q1 The skeletal formulae of three compounds are shown on the right.

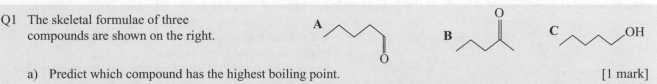

a) Predict which compound has the highest boiling point. [1 mark]

b) Which compound(s) do not form silver precipitates when reacted with Tollens' reagent? [1 mark]

c) Compound B is heated with potassium dichromate(VI) and dilute sulfuric acid. No colour changes occur. Explain why. [1 mark]

Silver mirror on the wall, who's the most 'aldehydey' of them all...

Benedict Cumberbatch. What a guy. Unfortunately he's not the Benedict who the solution is named after. Better luck next time Cumberbatch... You don't have to be Sherlock Holmes to know you have to learn the tests for an aldehyde.

Reactions of Aldehydes and Ketones

So I bet you were wondering 'I know how to distinguish between aldehydes and ketones and have learnt about their properties but what more reactions can they do?' Well, wonder no more my brave chemistry friend.

You can **Reduce** Aldehydes and Ketones Back to **Alcohols**

Using a **reducing agent** [H] you can:

1) Reduce an **aldehyde** to a **primary alcohol**.

$$R-C\substack{=O\\ \\ \backslash H} + 2[H] \longrightarrow R-CH_2-OH$$

2) Reduce a **ketone** to a **secondary alcohol**.

$$R-C\substack{=O\\ \\ \backslash R'} + 2[H] \longrightarrow R-\underset{R'}{\overset{H}{C}}-OH$$

For the **reducing agent,** you could use **LiAlH$_4$** (lithium tetrahydridoaluminate(III) or lithium aluminium hydride) in **dry ether** — it's a very powerful reducing agent, which reacts violently with water, bursting into flames. Eeek.

These are nucleophilic addition reactions (see below) — the reducing agent supplies an H$^-$ that acts as a nucleophile and attacks the δ+ carbon.

Mr White went OTT with the LiAlH$_4$ again...

Hydrogen Cyanide will React with Carbonyls by **Nucleophilic Addition**

Hydrogen cyanide reacts with carbonyl compounds to produce **hydroxynitriles** (molecules with a CN and an OH group). It's a **nucleophilic addition reaction** — a **nucleophile** attacks the molecule, and adds itself.

Hydrogen cyanide is a **weak acid** — it partially dissociates in water to form **H$^+$** and **CN$^-$** ions.

$$HCN \rightleftharpoons H^+ + CN^-$$

You can also use acidified potassium cyanide (which dissociates in water to form K$^+$ ions and CN$^-$ ions). It needs to be acidified so there's a source of H$^+$ for this step.

1) The CN$^-$ ion **attacks** the slightly positive carbon atom and **donates** a pair of electrons to it. Both electrons from the double bond transfer to the oxygen.

2) H$^+$ (from either hydrogen cyanide or water) bonds to the oxygen to form the **hydroxyl group** (OH).

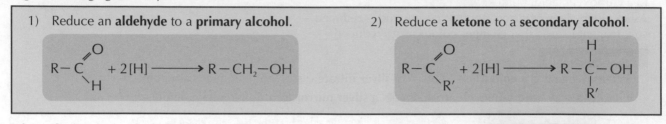

Hydrogen cyanide is a **highly toxic** gas. When this reaction is done in the laboratory, a solution of **acidified potassium cyanide** is used instead, to reduce the risk. Even so, the reaction should be done in a **fume cupboard** while wearing a **lab coat**, **gloves** and **safety glasses**.

Information about the optical activity of the **hydroxynitrile** can provide **evidence** for the reaction mechanism.

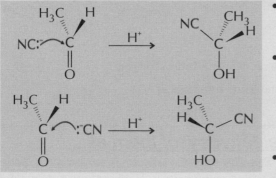

- The groups surrounding the carbonyl carbon in a ketone or aldehyde are **planar**. The nucleophile (CN$^-$ ion) can attack it from **either side**.
- When you react an aldehyde or asymmetric ketone with CN$^-$, you get a **racemic mixture** of **two optical isomers**. This is exactly what you'd expect from the mechanism — the carbonyl group gets attacked equally from **each side**, producing **equal amounts** of the two products, which are optical isomers.
- Because the product is present in a racemic mixture, you would expect the product to be **optically inactive**.

Reactions of Aldehydes and Ketones

2,4-dinitrophenylhydrazine *Tests for a* **Carbonyl Group**

2,4-dinitrophenylhydrazine (2,4-DNPH) is dissolved in methanol and concentrated sulfuric acid.

The **2,4-dinitrophenylhydrazine** reacts to form a
bright orange precipitate if a carbonyl group is present.

This only happens with **C=O groups**, not with more complicated
ones like -COOH, so it only tests for **aldehydes** and **ketones**.

You have to be careful when handling 2,4-DNPH — it's harmful, flammable and can be explosive when dry.

The **Melting Point** of the Precipitate **Identifies** the Carbonyl Compound

The orange precipitate is a **derivative** of the carbonyl compound
which can be purified by **recrystallisation**.   Each different carbonyl
compound gives a crystalline derivative with a **different melting point**.

For details of how to do a recrystallisation, have a look at page 106.

If you measure the melting point of the crystals and compare it to a table of **known**
melting points of the possible derivatives, you can **identify** the carbonyl compound.

Some Carbonyls will React with **Iodine**

Carbonyls that contain a **methyl carbonyl** group react when heated with
iodine in the presence of an alkali. If there's a methyl carbonyl group you'll
get a **yellow precipitate** of triiodomethane (CHI_3) and an antiseptic smell.

This is a methyl carbonyl group: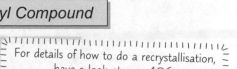

$$RCOCH_3 + 3I_2 + 4OH^- \rightarrow RCOO^- + CHI_3 + 3I^- + 3H_2O$$

If something contains a **methyl carbonyl** group, it must be:

Ethanal. or A **ketone** with **at least one** methyl group.

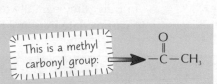

Practice Questions

Q1 What are the reagents and conditions necessary to convert an aldehyde into an alcohol?

Q2 What are the reagents and conditions necessary to convert a carbonyl into a hydroxynitrile?

Q3 Which aldehyde will react with iodine in the presence of an alkali?

Exam Questions

Q1 Substance Q reacts to give an orange precipitate with 2,4-dinitrophenylhydrazine. It produces a secondary alcohol
when reduced. It reacts with iodine to give a yellow precipitate. The molecular formula of Q is $C_7H_{14}O$.

a) Use the information to draw a possible structure for Q. Explain how each piece of information is useful. [4 marks]

b) Suggest and explain how the precipitate formed when Q reacts with 2,4-DNPH reagent
could be used to confirm your suggested structure.   [2 marks]

c) Draw the structure of the substance produced when Q reacts with $LiAlH_4$ in dry ether.   [1 mark]

Q2 Propanone and propanal are isomers with the molecular formula C_3H_6O.

a) Name the type of reaction that occurs when hydrogen cyanide reacts with carbonyl compounds.   [1 mark]

b) Draw: i)   the product obtained when hydrogen cyanide reacts with propanone.   [1 mark]

ii)   the mechanism of the reaction between HCN and propanone.   [4 marks]

c) When propanal reacts with HCN the resulting product forms a racemic mixture. Give reasons why.   [3 marks]

Spot the difference...

*If you can't remember which is aldehyde and which is ketone, this might help — 'a' comes at one end of the alphabet,
so CO is at the end of the molecule, 'k' is in the middle of the alphabet, so the CO is in the middle. Just an idea.*

Carboxylic Acids

Carboxylic acids are more interesting than cardboard boxes — as you're about to discover...

Carboxylic Acids Contain –COOH

1) **Carboxylic acids** contain the **carboxyl** functional group **–COOH**.

2) To name a carboxylic acid, you find and name the longest alkane chain containing the –COOH group, take off the 'e' and add **'–oic acid'**.

A carboxyl group contains a carbonyl group and a hydroxyl group.

The branches and other groups of carboxylic acids are named using the IUPAC rules. If you're unsure have a look at your Year 1 notes.

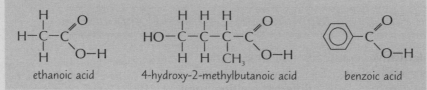

ethanoic acid   4-hydroxy-2-methylbutanoic acid   benzoic acid

3) The carboxyl group is always at the **end** of the molecule and when naming it's more important than any other functional groups — so all the other functional groups in the molecule are numbered starting from this carbon.

4) Carboxylic acids are **weak acids** — in water they partially dissociate into **carboxylate ions** and H^+ ions.

This equilibrium lies to the left because most of the molecules don't dissociate.

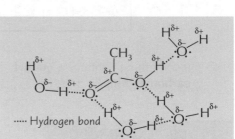

carboxylic acid   carboxylate ion

Carboxylic Acids are Very Soluble

1) Carboxylic acids molecules can form **hydrogen bonds** with each other. Because of this, carboxylic acids have relatively **high boiling points**.

2) The ability to form hydrogen bonds make small carboxylic acids **very soluble** in water, as they can form H bonds with the water molecules.

3) As with aldehydes and ketones (see page 76), the solubility of carboxylic acids **decreases** as the length of the carbon chain **increases**. The hydrocarbon chains can't form hydrogen bonds with water but, when mixed with water, disrupt the hydrogen bonds present between the water molecules. So, large carboxylic acids **don't dissolve** in water.

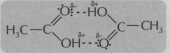

..... Hydrogen bond

In pure, liquid carboxylic acids, **dimers** can also form. This is when a molecule hydrogen bonds with just **one** other molecule. This effectively **increases** the **size** of the molecule, **increasing** the intermolecular forces, and so the boiling point.

Carboxylic Acids Can Be Formed from Alcohols, Aldehydes and Nitriles

Oxidation of Primary Alcohols and Aldehydes

[O] represents an oxidising agent, for example, acidified dichromate(VI) ions, $Cr_2O_7^{2-}$.

You can make a carboxylic acid by **oxidising** a **primary alcohol** to an **aldehyde**, and then to a carboxylic acid. Often, acidified potassium dichromate is used ($K_2Cr_2O_7/H_2SO_4$).

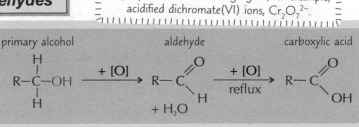

primary alcohol   aldehyde   carboxylic acid

Hydrolysis of Nitriles

Carboxylic acids can also be made by **hydrolysing** a **nitrile**. You reflux the nitrile with dilute hydrochloric acid, and then distil off the carboxylic acid.

Look at page 104 for more on distillation.

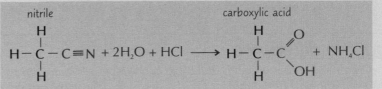

nitrile   carboxylic acid

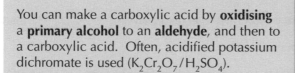

Carboxylic Acids

Carboxylic Acids React with *Bases* to Form *Salts*

1) Carboxylic acids are **neutralised** by **aqueous bases (alkalis)** to form **salts** and **water**.

$$CH_3COOH + NaOH \rightarrow CH_3COONa + H_2O$$

ethanoic acid   sodium ethanoate

Salts of carboxylic acids are called carboxylates and their names end with –oate.

2) Carboxylic acids react with **carbonates (CO_3^{2-})** or **hydrogencarbonates (HCO_3^-)** to form a **salt**, **carbon dioxide** and **water**.

$$2CH_3COOH_{(aq)} + Na_2CO_{3(s)} \rightarrow 2CH_3COONa_{(aq)} + H_2O_{(l)} + CO_{2(g)}$$

$$CH_3COOH_{(aq)} + NaHCO_{3(s)} \rightarrow CH_3COONa_{(aq)} + H_2O_{(l)} + CO_{2(g)}$$

ethanoic acid   sodium ethanoate

In these reactions, carbon dioxide fizzes out of the solution. This can be used as a test for carboxylic acids.

Other Reactions You'll Need to Know

It's quite **hard** to reduce a carboxylic acid, so you have to use a **powerful reducing agent** like **LiAlH$_4$** in **dry ether**.
It reduces the carboxylic acid right down to an **alcohol** in one go — you can't get the reduction to stop at the aldehyde.

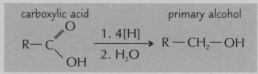

Mix a carboxylic acid with **phosphorus(V) chloride** (Phosphorous pentachloride) and you'll get an **acyl chloride**.

Acyl chlorides are covered on page 84.

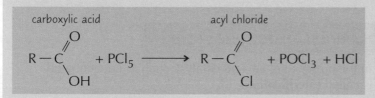

Practice Questions

Q1 Draw the structure of ethanoic acid.

Q2 Explain the relatively high boiling points of carboxylic acids.

Q3 Describe two ways of preparing carboxylic acids.

Q4 How can you make an acyl chloride from a carboxylic acid?

Exam Questions

Q1 A student is carrying out an experiment to synthesise propanoic acid from propan-1-ol.

   a) Describe how the student could make propanoic acid from propan-1-ol.   [2 marks]

   b) The student wants to know whether the synthesis has been successful.
       Describe a simple test tube reaction to distinguish between propan-1-ol and propanoic acid.
       Give the reagent(s) and state the observations expected.   [2 marks]

Q2 Methanoic acid, H_2COOH, and pentanoic acid, $CH_3(CH_2)_3COOH$, are carboxylic acids.

   a) Draw the structures of both compounds.   [2 marks]

   b) Explain why methanoic acid is more soluble in water than pentanoic acid.   [2 marks]

   c) Write a balanced equation for the reaction of 2-ethylpentanoic acid with phosphorous(V) chloride.   [1 mark]

Alright, so maybe cardboard boxes do have the edge after all...

So a few new reactions for you to get your head around here. When you think about it though, the reactions with bases and carbonates are just the same as they would be for any old acid. Also, learning the last section on forming acyl chlorides will be really useful for when we get on to their reactions later on. You'll have to wait for that treat though.

Esters

Time to embrace another functional group. You'll like this one, some of the compounds smell of fruit.

Esters have the Functional Group –COO–

The **name** of an **ester** is made up of **two parts** — the **first** bit comes from the **alcohol**, and the **second** bit from the **carboxylic acid**.

1) Look at the **alkyl** group that came from the **alcohol**. This is the first bit of the ester's name.

This is an **ethyl** group.

2) Now look at the part that came from the **carboxylic acid**. Swap its '-oic acid' ending for '-oate' to get the second bit of the name.

This came from **ethanoic acid**, so it is an **ethanoate**.

3) Put the two parts together. It's **ethyl ethanoate**
CH₃COOCH₂CH₃

The name's written the opposite way round from the formula.

This goes for molecules with benzene rings too. If you react methanol with benzoic acid, and you get methyl benzoate, $C_6H_5COOCH_3$.

If either of the carbon chains is **branched** you need to name the attached groups too. For an ester, number the carbons starting from the C atoms in the C–O–C bond.

ethyl 2-methylbutanoate
$CH_3CH_2CH(CH_3)COOCH_2CH_3$

1-methylpropyl methanoate
$HCOOCH(CH_3)CH_2CH_3$

Esters can be Made From Alcohols and Carboxylic Acids

1) If you heat a **carboxylic acid** with an **alcohol** in the presence of an **acid catalyst**, such as concentrated H_2SO_4 or HCl, you get an ester. The reaction is called **esterification**.

2) For example, to make **ethyl ethanoate** you reflux ethanoic acid with ethanol and concentrated sulfuric acid as the catalyst:

This oxygen comes from the alcohol.

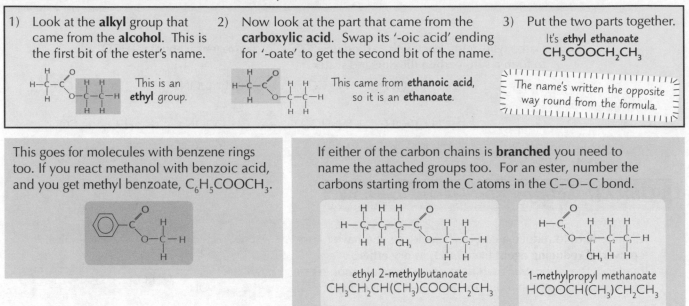

ethanoic acid   ethanol   ethyl ethanoate   water

It's a condensation reaction as two molecules react to produce a large molecule, and a small molecule (in this case water) is released.

3) The reaction is **reversible**, so you need to separate out the product **as it's formed**. You do this by **distillation**, collecting the liquid that comes off just **below** 80 °C.

4) The product is then mixed with **sodium carbonate** solution to react with any **carboxylic acid** that might have snuck in. The **ethyl ethanoate** forms a layer on the **top** of the aqueous layer and can be easily separated using a separating funnel.

5) Ethyl ethanoate is often used as a **solvent** in chromatography and as a **pineapple flavouring**.

Esters can be Broken Up in Hydrolysis Reactions

Acid Hydrolysis

As it's a reversible reaction, you need to use lots of water to push the equilibrium over to the right.

Acid hydrolysis splits the ester into an **acid** and an **alcohol** — it's just the **reverse** of the condensation reaction above. You have to **reflux** the ester with a **dilute acid**, such as hydrochloric or sulfuric. For example:

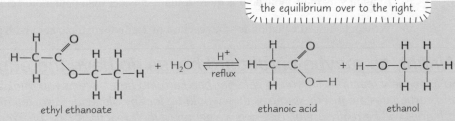

ethyl ethanoate   ethanoic acid   ethanol

Esters

Base Hydrolysis

This time you have to **reflux** the ester with a **dilute alkali**, such as sodium hydroxide. You get a **carboxylate ion** and an **alcohol**. This reaction is **irreversible** For example:

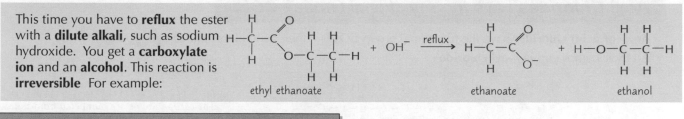

ethyl ethanoate + OH⁻ → (reflux) ethanoate + ethanol

Polyesters Contain lots of Ester Links

1) **Diols** contain **two** –OH functional groups and **dicarboxylic** acids contain **2** –COOH functional groups.

2) Dicarboxylic acids and diols can **react together** to form long **ester chains**, called **polyesters**. This reaction is known as a **condensation polymerisation** reaction.

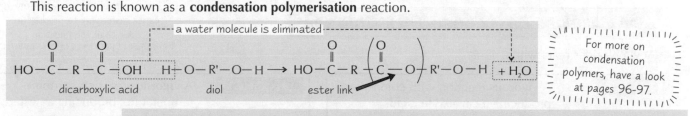

- - - - a water molecule is eliminated - - - -

dicarboxylic acid   diol   ester link   + H₂O

For more on condensation polymers, have a look at pages 96-97.

Example: Terylene™ (PET) — formed from **benzene-1,4-dicarboxylic acid** and **ethane-1,2-diol**.

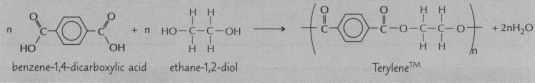

benzene-1,4-dicarboxylic acid   ethane-1,2-diol   Terylene™   + 2nH₂O

Jeremy didn't know the chemistry behind his outfit — he just knew he looked good.

Polyester fibres are **strong**, **flexible** and **abrasion-resistant**. Terylene™ is used in **clothes** to keep them crease-free and make them last longer. Polyesters are also used in **carpets**.

You can treat polyesters (by stretching and heat-treating them) to make them stronger. Treated Terylene™ is used to make fizzy drink bottles and food containers.

Practice Questions

Q1 Draw the structure of ethyl ethanoate.

Q2 Suggest the reactants necessary to form ethyl ethanoate via an esterification reaction.

Q3 Name the products formed when ethyl ethanoate undergoes acid hydrolysis.

Exam Questions

Q1 Compound C, shown on the right, is found in raspberries.

a) Name compound C. [1 mark]

b) Draw and name the structures of the products formed when compound C is refluxed with dilute sulfuric acid. What kind of reaction is this? [5 marks]

Q2 1-methylethyl methanoate is an ester.

a) Draw the structure of this ester. [1 mark]

b) Write an equation to show the formation of this ester from a suitable acid and an alcohol. [3 marks]

c) Name the type of reaction that is taking place to form this ester. [1 mark]

Carboxylic acid + alcohol produces ester — well, that's life...

Those two ways of hydrolysing esters are just similar enough that it's easy to get in a muddle. Remember — hydrolysis in acidic conditions is reversible, and you get a carboxylic acid as well as an alcohol. Hydrolysis with a base is a one way reaction that gives you an alcohol and a carboxylate ion. Now we've got that sorted, I think it's time for a cuppa.

TOPIC 17 – ORGANIC CHEMISTRY II

Acyl Chlorides

Told you we'd get on to acyl chlorides later. Can you imagine a better way to end the topic? OK, maybe ice cream...

Acyl Chlorides have the Functional Group –COCl

Acyl (or acid) chlorides have the functional group **COCl** — their general formula is $C_nH_{2n-1}OCl$.
All their names end in '**–oyl chloride**'.

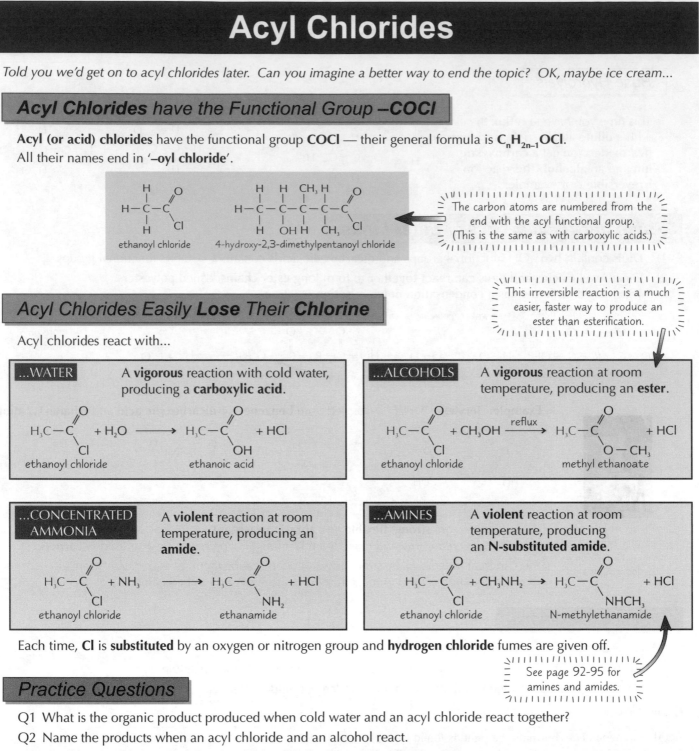

ethanoyl chloride

4-hydroxy-2,3-dimethylpentanoyl chloride

> The carbon atoms are numbered from the end with the acyl functional group. (This is the same as with carboxylic acids.)

Acyl Chlorides Easily Lose Their Chlorine

> This irreversible reaction is a much easier, faster way to produce an ester than esterification.

Acyl chlorides react with...

...WATER — A **vigorous** reaction with cold water, producing a **carboxylic acid**.

$$H_3C-C{O \atop Cl} + H_2O \longrightarrow H_3C-C{O \atop OH} + HCl$$

ethanoyl chloride → ethanoic acid

...ALCOHOLS — A **vigorous** reaction at room temperature, producing an **ester**.

$$H_3C-C{O \atop Cl} + CH_3OH \xrightarrow{reflux} H_3C-C{O \atop O-CH_3} + HCl$$

ethanoyl chloride → methyl ethanoate

...CONCENTRATED AMMONIA — A **violent** reaction at room temperature, producing an **amide**.

$$H_3C-C{O \atop Cl} + NH_3 \longrightarrow H_3C-C{O \atop NH_2} + HCl$$

ethanoyl chloride → ethanamide

...AMINES — A **violent** reaction at room temperature, producing an **N-substituted amide**.

$$H_3C-C{O \atop Cl} + CH_3NH_2 \longrightarrow H_3C-C{O \atop NHCH_3} + HCl$$

ethanoyl chloride → N-methylethanamide

Each time, **Cl** is **substituted** by an oxygen or nitrogen group and **hydrogen chloride** fumes are given off.

> See page 92-95 for amines and amides.

Practice Questions

Q1 What is the organic product produced when cold water and an acyl chloride react together?

Q2 Name the products when an acyl chloride and an alcohol react.

Q3 Give the reagent(s) required to form an amide from an acyl chloride.

Exam Question

Q1 2-methylbutanoyl chloride is an acyl chloride.

a) Draw the structure of 2-methylbutanoyl chloride. [1 mark]

b) 2-methylbutanoyl chloride is reacted with compound X to give N-propyl 2-methylbutanamide.

i) Give the structure of compound X. [1 mark]

ii) Write a balance equation for the reaction. [1 mark]

Learn this page and you can become a real ace at acyl chloride reactions...

Acyl chlorides love to react. I just stared at one once, and it lost it's chlorine right there and then... You might find it useful to learn the structure of the functional group and get to grips with their various reactions. And when I say useful, I mean really very important. Better get to it. Once you're done, congratulate yourself on finishing the topic unscathed.

Aromatic Compounds

We begin this topic with a fantastical tale about the discovery of the magical rings of Benzene.
Our story opens in a shire where four hobbits are getting up to mischief... Actually no, that's something else...

Benzene has a **Ring Of Carbon Atoms**

Benzene has the formula C_6H_6. It has a cyclic structure, with its six carbon atoms joined together in a ring.
There are two ways of representing it — the **Kekulé model** and the **delocalised model**.

The **Kekulé Model** Came First

1) In 1865, the German chemist Friedrich August Kekulé proposed that **benzene** was made up of a **planar** (flat) **ring** of **carbon** atoms with **alternating single** and **double** bonds between them.

2) In Kekulé's model, each carbon atom is also bonded to **one hydrogen** atom.

3) He later adapted the model to say that the benzene molecule was constantly **flipping** between two forms (**isomers**) by switching over the double and single bonds:

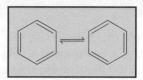

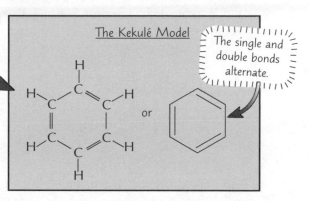

The Kekulé Model

The single and double bonds alternate.

or

4) If the Kekulé model was correct, you'd expect benzene to have three bonds with the length of a **C–C bond** (154 pm) and three bonds with the length of a **C=C bond** (134 pm).

5) However **X-ray diffraction studies** have shown that all the carbon-carbon bonds in benzene have the **same length** of 140 pm — i.e. they're **between** the length of a single bond and a double bond. So the Kekulé structure **can't** be completely right...

Even though it's not completely right, chemists still draw the Kekulé structure of benzene as it's useful when drawing reaction mechanisms.

The **Delocalised Model** Replaced Kekulé's Model

The bond-length observations are explained by a different model — the **delocalised** model.

1) In the delocalised model, each carbon atom forms three σ-bonds — one to a hydrogen atom, and one to each of its neighbouring carbon atoms. These bonds form due to **head-on** overlap of their atomic orbitals.

2) Each carbon atom then has **one remaining** p-orbital, containing one electron, which sticks out **above** and **below** the plane of the ring. These p-orbitals on each of the carbon atoms overlap **sideways** to form a **ring** of π-bonds that are **delocalised** around the carbon ring.

3) The delocalised π-bonds are made up of two **ring-shaped** clouds of electrons — one above and one below the plane of the six carbon atoms.

4) All the bonds in the ring are the same — so, they're all the **same length**.

5) The electrons in the rings are said to be **delocalised** because they don't belong to a **specific** carbon atom. They are represented as a **circle** inside the ring of carbons rather than as double or single bonds.

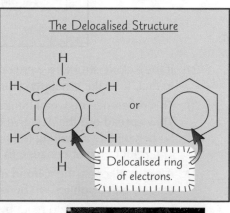

The Delocalised Structure

or

Delocalised ring of electrons.

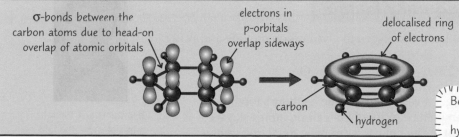

σ-bonds between the carbon atoms due to head-on overlap of atomic orbitals

electrons in p-orbitals overlap sideways

delocalised ring of electrons

carbon

hydrogen

Gary woke up after the stag party to find himself in a delocalised orbit.

Benzene is a planar (flat) molecule — it's got a ring of carbon atoms with their hydrogens sticking out all on a flat plane.

Aromatic Compounds

Enthalpy Changes of Hydrogenation Give More Evidence for Delocalisation

1) If you react an **alkene** with **hydrogen gas**, two atoms of hydrogen add across the **double bond**. This is called **hydrogenation**, and the enthalpy change of the reaction is the **enthalpy change of hydrogenation**.

2) Cyclohexene has **one** double bond. When it's hydrogenated, the enthalpy change is **–120 kJ mol⁻¹**. If benzene had three double bonds (as in the Kekulé structure), you'd expect the enthalpy of hydrogenation to be (3 × 120 =) **–360 kJ mol⁻¹**.

3) But the **experimental** enthalpy of hydrogenation of benzene is **–208 kJ mol⁻¹** — far **less exothermic** than expected.

4) Energy is put in to break bonds and released when bonds are made. So **more energy** must have been put in to break the bonds in benzene than would be needed to break the bonds in the Kekulé structure.

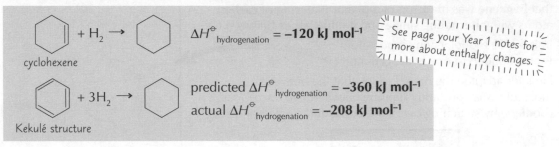

cyclohexene

$\Delta H^{\ominus}_{\text{hydrogenation}} = \mathbf{-120\ kJ\ mol^{-1}}$

See page your Year 1 notes for more about enthalpy changes.

Kekulé structure

predicted $\Delta H^{\ominus}_{\text{hydrogenation}} = \mathbf{-360\ kJ\ mol^{-1}}$

actual $\Delta H^{\ominus}_{\text{hydrogenation}} = \mathbf{-208\ kJ\ mol^{-1}}$

5) This difference indicates that benzene is **more stable** than the Kekulé structure would be. Benzene's **resistance to reaction** (see below) gives more evidence for it being **more stable** than the Kekulé structure suggests. The extra stability is thought to be due to the **delocalised ring of electrons**.

Alkenes usually like Addition Reactions, but Not Benzene

1) **Alkenes** react easily with **bromine** water at room temperature. This **decolourises** the brown bromine water. It's an **electrophilic addition reaction** — the bromine atoms are added across the double bond of the alkene (see your Year 1 notes). For example:

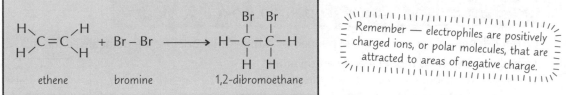

ethene   bromine   1,2-dibromoethane

Remember — electrophiles are positively charged ions, or polar molecules, that are attracted to areas of negative charge.

2) If the Kekulé structure were correct, you'd expect a **similar reaction** between benzene and bromine. In fact, to make it happen you need **hot benzene** and **ultraviolet light** — and it's still a real **struggle**.

3) This difference between benzene and other alkenes is explained by the **delocalised π-bonds** in benzene. They **spread out** the negative charge and make the benzene ring very **stable**. So benzene is **unwilling** to undergo **addition reactions** which would destroy the stable ring. The **reluctance** of benzene to undergo addition reactions is **more evidence** supporting the **delocalised model**.

4) Also, in alkenes, the **π-bond** in the C=C double bond is an area of localised **high electron density** which strongly attracts **electrophiles**. In benzene, this attraction is reduced due to the negative charge being spread out.

5) So benzene prefers to react by **electrophilic substitution** (see pages 88-90).

Benzene Burns with a Smoky Flame

Benzene is a **hydrocarbon**, so it burns in oxygen to give carbon dioxide and water:

$$2C_6H_6 + 15O_2 \rightarrow 12CO_2 + 6H_2O$$

If you burn benzene in **air**, you get a very **smoky flame** — there's too little oxygen to burn the benzene completely. A lot of the carbon atoms stay as carbon and form particles of **soot** in the hot gas — making the flame **smoke**.

Ben didn't just think he was hot... He thought he was smoking hot.

Aromatic Compounds

Aromatic Compounds are Derived from Benzene

1) Compounds containing a **benzene ring** are called **arenes** or 'aromatic compounds'. There are **two** ways of **naming** arenes, but there's no easy rule to know which name to give them. Here are some examples:

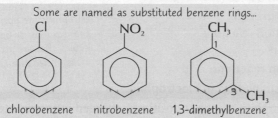

Some are named as substituted benzene rings...

chlorobenzene   nitrobenzene   1,3-dimethylbenzene

...others are named as compounds with a phenyl group (C_6H_5) attached.

phenol   phenylamine

2) If there's **more than one** functional group attached to the benzene ring you have to **number** the **carbons** to show where the groups are.

- If all the functional groups are the **same**, pick the group to start from that gives the **smallest** numbers when you count round.

- If the functional groups are **different**, start from whichever functional group gives the molecule its **suffix** (e.g. the -OH group for a phenol) and continue counting round the way that gives the **smallest** numbers.

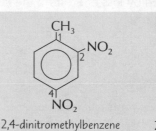

2,4-dinitromethylbenzene   2-methylphenol

Practice Questions

Q1 Draw the Kekulé and delocalised models of benzene.

Q2 Write an equation for the combustion of benzene in excess oxygen.

Exam Questions

Q1 When cyclohexene reacts with hydrogen, one mole of H_2 adds across the double bond in one mole of cyclohexene. 120 kJ of energy is released.

$$\text{⬡} + H_2 \rightarrow \text{⬡} \qquad \Delta H = -120 \text{ kJ mol}^{-1}$$

Use the structures of the following molecules, along with the information above, to answer the following questions:

⬡ Cyclohexa-1,3-diene   ⬡ Benzene (Kekulé structure)

a) i) Predict the number of moles of H_2 that one mole of cyclohexa-1,3-diene will react with. [1 mark]

   ii) Predict how much energy will be released during this reaction. [1 mark]

b) Look at the Kekulé structure for benzene. Explain why this model would lead to the prediction that 360 kJ of energy would be released during the reaction between benzene and H_2. [1 mark]

c) One mole of benzene actually releases 208 kJ of energy when it reacts with hydrogen. Suggest how the delocalised model of benzene explains the difference between this number and the prediction of 360 kJ based on the Kekulé structure. [2 marks]

d) By referring to the structure and reactivity of benzene, outline two further pieces of evidence which support the delocalised structure as a better representation of benzene than the Kekulé structure. [4 marks]

Q2 A student takes two test tubes, each containing bromine water. He adds cyclohexene to one of the test tubes and benzene to the other. Describe and explain what the student will see. [3 marks]

Everyone needs a bit of stability in their life...

The structure of benzene is bizarre — even top scientists struggled to find out what its molecular structure looked like. Make sure you can draw all the different representations of benzene given on these pages, including the ones showing the Cs and Hs. Yes, and don't forget there's a hydrogen at every point on the ring — it's easy to forget they're there.

Electrophilic Substitution Reactions

Benzene is an alkene but it often doesn't behave like one — whenever this is the case, you can pretty much guarantee that our kooky friend Mr Delocalised Electron Ring is up to his old tricks again...

Arenes Undergo **Electrophilic Substitution** Reactions

1) As you saw on page 86, benzene **doesn't** undergo electrophilic addition reactions as alkenes do. This is because addition reactions would break the very **stable** ring of delocalised π-bonds.

Electrophiles are positively charged ions, or polar molecules, that are attracted to areas of negative charge.

2) Instead, benzene takes part in **electrophilic substitution reactions**.

3) In these reactions, a **hydrogen** atom in benzene is substituted by an **electrophile**.

4) The mechanism has two steps — addition of the **electrophile** to form a **positively charged intermediate**, followed by loss of **H⁺** from the carbon atom attached to the electrophile. This **reforms** the delocalised ring.

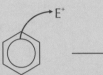

Benzene reacts with the electrophile, breaking the delocalised ring.

An unstable intermediate forms.

H⁺ is lost, and the delocalised ring is reformed.

E is an electrophile.

Halogen Carriers Help to Make **Good Electrophiles**

1) The **delocalised** π-bonds in benzene means that the charge density is **spread out** across the ring. This means that an electrophile has to have a pretty strong **positive charge** to be able to attack the benzene ring. Most compounds just **aren't polarised enough** — but some can be made into **stronger electrophiles** using a catalyst called a **halogen carrier**.

2) A halogen carrier accepts a **lone pair of electrons** from a **halogen** atom on an **electrophile**. As the lone pair of electrons is pulled away, the **polarisation** in the molecule **increases** and sometimes a **carbocation** forms. This makes the electrophile **stronger**.

$$\overset{\delta+}{R}\!-\!\overset{\delta-}{Cl}\!:\cdots\!\!\!\longrightarrow AlCl_3 \longrightarrow R^+ \ AlCl_4^-$$

halogenoalkane   halogen   carbocation
              carrier

Although R⁺ gets shown as a free ion, it probably remains associated with $AlCl_4^-$ — this doesn't affect how R⁺ reacts though.

Halogen carriers can increase how electrophilic (how strongly something reacts as an electrophile) halogens, acyl chlorides and halogenoalkanes are.

3) Halogen carriers include **aluminium halides**, **iron halides** and **iron**.

Halogen Carriers Help **Halogens Substitute** into the Benzene Ring

1) Benzene will react with **halogens** (e.g. Br₂) at room temperature in the presence of a halogen carrier catalyst, e.g **iron(III) bromide**, FeBr₃.

2) The catalyst **polarises** the halogen, allowing one of the halogen atoms to act as an **electrophile**.

3) During the reaction, a halogen atom is **substituted** in place of a H atom — this is called **halogenation**.

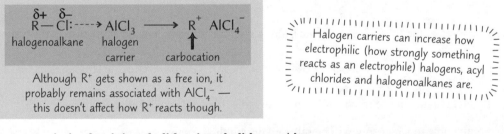

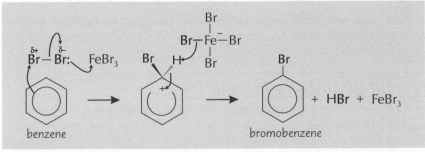

benzene

bromobenzene

Electrophilic Substitution Reactions

Friedel-Crafts Reactions Form C–C Bonds

Friedel-Crafts reactions are really useful for forming C–C bonds in organic synthesis. They are carried out by refluxing benzene with a halogen carrier and either a **halogenoalkane** or an **acyl chloride**. There are two types:

Friedel-Crafts Alkylation Puts an Alkyl Group on Benzene

Friedel-Crafts alkylation puts **any alkyl group** onto a benzene ring using a **halogenoalkane** and a halogen carrier. The general reaction is:

$$C_6H_6 + R{-}X \xrightarrow[\text{Reflux}]{AlCl_3} C_6H_5R + HX$$

Here's how the **mechanism** for the reaction works, using a chloroalkane and $AlCl_3$ as an example:

A **carbocation** is formed from the chloroalkane and $AlCl_3$.

The carbocation then reacts with benzene via **electrophilic substitution**:

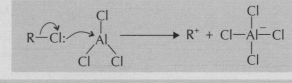

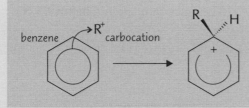

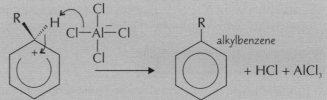

1) The **carbocation** is the **electrophile**. It attracts the electrons in the delocalised ring to form a **new C–C bond**. The delocalised ring of electrons is **broken** and an unstable intermediate forms.

2) $AlCl_4^-$ reacts with the unstable intermediate to remove a **hydrogen ion** and the delocalised ring is **reformed**. An alkylbenzene and hydrogen chloride are made and the $AlCl_3$ catalyst is regenerated.

Friedel-Crafts alkylation can also occur with other **electrophiles**.

Electrophiles that are made up of alkyl chains containing $OAlCl_3^-$ groups can be added to benzene rings to create **alcohols**.

Because the oxygen in the alkyl chain has a **lone pair** of electrons, it can act as a nucleophile.

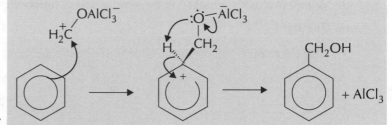

Friedel-Crafts Acylation Produces Phenylketones

Friedel-Crafts acylation substitutes an **acyl group** for an H atom on benzene. You have to reflux benzene with an **acyl chloride** instead of a halogenoalkane. This produces **phenylketones** (unless R = H, in which case an aldehyde called benzenecarbaldehyde, or benzaldehyde, is formed). The reactants need to be **heated under reflux** in a **non-aqueous solvent** (like dry ether) for the reaction to occur.

The general reaction is:

$$C_6H_6 + RCOCl \xrightarrow[\text{Reflux}]{AlCl_3} C_6H_5COR + HCl$$

The mechanism for this is the same as for the formation of a carbocation in Friedel-Crafts alkylation, except with an acyl chloride instead of a halogenoalkane.

Again, the **carbocation** is formed from the acyl chloride and $AlCl_3$: $CH_3COCl + AlCl_3 \rightarrow CH_3CO^+ + AlCl_4^-$

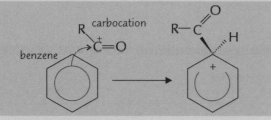

1) **Electrons** in the benzene ring are **attracted** to the positively charged **carbocation**. Two electrons from the benzene **bond** with the carbocation. This **partially breaks** the delocalised ring and gives it a **positive charge**.

2) The **negatively charged** $AlCl_4^-$ ion is attracted to the **positively charged ring**. One **chloride ion** breaks away from the aluminium chloride ion and **bonds** with the **hydrogen ion**. This **removes the hydrogen** from the ring forming **HCl**. It also reforms the catalyst.

Electrophilic Substitution Reactions

Nitric Acid Acts as an Electrophile with a Sulfuric Acid Catalyst

When you warm **benzene** with **concentrated nitric acid** and **concentrated sulfuric acid**, you get a **nitration reaction** and **nitrobenzene** is formed.

Sulfuric acid is a **catalyst** — it helps make the nitronium ion, NO_2^+, which is the **electrophile**:

$$HNO_3 + H_2SO_4 \rightarrow H_2NO_3^+ + HSO_4^-$$
$$H_2NO_3^+ \rightarrow NO_2^+ + H_2O$$

The NO_2^+ electrophile then reacts with the benzene ring to form nitrobenzene:

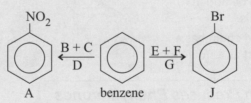

This H^+ ion reacts with HSO_4^- to reform the catalyst, H_2SO_4.

If you only want one NO_2 group added (**mononitration**), you need to keep the temperature **below 55 °C**. Above this temperature you'll get lots of substitutions.

Practice Questions

Q1 What type of reaction does benzene tend to undergo?

Q2 Describe the role of a halogen carrier in electrophilic substitution reactions.

Q3 Name two substances that are used as halogen carriers in substitution reactions of benzene.

Q4 Describe two ways of making C–C bonds with benzene.

Q5 What type of compounds are normally formed in Friedel-Crafts acylation reactions?

Q6 Which two acids are used in the production of nitrobenzene?

Exam Questions

Q1 Two electrophilic substitution reactions of benzene are summarised in the diagram below:

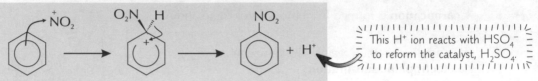

a) i) Name product A, the reagents B and C, and give the conditions, D. [4 marks]

   ii) Write equations to show the formation of the electrophile in this reaction. [2 marks]

   iii) Outline a mechanism for the reaction of benzene with the electrophile formed in ii). [2 marks]

b) i) Name product J. [1 mark]

   ii) Name reagents E and F, and give the conditions, G, needed in the reaction to make J. [3 marks]

Q2 A halogen carrier, such as $AlCl_3$, is used as a catalyst in the reaction between benzene and ethanoyl chloride.

a) Describe the conditions needed for this reaction. [1 mark]

b) Explain why the halogen carrier is needed as a catalyst for this reaction to occur. [2 marks]

c) Draw the structure of the electrophile that attacks the benzene ring. [1 mark]

Shhhh... Don't disturb The Ring...

Benzene really likes Mr Delocalised Electron Ring and it won't give him up for nobody, at least not without one heck of a fight. It'd much rather get tangled up in an electrophilic substitution reaction. I mean, those hydrogen atoms weren't good for much anyway, so it's not as if anyone's going to miss them. Anything not to bother The Ring.

Phenols

Phenols are like benzene, but they have a hydroxyl group on the benzene ring. This changes their reactivity.

Phenols Have Benzene Rings with -OH Groups Attached

Phenol has the formula C_6H_5OH.
Other phenol derivatives have various groups attached to the benzene ring:

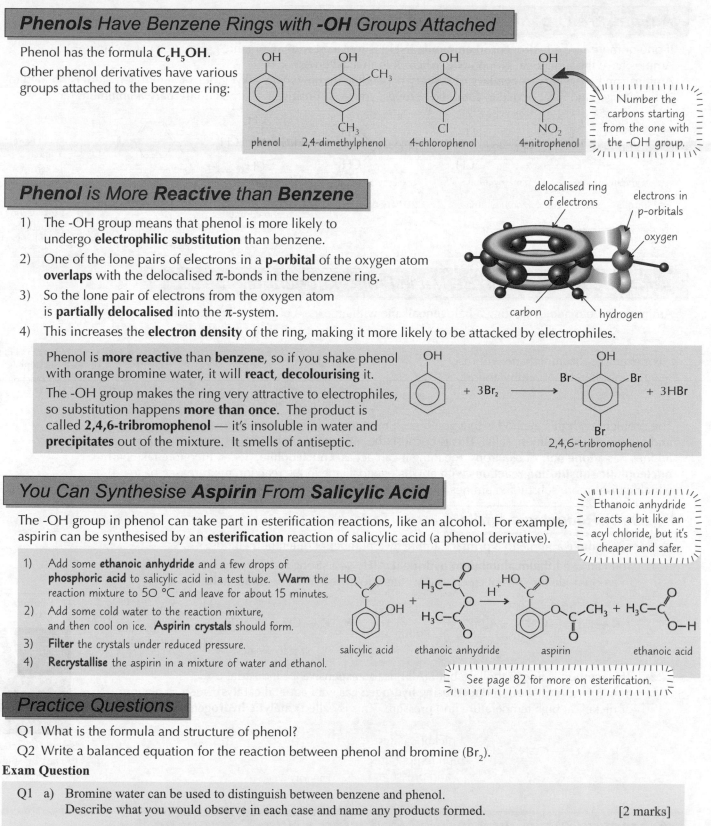

phenol   2,4-dimethylphenol   4-chlorophenol   4-nitrophenol

Number the carbons starting from the one with the -OH group.

Phenol is More Reactive than Benzene

1) The -OH group means that phenol is more likely to undergo **electrophilic substitution** than benzene.

2) One of the lone pairs of electrons in a **p-orbital** of the oxygen atom **overlaps** with the delocalised π-bonds in the benzene ring.

3) So the lone pair of electrons from the oxygen atom is **partially delocalised** into the π-system.

4) This increases the **electron density** of the ring, making it more likely to be attacked by electrophiles.

delocalised ring of electrons

electrons in p-orbitals

oxygen

carbon   hydrogen

Phenol is **more reactive** than **benzene**, so if you shake phenol with orange bromine water, it will **react**, **decolourising** it.

The -OH group makes the ring very attractive to electrophiles, so substitution happens **more than once**. The product is called **2,4,6-tribromophenol** — it's insoluble in water and **precipitates** out of the mixture. It smells of antiseptic.

2,4,6-tribromophenol

You Can Synthesise Aspirin From Salicylic Acid

Ethanoic anhydride reacts a bit like an acyl chloride, but it's cheaper and safer.

The -OH group in phenol can take part in esterification reactions, like an alcohol. For example, aspirin can be synthesised by an **esterification** reaction of salicylic acid (a phenol derivative).

1) Add some **ethanoic anhydride** and a few drops of **phosphoric acid** to salicylic acid in a test tube. **Warm** the reaction mixture to 50 °C and leave for about 15 minutes.

2) Add some cold water to the reaction mixture, and then cool on ice. **Aspirin crystals** should form.

3) **Filter** the crystals under reduced pressure.

4) **Recrystallise** the aspirin in a mixture of water and ethanol.

salicylic acid   ethanoic anhydride   aspirin   ethanoic acid

See page 82 for more on esterification.

Practice Questions

Q1 What is the formula and structure of phenol?

Q2 Write a balanced equation for the reaction between phenol and bromine (Br_2).

Exam Question

Q1 a) Bromine water can be used to distinguish between benzene and phenol.
Describe what you would observe in each case and name any products formed. [2 marks]

b) Explain why phenol reacts differently from benzene. [2 marks]

c) Name the type of reaction that occurs between phenol and bromine. [1 mark]

Phenol Destination 4 — more compounds, more equations, more horror...

The electrophilic substitution reactions of phenol are all pretty similar to benzene — phenol's just more reactive so the reaction conditions can be a bit milder. Make sure you can explain why phenol is more reactive than benzene.

Amines

Another type of organic compound coming up. Amines all contain nitrogen. Luckily, they're not as mean as they sound.

Amines are Organic Derivatives of **Ammonia**

If one or more of the **hydrogens** in **ammonia** (NH_3) is replaced with an organic group, you get an **amine**.
Amines have the functional group **$-NR_2$** where R is an **alkyl group** or **H**.
Amines can be **primary**, **secondary** or **tertiary** depending on how many **alkyl** groups the nitrogen atom is bonded to.
If the nitrogen atom is bonded to **four** alkyl groups, you get a **positively** charged **quaternary ammonium** ion.

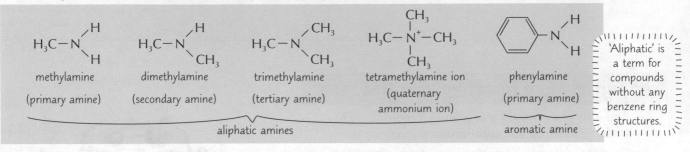

methylamine
(primary amine)

dimethylamine
(secondary amine)

trimethylamine
(tertiary amine)

tetramethylamine ion
(quaternary
ammonium ion)

phenylamine
(primary amine)

aliphatic amines

aromatic amine

'Aliphatic' is a term for compounds without any benzene ring structures.

Aliphatic Amines Can Be Made From *Halogenoalkanes...*

Amines can be made by heating a **halogenoalkane** with an excess of **ethanolic ammonia**.

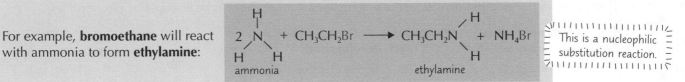

For example, **bromoethane** will react with ammonia to form **ethylamine**:

$$2\ \overset{H}{\underset{H}{N}}{-}H + CH_3CH_2Br \longrightarrow CH_3CH_2\overset{H}{\underset{H}{N}} + NH_4Br$$

ammonia

ethylamine

This is a nucleophilic substitution reaction.

The problem with this method is that you'll get a **mixture** of primary, secondary and tertiary amines, and quaternary ammonium salts. This is because the nitrogen atom in primary, secondary and tertiary amines has a **lone pair** of electrons, meaning it can act as a **nucleophile**. It can therefore take part in **nucleophilic substitution reactions** with any halogenoalkane in the reaction mixture (see page 94), which causes more substituted amines to be produced, where more than one hydrogen is replaced.

...Or By **Reducing** a **Nitrile**

You can **reduce** a nitrile to a **primary amine** by a number of different methods:

1) You can use **lithium aluminium hydride** (**$LiAlH_4$** — a strong reducing agent) in a non-aqueous solvent (such as dry ether), followed by some **dilute acid**.

$$R{-}CH_2{-}C{\equiv}N + 4[H] \xrightarrow[\text{(2) dilute acid}]{\text{(1) } LiAlH_4} R{-}CH_2{-}CH_2\overset{H}{\underset{H}{N}}$$

nitrile

primary amine

[H] is just the reducing agent (here it's $LiAlH_4$).

I can't afford $LiAlH_4$...

2) This method is fine in the lab, but $LiAlH_4$ is too **expensive** for industrial use. In industry, nitriles are reduced using **hydrogen gas** with a **metal catalyst**, such as platinum or nickel, at high temperature and pressure. This is called **catalytic hydrogenation**.

$$R{-}CH_2{-}C{\equiv}N + 2H_2 \xrightarrow[\text{high temperature and pressure}]{\text{nickel catalyst}} R{-}CH_2{-}CH_2\overset{H}{\underset{H}{N}}$$

nitrile

primary amine

Becky was reduced to tears by lithium aluminium hydride.

Aromatic Amines are Made by *Reducing* a *Nitro Compound*

Aromatic nitro compounds, e.g. **nitrobenzene**, are reduced in two steps:

1) Heat a mixture of a **nitro compound**, **tin metal** and **concentrated hydrochloric acid** under **reflux** — this makes a **salt**.

2) To get the **aromatic amine**, add **sodium hydroxide**.

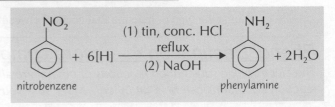

$$\text{nitrobenzene} + 6[H] \xrightarrow[\text{(2) NaOH}]{\text{(1) tin, conc. HCl} \atop \text{reflux}} \text{phenylamine} + 2H_2O$$

Amines

Amines Are *Bases*

1) Amines act as **weak bases** because they **accept protons**. There's a **lone pair of electrons** on the **nitrogen** atom that can form a **dative covalent (coordinate) bond** with an H^+ ion.

2) The **strength** of the **base** depends on how **available** the nitrogen's lone pair of electrons is. The more **available** the **lone pair** is, the more likely the amine is to **accept a proton**, and the **stronger** a base it will be. A **lone pair** of electrons will be **more available** if its **electron density** is **higher**.

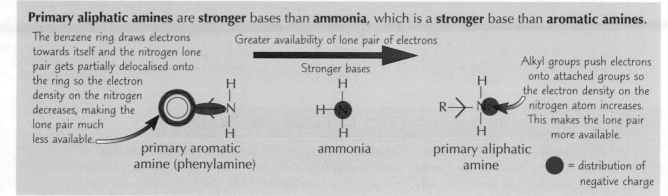

Primary aliphatic amines are **stronger** bases than **ammonia**, which is a **stronger** base than **aromatic amines**.

The benzene ring draws electrons towards itself and the nitrogen lone pair gets partially delocalised onto the ring so the electron density on the nitrogen decreases, making the lone pair much less available.

Greater availability of lone pair of electrons

Stronger bases

Alkyl groups push electrons onto attached groups so the electron density on the nitrogen atom increases. This makes the lone pair more available.

primary aromatic amine (phenylamine)

ammonia

primary aliphatic amine

= distribution of negative charge

3) The lone pair of electrons also means that amines are **nucleophiles**. They react with **halogenoalkanes** in a **nucleophilic substitution reaction** (see next page), or with **acyl chlorides** to form **N-substituted amides** (p.95).

4) Amines are **neutralised** by **acids** to make **ammonium salts**. E.g. **butylamine** reacts with **hydrochloric acid** to form butylammonium chloride:

$$CH_3CH_2CH_2CH_2NH_2 + HCl \rightarrow CH_3CH_2CH_2CH_2NH_3^+Cl^-$$

Small Amines *Dissolve* in Water to Form an *Alkaline* Solution

1) **Small amines** are **soluble in water** as the amine group can form **hydrogen bonds** with the water molecules.

2) The **bigger** the amine, the **greater** the **London forces** (see your Year 1 notes) between the amine molecules and the more energy it takes to overcome the London forces. The larger carbon chains in larger amines also disrupt the hydrogen bonding in water, but can't form hydrogen bonds with water themselves. So **large amines** are **less soluble** in water than small ones.

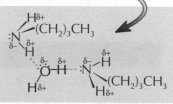

3) When they dissolve, amines form **alkaline** solutions. Some of the amine molecules in the solution take a hydrogen ion from water, forming **alkyl ammonium ions** and **hydroxide ions**.

$$CH_3CH_2CH_2CH_2NH_{2(aq)} + H_2O_{(l)} \rightleftharpoons CH_3CH_2CH_2CH_2NH_3^+{}_{(aq)} + OH^-{}_{(aq)}$$

Amines will Form a *Complex Ion* With *Copper(II) Ions*

1) In **copper(II) sulfate** solution, the Cu^{2+} ions form $[Cu(H_2O)_6]^{2+}$ complexes with water. This solution's **blue**.

2) If you add a **small** amount of **butylamine solution** to copper(II) sulfate solution you get a **pale blue precipitate** — the amine acts as a **base** (proton acceptor) and takes two H^+ ions from the complex. This leaves a pale blue precipitate of copper hydroxide, $[Cu(OH)_2(H_2O)_4]$, which is insoluble.

3) Add more butylamine solution, and the **precipitate dissolves** to form a beautiful **deep blue solution**. Some of the ligands are replaced by butylamine molecules, which donate their lone pairs to form dative covalent bonds with the Cu^{2+} ion. This forms soluble $[Cu(CH_3(CH_2)_3NH_2)_4(H_2O)_2]^{2+}$ complex ions.

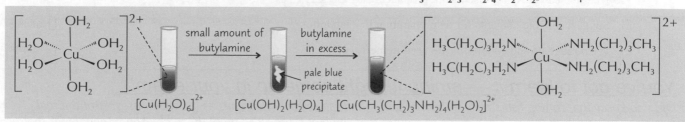

small amount of butylamine

butylamine in excess

pale blue precipitate

$[Cu(H_2O)_6]^{2+}$ $[Cu(OH)_2(H_2O)_4]$ $[Cu(CH_3(CH_2)_3NH_2)_4(H_2O)_2]^{2+}$

4) The **same** set of reactions will happen with **other** amine molecules. For **larger** amines, the final product may **change** because the amine molecules just **can't fit** around the copper ion.

TOPIC 18 — ORGANIC CHEMISTRY III

Amines

Amines React with *Halogenoalkanes* in *Nucleophilic Substitution* Reactions

1) As you saw on page 92, primary amines can be made from the reaction between **ammonia** and a **halogenoalkane**. It's a **nucleophilic substitution reaction** — the **lone pair** on the ammonia molecule is attracted to the δ+ carbon in the halogenoalkane and reacts with it to remove the halogen and form a primary amine.

2) The nitrogen atom in the primary amine that is formed has a lone pair of electrons, so it is **also** a **nucleophile**. In fact, **primary**, **secondary** and **tertiary** amines all have a lone pair of electrons on their nitrogen atom, so are able to react with halogenoalkanes in nucleophilic substitution reactions to form more substituted amines:

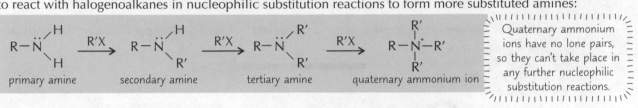

Quaternary ammonium ions have no lone pairs, so they can't take place in any further nucleophilic substitution reactions.

Amines Can Be *Acylated* to Form *N-Substituted Amides*

When amines react with acyl chlorides, an **H atom** on the amine is swapped for the **acyl group**, RCO, to produce an **N-substituted amide** (see the next page) and **HCl**. The HCl reacts with another molecule of the amine to produce a **salt**. In the case of **butylamine** ($C_4H_9NH_2$), the reactions are:

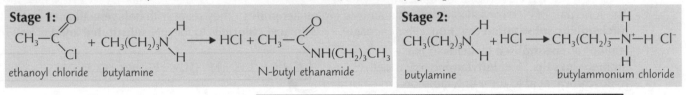

The combined equation for this reaction is: $CH_3COCl + 2C_4H_9NH_2 \rightarrow CH_3CONHC_4H_9 + [C_4H_9NH_3]^+Cl^-$

To carry out this reaction, ethanoyl chloride is added to a **concentrated aqueous solution** of the amine. A violent reaction occurs, which produces a **solid, white mixture** of the products.

This is the 'halogenoalkane + ammonia' reaction you met in Year 1.

Practice Questions

Q1 Draw examples of a primary, secondary and tertiary amine, and a quaternary ammonium ion.

Q2 What conditions are needed to reduce nitrobenzene to phenylamine?

Q3 Explain why small amines dissolve in water but large ones don't.

Exam Questions

Q1 Butylamine solution will react with ethanoyl chloride, CH_3COCl, to form N-butylethanamide, $CH_3CONH(C_4H_9)$.

   a) Butylamine solution is alkaline. Explain why this is. [2 marks]

   b) Write balanced equations for the two stages of the reaction between butylamine and ethanoyl chloride. [2 marks]

Q2 a) Explain how methylamine, CH_3NH_2, can act as a base. [1 mark]

   b) Methylamine is a stronger base than ammonia, NH_3. However, phenylamine, $C_6H_5NH_2$, is a weaker base than ammonia. Explain these differences in base strength. [2 marks]

Q3 Propylamine can be synthesised from propanenitrile, CH_3CH_2CN.

   a) Suggest suitable reagents for its preparation in a laboratory. [1 mark]

   b) What reagents and conditions are used in industry? [2 marks]

You've got to learn it — amine it might come up in your exam...

Did you know that rotting fish smells so bad because the flesh releases diamines as it decomposes? But the real question is: is it fish that smells of amines or amines that smell of fish — it's one of those chicken or egg things that no one can answer. Well, enough philosophical pondering — we all know the answer to the meaning of life. It's 42.

Amides

Some more nitrogen-containing organic compounds to keep you entertained. Amides look like carboxylic acids, but the -OH group is replaced by -NH₂ or -NHR. You need to be able to recognise them and know how they're made.

Amides are Carboxylic Acid Derivatives

Amides contain the functional group **-CONH₂**.

The **carbonyl group** pulls electrons away from the rest of the -CONH₂ group, so amides behave differently from amines.

You get **primary amides** and **N-substituted amides** depending on how many **carbon atoms** the nitrogen is bonded to.

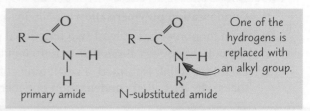

primary amide   N-substituted amide

One of the hydrogens is replaced with an alkyl group.

You Name Amides Using the Suffix '-amide'

1) Amides all have the suffix **-amide**. If the molecule is a **primary amide**, then the name is simply the stem of the carbon chain, followed by -amide.

2) **N-substituted amides** also have a prefix to describe the alkyl chain that is attached directly to the nitrogen atom. The prefix has the general form **N-alkyl-**.

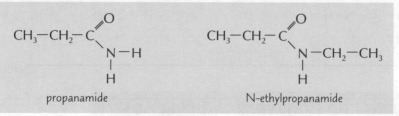

propanamide   N-ethylpropanamide

Charlie was trying the new, protein-heavy hen-substituted diet.

Amides Can Be Made From Acyl Chlorides

If you can react an acyl chloride with **ammonia** or a **primary amine**, you'll form an **amide**.

1) The reaction with concentrated **ammonia** at **room temperature** forms a **primary amide**:

$$H_3C-C \underset{Cl}{\overset{O}{<}} + NH_3 \longrightarrow H_3C-C \underset{NH_2}{\overset{O}{<}} + HCl$$

ethanoyl chloride   ethanamide

2) The reaction with a **primary amine** at **room temperature** forms an **N-substituted amide**:

$$H_3C-C \underset{Cl}{\overset{O}{<}} + CH_3NH_2 \longrightarrow H_3C-C \underset{NHCH_3}{\overset{O}{<}} + HCl$$

ethanoyl chloride   N-methylethanamide

Practice Questions

Q1 Draw the general structures of a primary amide and an N-substituted amide, using R and R' to represent any alkyl groups.

Q2 Give the reagents and conditions you could use to make a primary amide from an acyl chloride.

Exam Question

Q1 An N-substituted amide is shown on the right.

a) Name the amide.

$$CH_3CH_2CH_2-C \underset{NHCH_2CH_2CH_3}{\overset{O}{<}}$$

[1 mark]

b) The amide can be made through the reaction of an acyl chloride.
Name the acyl chloride, and give any other reagents and conditions needed for this reaction.

[3 marks]

I think, therefore I amide...

'Amine' and 'amide' might sound pretty similar, but that C=O group makes a world of difference. Check that you can tell the difference between them, and make sure you know how to make both primary and N-substituted amides.

Condensation Polymers

You met addition polymerisation back in Year 1. Now it's time for a second type — condensation polymerisation.

Condensation Polymers Include **Polyesters**, **Polyamides** and **Polypeptides**

1) **Condensation polymerisation** usually involves two different types of monomers.

2) Each monomer has at least **two functional groups**. Each functional group reacts with a group on another monomer to form a link, creating polymer chains.

3) Each time a link is formed, a small molecule (often water) is lost — that's why it's called **condensation** polymerisation.

Reactions Between **Dicarboxylic Acids** and **Diamines** Make **Polyamides**

1) **Carboxyl** (–COOH) groups react with **amino** (–NH$_2$) groups to form **amide** (–CONH–) links.

2) A water molecule is lost each time an amide link is formed — it's a **condensation** reaction.

3) The condensation polymer formed is a **polyamide**.

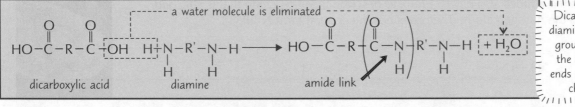

Dicarboxylic acids and diamines have functional groups at each end of the molecule, so both ends can react and long chains can form.

Proteins are **Condensation Polymers** of Amino Acids

1) Amino acids are molecules that contain **both** an **amine** and a **carboxylic acid** group (see page 98).

2) Amino acid monomers can react together in condensation polymerisation reactions to form **proteins**. The **amino acid monomers** are connected by amide links — in proteins these are called **peptide links**.

3) The **amine group** of one amino acid can react with the **carboxylic acid group** of another in a **condensation** reaction.

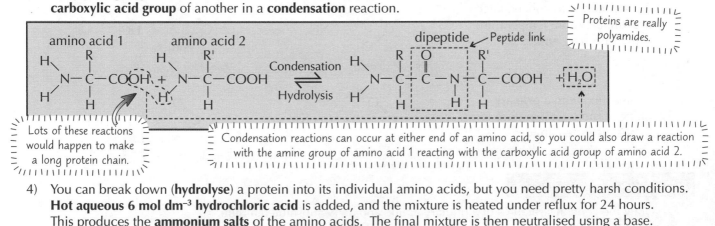

Proteins are really polyamides.

Lots of these reactions would happen to make a long protein chain.

Condensation reactions can occur at either end of an amino acid, so you could also draw a reaction with the amine group of amino acid 1 reacting with the carboxylic acid group of amino acid 2.

4) You can break down (**hydrolyse**) a protein into its individual amino acids, but you need pretty harsh conditions. **Hot aqueous 6 mol dm^{-3} hydrochloric acid** is added, and the mixture is heated under reflux for 24 hours. This produces the **ammonium salts** of the amino acids. The final mixture is then neutralised using a base.

5) Once you've hydrolysed a protein, you can use **chromatography** (see page 99) to identify the amino acid monomers that it was made from.

Reactions Between **Dicarboxylic Acids** and **Diols** Make **Polyesters**

Carboxyl groups (–COOH) react with **hydroxyl** (–OH) groups to form **ester links** (–COO–). It's another **condensation** reaction, and the polymer formed is a **polyester**

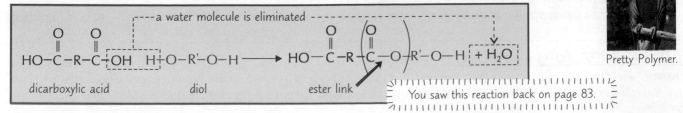

You saw this reaction back on page 83.

Pretty Polymer.

Condensation Polymers

Break the *Amide* or *Ester* Link to Find the *Monomers* of a *Condensation* Polymer

You can find the formulae of the **monomers** used to make a condensation polymer by looking at its repeat unit.

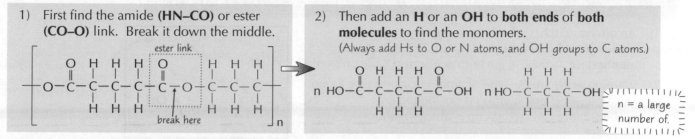

1) First find the amide (**HN–CO**) or ester (**CO–O**) link. Break it down the middle.

2) Then add an **H** or an **OH** to **both ends** of **both molecules** to find the monomers.
   (Always add Hs to O or N atoms, and OH groups to C atoms.)

n = a large number of.

Join the *Monomer Functional Groups* to Find a *Condensation Polymer*

If you know the **formulae** of a pair of **monomers** that react together in a **condensation polymerisation** reaction, you can work out the **repeat unit** of the condensation polymer that they would form.

Example: A condensation polymer is made from 1,4-diaminobutane, $H_2N(CH_2)_4NH_2$, and decanedioic acid, $HOOC(CH_2)_8COOH$. Draw the repeat unit of the polymer that is formed.

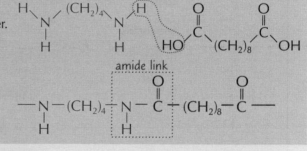

1) Draw out the two **monomer** molecules next to each other.
2) Remove an **OH** from the **dicarboxylic acid**, and an **H** from the **diamine** — that gives you a water molecule.
3) Join the C and the N together to make an **amide link**.
4) Take another **H** and **OH** off the ends of your molecule, and there's your **repeat unit**.

If the monomer molecules are a **dicarboxylic acid** and a **diol**, then you take an **H** atom from the **diol** and an **-OH** group from the **dicarboxylic acid**, and form an **ester** link instead.

Practice Questions

Q1 Why are polyamides and polyesters called 'condensation polymers'?

Q2 Which two types of molecules react together to make a polyamide?

Q3 What type of molecules react together to form a polypeptide?

Exam Questions

Q1 The monomers shown on the right are used to make a polymer called poly(butylene succinate), or PBS.

butanedioic acid   butane-1,4-diol

a) Draw the repeat unit of the polymer made from these two monomers. (It is not necessary to draw the carbon chains out in full.) [2 marks]

b) Give a name for the type of link formed between the monomers. [1 mark]

Q2 The polyamide nylon (6,6) is formed by the reaction between the monomers hexanedioic acid and 1,6-hexanediamine.

a) Draw the repeat unit for nylon (6,6). [2 marks]

b) Explain why this is an example of condensation polymerisation. [1 mark]

Conversation polymerisation — when someone just goes on and on and on...

If you need to work out a repeat unit for a polymer that's made up of two complicated looking monomers, don't worry. All that matters is finding the carboxylic acid group and the amine or alcohol group and linking them up. Then write down everything that comes in between just as it's been given to you, take off an -H and an -OH, and there you go.

Amino Acids

Amino acids are often called the building blocks of life. They're like little plastic building bricks, but hurt less if you tread on one. Instead of putting them together to make houses and rockets, they're used to make all the proteins in your body.

Amino Acids have an **Amino Group** and a **Carboxyl Group**

1) An amino acid has a **basic amino group** (NH₂) and an **acidic carboxyl group** (COOH). This makes them **amphoteric** — they've got both acidic and basic properties.

2) **2-amino acids** are the type of amino acids that are found in nature. The **amino** group is positioned on **carbon-2** (the carboxyl group is always carbon-1).

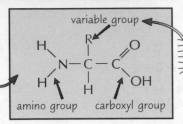

variable group

The R group is different for different amino acids.

amino group   carboxyl group

Amino Acids Can Exist As **Zwitterions**

A **zwitterion** is an **overall neutral** molecule that has both a **positive** and a **negative charge** in different parts of the molecule. An amino acid can only exist as a zwitterion near its **isoelectric point** — this is the **pH** where the **overall charge** on the amino acid is zero. It's different for different amino acids — it depends on their R group.

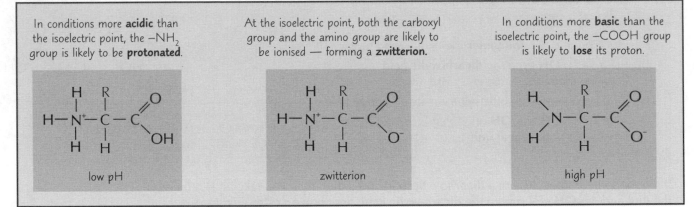

In conditions more **acidic** than the isoelectric point, the –NH₂ group is likely to be **protonated**.

low pH

At the isoelectric point, both the carboxyl group and the amino group are likely to be ionised — forming a **zwitterion**.

zwitterion

In conditions more **basic** than the isoelectric point, the –COOH group is likely to **lose** its proton.

high pH

In general, if the amino acid contains **the same number** of carboxyl groups as amino groups, it will exist as a zwitterion when it is dissolved in solution, and will have a pH of about 7 (it will be roughly **neutral**).

Most **2-Amino Acids** Are **Chiral**

1) There are usually **four** different groups attached to carbon-2 of a 2-amino acid — the carboxyl group, the amino group, a hydrogen atom and the R group. This means that they are **chiral** molecules and have two **optical isomers** (see page 74).

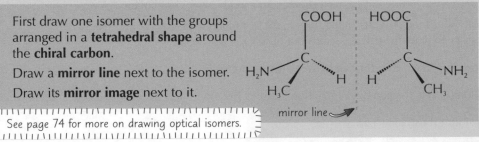

Example: Draw both possible enantiomers of the 2-amino acid alanine, CH₃CH(NH₂)COOH.

1) First draw one isomer with the groups arranged in a **tetrahedral shape** around the **chiral carbon**.
2) Draw a **mirror line** next to the isomer.
3) Draw its **mirror image** next to it.

See page 74 for more on drawing optical isomers.

mirror line

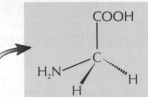

Sweet dreams are made of cheese..

A choral protein.

2) If **plane-polarised, monochromatic light** is shone through an aqueous solution that contains just **one** of the enantiomers of a 2–amino acid, the plane of the light gets **rotated** because of the **chiral carbon**.

3) The exception to this is **glycine** where the **R group** is a hydrogen atom. It has two H atoms attached to the central carbon, so it **isn't chiral** (it's **achiral**), and it won't rotate the plane of plane-polarised light.

Amino Acids

Paper Chromatography can be used to Identify Unknown Amino Acids

You can easily identify amino acids in a mixture using a simple **paper** (one-way) **chromatography experiment**.

1) Draw a **pencil line** near the bottom of a piece of chromatography paper and put a **concentrated spot** of the mixture you want to investigate on it.

2) Place the paper into a **beaker** containing a small amount of **solvent**, so that the solvent level is **below** the spot of mixture. Place a **watch glass** on top of the beaker to stop any solvent **evaporating** out.

3) Different substances have **different solubilities** in the solvent. As the solvent spreads up the paper, the different chemicals in the mixture move with it, but at **different rates**, so they separate out.

4) When the solvent's **nearly** reached the top, take the paper out and **mark** where the solvent has reached with a pencil. This is the **solvent front**.

5) Identify the positions of the spots of different chemicals on the paper. Some chemicals, such as amino acids, aren't coloured so you first have to make them **visible**. You can do this by spraying **ninhydrin solution** (a developing agent) on the paper to turn them purple. You can also dip the paper into a jar containing a few crystals of **iodine**. Iodine **sublimes** from a solid straight to a gas, and the iodine gas causes the spots to turn **brown**. However you visualise your spots, you should **circle** their positions with a pencil.

watch glass

distance moved by solvent ('solvent front')

spot of component in mixture

B

A

solvent

point of origin

6) You can work out the R_f **values** of the substances using this formula:

$$R_f \text{ value} = \frac{A}{B} = \frac{\text{distance travelled by spot}}{\text{distance travelled by solvent}}$$

There's more on chromatography on pages 116-117.

7) If you've done your experiment under **standard conditions**, you can use a **table of known R_f values** to identify the components of the mixture. Otherwise, you should **repeat** the experiment with a spot of a substance you think is in the mixture, alongside the mixture, to see if they have the same R_f value.

Thin-layer chromatography can also be used to separate and identify amino acids. The method is the same as for paper chromatography, but instead of chromatography paper, you use a plate covered in a **thin layer** of **silica** (SiO_2) or **alumina** (Al_2O_3) as the **stationary phase**.

Practice Questions

Q1 Draw the general structure of a 2-amino acid.

Q2 What is a zwitterion?

Exam Questions

Q1 Glycine and cysteine, shown on the right, are two naturally occurring 2-amino acids.

COOH   COOH

H_2N—C—H H_2N—C—H
    H HSH_2C

Glycine   **Cysteine**

a) One way of distinguishing between glycine and cysteine is to observe their effect on plane-polarised monochromatic light. Explain why this method works. [2 marks]

b)* Explain how paper chromatography could be used to separate and identify a mixture of amino acids. [6 marks]

Q2 Amino acids are organic molecules that contain both a carboxyl group and an amino group.

a) Explain what is meant by the 'isoelectric point' of an amino acid. [1 mark]

b) The 2-amino acid serine has the formula $HOOCCH(NH_2)CH_2OH$.

i) Draw the displayed formula of serine. [1 mark]

ii) Draw the structure that serine will take in a solution with a high pH. [1 mark]

Twitterions — when amino acids get let loose on social media...

Well, these pages aren't too bad. Another organic structure, a bit of drawing chiral molecules, and a nice experimental technique. Make sure you know how chromatography is used to separate and identify amino acids and you're away.

* The quality of your extended response will be assessed for this question.

Grignard Reagents

The whole of Organic Chemistry revolves around carbon compounds and how they react, but getting one carbon to react with another and form a new carbon-carbon bond is surprisingly hard. Fortunately, Grignard reagents let you do it.

Grignard Reagents Are **Made** by Reacting **Halogenoalkanes** With **Magnesium**

1) Grignard (Grin-yard) reagents have the general formula **RMgX**, where R is an **alkyl group** and X is a **halogen**.

$$R–X \xrightarrow[\text{dry ether}]{\text{Mg}} RMgX$$

2) They're made by refluxing a halogenoalkane with magnesium in **dry ether**.

3) For example, refluxing **bromoethane** with magnesium in dry ether would create the following Grignard reagent:

$$CH_3CH_2Br + Mg \xrightarrow{\text{dry ether}} CH_3CH_2MgBr$$

Grignard Reagents React With **Carbon Dioxide**...

You can make a **carboxylic acid** from a Grignard reagent in **two steps**.

1) First, bubble **carbon dioxide gas** through a Grignard reagent in **dry ether**. Then add a dilute acid, such as hydrochloric acid.

2) During the reaction, **a new C–C bond** forms between the carbon atom in carbon dioxide and the C–Mg carbon from the Grignard reagent. One of the C=O bonds in carbon dioxide is broken to form a **-COO⁻ group**, which is **protonated** when the dilute acid is added to form -COOH.

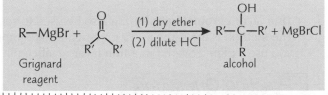

Example: Butanoic acid can be synthesised from bromopropane in three steps. Give the reagents and conditions needed for each step, and the product formed at each stage of the synthesis.

$$CH_3CH_2CH_2Br \xrightarrow[\text{dry ether}]{\text{Mg}} CH_3CH_2CH_2MgBr \xrightarrow[\text{(2) dilute HCl}]{\text{(1) } CO_2\text{, dry ether}} CH_3CH_2CH_2COOH + MgBrCl$$

...And With **Carbonyl Compounds**

1) Grignard reagents react with aldehydes and ketones to make **alcohols**. A **new C–C bond** forms between the C–Mg carbon atom from the Grignard reagent and the C=O carbon of the carbonyl. This causes the C=O bond to break and, when acid is added, an **-OH group** is formed.

2) Again, there are **two steps** to the reaction. First the carbonyl compound is added to the **Grignard reagent** in **dry ether**, and then **dilute acid** is added to the reaction mixture.

Reacting a Grignard reagent with an aldehyde will make a secondary alcohol (unless it's methanal which makes a primary alcohol). Reacting a Grignard reagent with a ketone will make a tertiary alcohol.

Practice Questions

Q1 Write the general formula of a Grignard reagent.

Q2 Give the reagents and conditions needed to make a Grignard reagent from a bromoalkane.

Q3 What type of organic product is formed when a Grignard reagent is reacted with carbon dioxide and then hydrolysed with dilute acid?

Exam Question

Q1 a) Give the reagents and conditions needed to make the Grignard reagent, **X**.   (structure) **X**   [1 mark]

b) Give the reagent and conditions needed to make the following compounds using Grignard reagent **X**:

i) Hexan-2-ol   [1 mark]

ii) Pentanoic acid   [1 mark]

You may not like Organic Chemistry, but you'll have to Grignard bear it...

Grignard reagents are quite unstable, so you can't just get them out of a bottle. Instead, you need to know how they're made. Don't forget that the reactions are in dry ether except in the last step — otherwise the reaction won't work.

Organic Synthesis

There are lots of organic compounds and reactions coming up. Don't panic. It's a summary of things you've met before.

Functional Groups are the Most Important Parts of a Molecule

Functional groups are the parts of a molecule that are responsible for the way the molecule reacts.
Substances are grouped into families called **homologous series** based on what functional groups they contain.
Here's a round-up of all the ones you've studied:

Homologous series	Functional group	Properties	Typical reactions
Alkane	C–C	Non-polar, unreactive.	Radical substitution
Alkene	C=C	Non-polar, electron-rich double bond.	Electrophilic addition
Aromatic compounds	C_6H_5-	Stable delocalised ring of electrons.	Electrophilic substitution
Alcohol	C-OH	Polar C-OH bond.	Nucleophilic substitution Dehydration/elimination
		Lone pair on oxygen can act as a nucleophile.	Esterification Nucleophilic substitution
Halogenoalkane	C–X	Polar C–X bond.	Nucleophilic substitution Elimination
Amine	$C–NH_2$ / $C–NR_2$	Lone pair on nitrogen is basic and can act as a nucleophile.	Neutralisation Nucleophilic substitution
Amide	$-CONH_2$ / -CONHR	–	–
Nitrile	$C–C\equiv N$	Electron deficient carbon centre.	Reduction Hydrolysis
Aldehyde/Ketone	C=O	Polar C=O bond.	Nucleophilic addition Reduction Aldehydes will oxidise.
Carboxylic acid	-COOH	Electron deficient carbon centre.	Neutralisation Esterification Reduction
Ester	RCOOR′	Electron deficient carbon centre.	Hydrolysis
Acyl chloride	-COCl	Electron deficient carbon centre.	Nucleophilic addition-elimination Condensation (lose HCl) Friedel-Crafts acylation

The functional groups in a molecule give you clues about its **properties** and **reactions**.
For example, a **–COOH group** will (usually) make the molecule **acidic** and mean it will **form esters** with alcohols.

Chemists Use Synthetic Routes to Get from One Compound to Another

1) Chemists need to be able to make one compound from another. It's vital for things such as **designing medicines**.

2) It's not always possible to synthesise a desired product from a starting material in **just one** reaction.

3) A **synthetic route** shows how you get from one compound to another. It shows all the **reactions** with the **intermediate products**, and the **reagents** needed for each reaction.

Example: Starting with ethene, you can synthesise ethanamide in four steps. The synthetic route is:

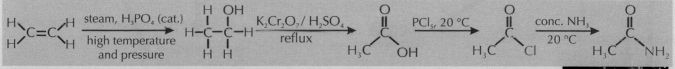

If you're asked how to make one compound from another in the exam, make sure you include:

1) Any **special procedures**, such as refluxing.

2) The **conditions** needed, e.g. high temperature or pressure, or the presence of a catalyst.

3) Any **safety** precautions, e.g. do it in a fume cupboard.

Jon and Patricia loved their new synthetic roots.

Organic Synthesis

Chemists Have to Carefully **Plan** a **Synthetic Route**

When chemists plan the synthesis of a molecule there are some things they need to keep in mind:

1) **Stereoisomers**: Making the correct stereoisomer is important in the pharmaceutical industry because different **stereoisomers** might have **different properties**. Understanding the **mechanism** of a reaction lets chemists plan which stereoisomer will be produced (p.75). E.g. S_N2 nucleophilic substitution can produce a **single isomer** product if a single isomer is used as the starting molecule.

2) **Safety**: To reduce the risks posed by any of the organic chemicals or reagents used in an organic synthesis method, **safety measures** must be considered. For example, reactions can be performed in **fume hoods** to remove toxic gases and **electric mantles**, **water baths** or **sand baths** can be used to heat solutions so there are no naked flames near flammable reagents.

Synthesis Routes for Making **Aliphatic Compounds**

Here's a round-up of the reactions to convert between functional groups that you've covered in the A-Level course:

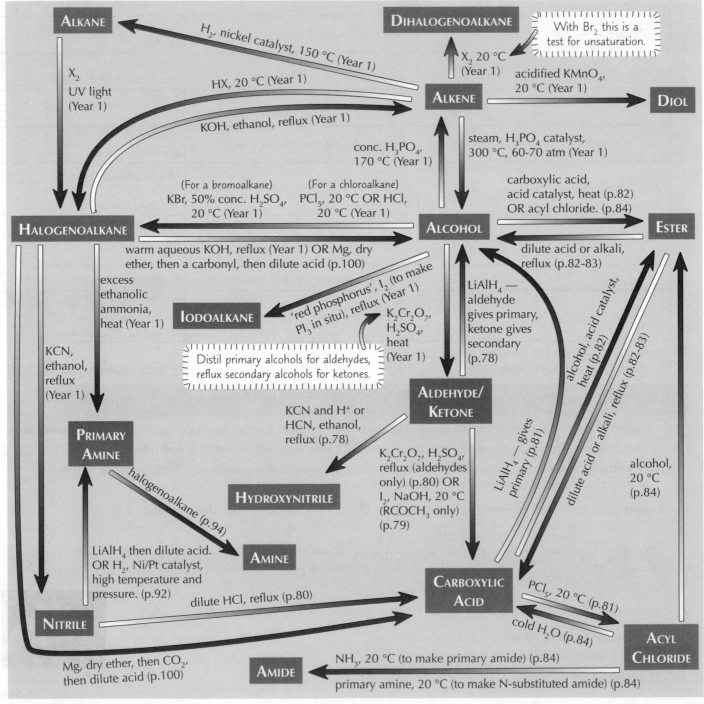

Organic Synthesis

Synthesis Routes for Making *Aromatic Compounds*

There aren't so many of these reactions to learn — so make sure you know all the itty-bitty details.
If you can't remember any of the reactions, look back to the relevant pages and take a quick peek over them.

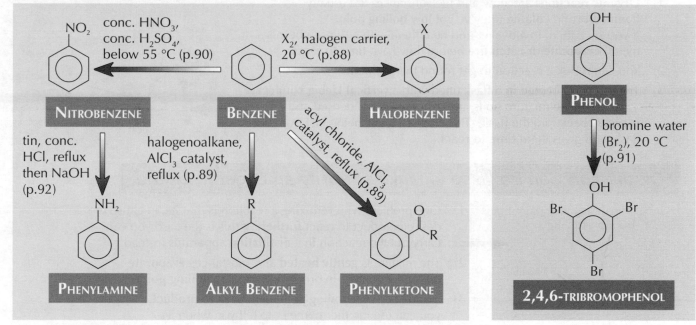

Practice Questions

Q1 What type of reactions do alkenes typically take part in?

Q2 What is shown in a synthetic route?

Q3 How do you make an alkene from an aldehyde?

Q4 How do you make phenylamine from benzene?

Exam Questions

Q1 Ethyl methanoate is one of the compounds responsible for the smell of raspberries.
Outline, with reaction conditions, how it could be synthesised in the laboratory from methanol. [2 marks]

Q2 How would you synthesise propanol starting with propane?
State the reaction conditions and reagents needed for each step. [2 marks]

Q3 The diagram below shows a possible reaction pathway for the two-step synthesis of a ketone from a halogenoalkane.

$$H-\underset{\underset{H}{|}}{\overset{\overset{H}{|}}{C}}-\underset{\underset{H}{|}}{\overset{\overset{X}{|}}{C}}-\underset{\underset{H}{|}}{\overset{\overset{H}{|}}{C}}-H \xrightarrow[\text{NaOH}]{\text{Step 1}} H-\underset{\underset{H}{|}}{\overset{\overset{H}{|}}{C}}-\underset{\underset{H}{|}}{\overset{\overset{OH}{|}}{C}}-\underset{\underset{H}{|}}{\overset{\overset{H}{|}}{C}}-H \xrightarrow{\text{Step 2}} H-\underset{\underset{H}{|}}{\overset{\overset{H}{|}}{C}}-\overset{\overset{O}{\|}}{C}-\underset{\underset{H}{|}}{\overset{\overset{H}{|}}{C}}-H$$

$$\textbf{P} \qquad\qquad\qquad \textbf{Q} \qquad\qquad\qquad \textbf{R}$$

a) Give the conditions needed to carry out Step 1. [1 mark]

b) Give the reagents and the conditions needed to carry out Step 2. [2 marks]

Q4 A chemist synthesises compound **A** in three steps, starting from benzene.
Given that, in the second step, a Grignard reagent is formed, suggest a
synthesis route the chemist could have taken. Give the reagents and conditions,
as well as the organic compounds formed, at each step of the synthesis. **A** [6 marks]

Big red buses are great at Organic Synthesis — they're Route Masters...

There's loads of information here. Tons and tons of it. But you've covered pretty much all of it before, so it shouldn't be too hard to make sure it's firmly embedded in your head. If it's not, you know what to do — go back over it again. Then cover the diagrams up and try to draw them out from memory. Keep going until you can do it perfectly.

Practical Techniques

You can't call yourself a chemist unless you know these practical techniques. Not unless your name's Boots.

Reactions *Often Need to be* Heated *to* Work

1) **Organic reactions** are **slow** and the substances are usually **flammable** and **volatile** (they've got **low boiling points**). If you stick them in a beaker and heat them with a Bunsen burner they'll **evaporate** or **catch fire** before they have **time to react**.

2) You can **reflux** a reaction to get round this problem.

3) The mixture's **heated in a flask** fitted with a **vertical Liebig condenser** — so when the mixture boils, the vapours are condensed and **recycled** back into the flask. This stops reagents being **lost** from the flask, and gives them **time to react**.

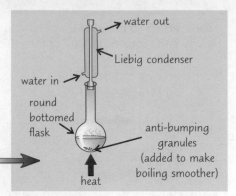

Distillation *Can Be Used to* Make *or* Purify *an* Organic Liquid

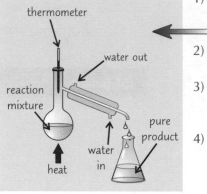

1) One problem with **refluxing** a reaction is that it can cause the desired product to **react further**. If this is the case you can carry out the reaction in a **distillation apparatus** instead.

2) The mixture is **gently heated** and substances **evaporate** out of the mixture in order of **increasing boiling point**.

3) If you know the boiling point of your **pure product**, you can use the thermometer to tell you when it's evaporating, and therefore when it's condensing.

4) If the **product** of a reaction has a **lower boiling point** than the **starting materials** then the reaction mixture can be **heated** so that the product **evaporates** from the reaction mixture as it forms. The **starting materials** will stay in the reaction mixture as long as the temperature is **controlled**.

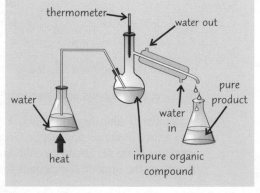

David had no need for distillation — he was pure class.

- If a product and its impurities have **different boiling points**, then distillation can be used to **separate** them. You use the distillation apparatus shown above, but this time you're heating an **impure product**, instead of the reaction mixture.

- When the liquid you want **boils** (this is when the thermometer is at the boiling point of the liquid), you place a flask at the open end of the condenser ready to collect your product.

- When the thermometer shows the temperature is changing, put another flask at the end of the condenser because a **different liquid** is about to be delivered.

Steam Distillation Lowers *the Boiling Point of an Organic Liquid*

1) Some organic liquids have **high** boiling points or **decompose** when they're **heated**. This means you **can't** purify them using the distillation technique shown above. Instead, if the product you're collecting is immiscible with water, you can use **steam distillation**.

2) In steam distillation, the presence of steam **lowers** the **boiling point** of the immiscible product, allowing it to be distilled out of the impure mixture below its boiling point, and before it decomposes.

3) Using the apparatus shown on the right, you heat **water** in a flask until it evaporates, and then allow it to pass, as **steam**, into a flask containing the impure organic mixture.

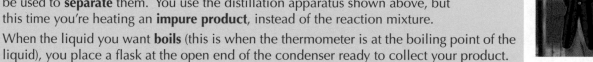

4) The steam **lowers** the **boiling points** of the compounds in the mixture, so they will evaporate at a **lower temperature**.

5) If the organic product you're trying to collect is less volatile than the components in the mixture you're separating it from, the organic product and the steam will evaporate out of the impure mixture **together**. You can then condense and collect them in a clean flask.

6) You can separate the organic product from water using a **separating funnel** (you may have to use the **solvent extraction** technique on the next page if the compound is slightly miscible with water).

Practical Techniques

Solvent Extraction *Removes* Partially Soluble *Compounds from* Water

You saw back in Year 1 that if a product is **insoluble** in water then you can
use **separation** to remove any impurities that **do dissolve** in water.

But, if your product and the impurities are **both** soluble in water, there's a
similar separation method called **solvent extraction** that you can use.

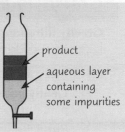

product
aqueous layer
containing
some impurities

1) Add the impure compound to a separating funnel and add some water. Shake well.

2) Then add an **organic solvent** in which the product is **more soluble** than it is
   in water. Shake the separating funnel well. The product will **dissolve** into
   the organic solvent, leaving the impurities dissolved in the water.

3) You could also add a **salt** (such as NaCl) to the mixture. This will cause the organic product to
   move into the organic layer, as it will be less soluble in the very polar salt and water layer.

4) You can then open the tap and run each layer off into a separate container.
   (In the example on the right, the impurities will be run off first, and the product collected second.)

Remove *Other* Impurities *by* Washing

The product of a reaction can be **contaminated** with leftover reagents or unwanted side products.
You can **remove** some of these by **washing** the product (which in this case means adding another liquid and shaking).

For example, if one of your reactants was an **organic acid**, it might be dissolved as an impurity
in the **organic layer**, along with your product. To remove it, you could add aqueous **sodium
hydrogencarbonate** which will react with the acid to give CO_2 gas and a **salt** of the acid. The salt will
then dissolve in the **aqueous layer**. The organic **product** will be left in the organic layer, and can be
separated from the aqueous layer containing the reactant impurities using a **separating funnel** (as above).

Remove Water *from a Purified Product by* Drying *it*

1) If you use separation to purify a product, the organic layer will end up
   containing **trace amounts** of **water** — so it has to be **dried**.

2) To do this, you add an **anhydrous salt** such as **magnesium sulfate** ($MgSO_4$) or **calcium chloride**
   ($CaCl_2$). The salt is used as a **drying agent** — it **binds** to any water present to become **hydrated**.

3) When you first add the salt to the organic layer it will **clump** together.
   You keep adding drying agent until it disperses **evenly** when you swirl the flask.

4) Finally, you **filter** the mixture to remove the solid drying agent — pop a piece of filter
   paper into a funnel that feeds into a flask and pour the mixture into the filter paper.

*The filter paper can
be fluted (concertina
folded) to increase
its surface area.*

Practice Questions

Q1 Why is refluxing needed in many organic reactions?

Q2 Draw the set-up that you could use to carry out a simple distillation.

Q3 How could you remove an organic acid from the organic layer in a separating funnel?

Exam Question

Q1 A chemist synthesises phenylamine by refluxing nitrobenzene with tin and concentrated hydrochloric acid and
then adding sodium hydroxide.

   a) Phenylamine is immiscible with water and decomposes before it boils.
      Draw and label a diagram to show the distillation set-up the chemist
      should use to separate pure phenylamine from the impure mixture. [3 marks]

   b) Describe a method that could be used to separate the condensed phenylamine from water after
      distillation, given that phenylamine is slightly soluble in water and also soluble in ether. [4 marks]

My organic compound isn't volatile — it's just highly strung...

*Scientists need to know why they do the things they do — that way they can plan new experiments to make new
compounds. Learning the details of how experiments are carried out and how products are purified may not be the most
interesting thing in the world, but you should get to try out some of these methods in practicals, which is a lot more fun.*

More Practical Techniques

Don't take your lab coat off or put down your safety specs just yet. There are more practical techniques coming up...

Gravity Filtration is Used to Remove a Solid From a Liquid

Gravity filtration is normally used when you want to keep the **liquid** (the filtrate) and discard the **solid**. For example, it can be used to remove the solid drying agent from the organic layer of a liquid that has been purified by separation.

1) Place a piece of **fluted filter paper** in a funnel that feeds into a conical flask.

2) **Gently pour** the mixture to be separated into the filter paper. The solution will pass through the filter paper into the conical flask, and the **solid** will be **trapped**.

3) **Rinse** the solid left in the filter paper with a **pure sample** of the solvent present in the solution. This makes sure that all the **soluble material** has passed through the filter paper and has been collected in the conical flask.

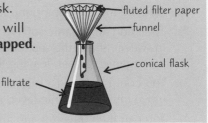

fluted filter paper
funnel
conical flask
filtrate

Filtration Under Reduced Pressure is Used to Remove a Liquid From a Solid

Filtration under reduced pressure is normally used when you want to keep the **solid** and discard the **liquid** (filtrate).

1) Place a piece of **filter paper**, slightly smaller than the diameter of the funnel, on the bottom of the Büchner funnel so that it lies flat and covers all the holes.

2) **Wet** the paper with a little solvent, so that it **sticks** to the bottom of the funnel, and doesn't slip around when you pour in your mixture.

3) Turn the **vacuum** on, and then pour your mixture into the funnel. As the flask is under **reduced pressure**, the **liquid** is sucked through the funnel into the flask, leaving the **solid** behind.

4) **Rinse** the solid with a little of the solvent that your mixture was in. This will **wash off** any of the original liquid from the mixture that stayed on your crystals (and also any soluble impurities), leaving you with a **more pure** solid.

5) Disconnect the vacuum line from the side-arm flask and then turn off the vacuum.

6) The solid will be a bit wet from the solvent, so leave it to **dry completely**.

solid crystals
filtration mixture
filter paper
Büchner funnel
bung
to vacuum line
unwanted liquid
side-arm flask

Organic Solids can be Purified by Recrystallisation

If the product of an organic reaction is a solid, then the simplest way of purifying it is a process called **recrystallisation**. First you dissolve your solid in a **hot** solvent to make a **saturated** solution. Then you let the solution cool. As the solution cools, the solubility of the product falls. When it reaches the point where it can't stay in solution, it starts to form crystals. Here's how it's done:

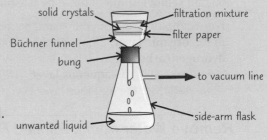

In a saturated solution, the maximum possible amount of solid is dissolved in the solvent.

1) **Very hot solvent** is added to the **impure** solid until it **just** dissolves – it's important not to add too much solvent. This should give a **saturated solution** of the **impure product**.

2) Filter the solution while it's still hot by **gravity filtration** to remove any insoluble impurities.

3) This solution is left to **cool** down **slowly**. **Crystals** of the **product** form as it cools. The **impurities** stay in solution as they're present in much smaller amounts than the product, so take much longer to crystallise out.

4) The crystals are removed by **filtration** under **reduced pressure** (see above) and **washed** with ice-cold solvent. Then they are dried, leaving you with crystals of your product that are **much purer** than the original solid.

The Choice of Solvent for Recrystallisation is Very Important

1) When you **recrystallise** a product, you must use an **appropriate solvent** for that particular substance. It will only work if the solid is **very soluble** in the **hot** solvent, but **nearly insoluble** when the solvent is **cold**.

2) If your product **isn't soluble enough** in the hot solvent you **won't** be able to dissolve it at all.

3) If your product **is too soluble** in the cold solvent, most of it will **stay in the solution** even after cooling. When you filter it, you'll **lose** most of your product, giving you a very low **yield**.

More Practical Techniques

Measuring **Boiling Point** is a Good Way to **Determine** the **Purity** of a Liquid

1) You can measure the purity of an organic, liquid product by looking at its boiling point.

2) If you've got a reasonable volume of liquid, you can determine its boiling point using a **distillation apparatus**, like the one shown on page 104.

3) If you **gently heat** the liquid in the distillation apparatus, until it evaporates, you can read the temperature at which it is distilled, using the thermometer in the top of the apparatus. This temperature is the **boiling point**.

Different organic liquids can have similar boiling points, so you should use other analytical techniques (see Topic 19) to help you determine your product's purity too.

4) You can then look up the boiling point of the substance in **data books** and compare it to your measurement.

5) If the sample contains **impurities**, then your measured boiling point will be **higher** than the recorded value. You may also find your product boils over a range of temperatures, rather than all evaporating at a single temperature.

Melting Points are Good Indicators of the **Purity** of an Organic Solid

Pure substances have a **specific melting point**. If they're **impure**, the **melting point's lowered**.
If they're **very impure**, melting will occur across a wide range of temperatures.

1) You can use **melting point apparatus** to accurately determine the melting point of an **organic solid**.

2) Pack a small sample of the solid into a **glass capillary tube** and place it inside the **heating element**.

3) **Increase the temperature** until the sample turns from solid to **liquid**.

4) You usually measure a **melting range**, which is the range of temperatures from where the solid **begins to melt** to where it has **melted completely**.

5) You can look up the melting point of a substance in **data books** and compare it to your measurements.

6) **Impurities** in the sample will **lower** the **melting point** and **broaden** the **melting range**.

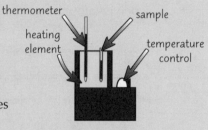

Practice Questions

Q1 How could you separate a solid product from liquid impurities? And a liquid product from solid impurities?

Q2 Give two factors you should consider when choosing a solvent for recrystallisation.

Exam Questions

Q1 Two samples of impure stearic acid melt at 69 °C and 64 °C respectively.
Stearic acid dissolves in hot propanone but not in water.

a) Explain which sample is purer. [1 mark]

b) Suggest a method that could be used to purify the impure sample. [1 mark]

c) How could the sample from b) be tested for purity? [1 mark]

Q2 A scientist has produced some impure solid sodium ethanoate, which she wants to purify using recrystallisation. She begins by dissolving the impure sodium ethanoate in the minimum possible amount of hot solvent.

a) Explain why the scientist used the minimum possible amount of hot solvent. [1 mark]

b) Outline the rest of the procedure that the scientist would need to follow to recrystallise the solid. [5 marks]

c) Describe the melting point range of the impure sodium ethanoate compared to the pure product. [1 mark]

Q3 A student is carrying out an experiment using the apparatus shown on the right. What type of experiment is she doing?

    A reflux   **B** filtration under reduced pressure

    C distillation   **D** recrystallisation [1 mark]

I hope that everything's now crystal clear...

Nobody wants loads of impurities in their reaction products. But now you're kitted out to get rid of them using these purification techniques. It doesn't even matter whether you have to purify a solid or a liquid — no excuses now.

Empirical and Molecular Formulae

It's the end of the Topic — hurray!!! But it's full of maths — boooo. But you've seen it before in Year 1— hurray!!!
I can't keep doing this — boooo. Oh go on then, one more — hurray!!! And don't forget to brush your teeth — ????

Empirical and Molecular Formulae Can Help Identify Organic Compounds

You first met calculations to find empirical and molecular formulae in Year 1. You can use empirical and molecular formulae, along with other data from, e.g. IR spectroscopy, to help you work out the structure of an unknown chemical.

In case you're feeling a bit hazy about what these formulae are, here's a quick reminder...

1) The **empirical formula** gives just the smallest whole number ratio of atoms in a compound.
    E.g. The empirical formula of ethane is CH_3.

2) The **molecular formula** gives the **actual** numbers of atoms in a molecule.
    It's made up of a **whole number** of empirical units. E.g. The molecular formula of ethane is C_2H_6.

Find Empirical and Molecular Formulae From Percentage Compositions

You saw calculations like this in Year 1 of the course. But here's a reminder...

Example: A compound has a molecular mass of 88. It is found to have percentage composition 54.5% carbon, 9.1% hydrogen and 36.4% oxygen by mass. Calculate its empirical and molecular formulae.

> *If you assume you've got 100 g of the compound, you can turn the % straight into mass, and then work out the number of moles as normal.*

In **100 g** of compound there are:

> *Use $n = \frac{mass}{M}$*

$\frac{54.5}{12.0} = 4.54$ moles of C $\qquad$ $\frac{9.1}{1.0} = 9.1$ moles of H $\qquad$ $\frac{36.4}{16.0} = 2.275$ moles of O

Divide each number of moles by the **smallest number** — in this case it's 2.275.

O: $\frac{4.54}{2.275} = 2.00$ $\qquad$ H: $\frac{9.1}{2.275} = 4.00$ $\qquad$ O: $\frac{2.275}{2.275} = 1.00$

The ratio of C : H : O = 2 : 4 : 1. So you know the empirical formula's got to be C_2H_4O.

The molecular mass of one empirical formula is $(2 \times 12.0) + (4 \times 1.0) + (1 \times 16.0) = 44$.

This is half the molecular mass of the compound, so the compound must contain two of the empirical formula and have the molecular formula $C_4H_8O_2$.

Combustion Analysis Uses Information From Burning an Organic Compound

When an organic compound containing carbon, hydrogen and oxygen combusts completely in oxygen, **water** and **carbon dioxide** are produced. All the **carbon atoms** in the carbon dioxide and all the **hydrogen atoms** in the water will have come from the organic compound. If you burn a **known amount** of the organic compound, you can use the amounts of water and carbon dioxide produced to help you work out its **empirical formula**.

Example: When 7.2 g of a carbonyl compound is burnt in excess oxygen, it produces 17.6 g of carbon dioxide and 7.2 g of water. Calculate the empirical formula for the carbonyl compound.

No. of moles of $CO_2 = \frac{mass}{M} = \frac{17.6}{44.0} = 0.40$ moles
1 mole of CO_2 contains 1 mole of C. So, 0.40 moles of CO_2 contains **0.40 moles of C**.

No. of moles $H_2O = \frac{mass}{M} = \frac{7.2}{18.0} = 0.40$ moles
1 mole of H_2O contains 2 moles of H. So, 0.40 moles of H_2O contain **0.80 moles of H**.

Mass of C = no. of moles $\times M = 0.40 \times 12.0 = 4.8$ g
Mass of H = no. of moles $\times M = 0.80 \times 1.0 = 0.80$ g
Mass of O = 7.2 − (4.8 + 0.80) = 1.6 g
Number of moles of O = $\frac{mass}{M} = \frac{1.6}{16.0} = 0.10$ moles

> *Now work out the mass of carbon and hydrogen in the alcohol. The rest of the mass of the carbonyl must be oxygen — so work out that too. Once you know the mass of O, you can work out how many moles there are of it.*

Molar Ratio = C : H : O = 0.40 : 0.80 : 0.10 = 4 : 8 : 1
Empirical formula = C_4H_8O

> *When you know the number of moles of each element, you've got the molar ratio. Divide each number by the smallest.*

Empirical and Molecular Formulae

Combustion Analysis Data Might Be Given As Volumes

1) Combustion reactions can happen between **gases**.

2) All gases at the same temperature and pressure have the same **molar volume**. This means you can use the **ratio** of the **volumes** of gases reacting together to calculate the **molar ratios**, and then work out the **molecular formula** of the **organic compound** that is combusting.

Example: 30 cm^3 of hydrocarbon X combusts completely with 180 cm^3 oxygen. 120 cm^3 carbon dioxide is produced. What is the molecular formula of hydrocarbon X?

* Using the volumes provided, the reaction equation can be written:

$$30X + 180O_2 \rightarrow 120CO_2 + ?H_2O$$

* This can be simplified by dividing everything by 30:

$$X + 6O_2 \rightarrow 4CO_2 + nH_2O$$

* 6 moles of oxygen reacts to form 4 moles of carbon dioxide and n moles of water. So any oxygen atoms (from O_2) that don't end up in CO_2, must be in H_2O. This means that **n = (6 × 2) – (4 × 2) = 4**.

* So, the combustion equation is: **X + 6O$_2$ → 4CO$_2$ + 4H$_2$O**. You can use this to identify X.

* All the carbon atoms from X end up in carbon dioxide molecules, and all the hydrogen atoms from X end up in water, so the number of **carbon** atoms in X is **4** and the number of **hydrogen** atoms in X is **8**.

* The molecular formula of X is **C$_4$H$_8$**.

This method is really handy because it gives you the molecular formula straight away, rather than the empirical formula (which in this example is CH$_2$).

Practice Questions

Q1 What's the difference between empirical and molecular formulae?

Q2 What's the empirical formula of ethane?

Q3 Where do the carbon atoms in carbon dioxide produced by burning an organic compound completely in oxygen come from?

Exam Questions

Q1 A carbonyl compound contains only carbon, hydrogen and oxygen. When it is burnt in excess oxygen 0.100 g of the compound gives 0.228 g of carbon dioxide and 0.0930 g of water.

  a) Calculate the empirical formula of this compound. [4 marks]

  b) What percentage of the compound by mass is hydrogen? [2 marks]

  c) If the molecular mass is 58.0, what is the molecular formula? [1 mark]

  d) When a sample of the compound is heated with Tollens' reagent, a silver mirror is formed. Predict, with reasoning, the structure of the molecule. [1 mark]

Q2 A common explosive contains 37.0% carbon, 2.2% hydrogen, 18.5% nitrogen and 42.3% oxygen, by mass. It has a molecular mass of 227 and can be made from benzene.

  a) Calculate the empirical formula of the compound and hence its molecular formula. [4 marks]

  b) Suggest a possible structure of the molecule. [1 mark]

Q3 A student was trying to identify an unknown hydrocarbon, X. When she combusted 25 cm^3 of X, completely with 125 cm^3 of oxygen, 75 cm^3 of carbon dioxide was produced.

  a) Calculate the molecular formula of X. [2 marks]

  b) The mass spectrum of X has an M peak at $m/z = 88$. What is the molecular formula of X? [2 marks]

These pages contain the formulae for A-Level Chemistry success...

These calculations aren't the only things you can use to work out the identity of an unknown molecule. Oh no. Coming up next there's loads more on analytical techniques. NMR and infrared spectroscopy, along with mass spectrometry, can really help to work out exactly what a certain substance is. Structure and all. Bet you can't wait.

High Resolution Mass Spectrometry

You met mass spectrometry back in Year 1 of the course, but who said the fun had to stop there? Time for more...

Mass Spectrometry Can Help to Identify Compounds

1) In a mass spectrometer, a **molecular ion** is formed when a molecule loses an **electron**.

2) The molecular ion produces a **molecular ion peak** on the mass spectrum of the compound.

3) For any compound, the **mass/charge** (m/z) value of the molecular
ion peak will be the same as the **molecular mass** of the compound
(assuming the ion has a +1 charge, which it normally will have).

Look back at your Year 1 notes for a reminder on how to work out atomic masses and molecular masses from mass spectra.

High Resolution Mass Spectrometry Measures Masses Precisely

1) Some mass spectrometers can measure atomic and molecular masses **extremely accurately**
(to several decimal places). These are known as **high resolution mass spectrometers**.

2) This can be useful for identifying compounds that appear to have
the **same M_r** when they're **rounded** to the nearest whole number.

3) For example, **propane** (C_3H_8) and **ethanal** (CH_3CHO) both have an M_r of **44** to the nearest whole number.
But on a **high resolution mass spectrum**, propane has a molecular ion peak with m/z = **44.0624** and
ethanal has a molecular ion peak with m/z = **44.0302**.

Example: On a high resolution mass spectrum, a compound had a molecular ion peak of 98.0448.
What was its molecular formula?

 A $C_5H_{10}N_2$ B $C_6H_{10}O$ C C_7H_{14} D $C_5H_6O_2$

Use these precise atomic masses to work out your answer:
^1H — 1.0078 ^{12}C — 12.0000 ^{14}N — 14.0064 ^{16}O — 15.9990

1) Work out the precise molecular mass of each compound:
$C_5H_{10}N_2$: M_r = (5 × 12.0000) + (10 × 1.0078) + (2 × 14.0064) = 98.0908
$C_6H_{10}O$: M_r = (6 × 12.0000) + (10 × 1.0078) + 15.9990 = 98.0770
C_7H_{14}: M_r = (7 × 12.0000) + (14 × 1.0078) = 98.1092
$C_5H_6O_2$: M_r = (5 × 12.0000) + (6 × 1.0078) + (2 × 15.9990) = 98.0448

On a normal (low resolution) mass spectrum, all of these molecules would show up as having an M_r of 98.

2) So the answer is **D, $C_5H_6O_2$**.

Practice Questions

Q1 Explain how you could find the molecular mass of a compound by looking at its mass spectrum.

Q2 Why is high resolution mass spectrometry useful for when studying molecules with similar molecular masses?

Exam Questions

Use the following precise atomic masses to answer the questions below:
^1H — 1.0078 ^{12}C — 12.0000 ^{14}N — 14.0064 ^{16}O — 15.9990

Q1 a) The high resolution mass spectrum of a compound has a molecular ion peak with m/z = 74.0908.
Which of the following could be the molecular formula of the compound?
 A $C_3H_6O_2$ B $C_4H_{10}O$ C $C_3H_{10}N_2$ D $C_2H_6N_2O$ [1 mark]

 b) Explain why low resolution mass spectrometry would not allow
you to distinguish between the options given in part a).   [1 mark]

Q2 A sample of an unknown hydrocarbon is injected into a high resolution mass spectrometer. It produces a
molecular ion peak at m/z = 56.0624. Draw a possible structure for and name the unknown hydrocarbon.   [2 marks]

I am highly resolved to improve my understanding of Chemistry...

*And you should be too if you want to ace your exams. This page is pretty easy. The only new bit is that stuff on high
resolution mass spectrometry. But fear not — it's just like normal mass spectrometry, but with more decimal places.*

NMR Spectroscopy

NMR isn't the easiest of things, so ingest this information one piece at a time — a bit like eating a bar of chocolate.

NMR Gives You Information about the Structure of Molecules

Nuclear magnetic resonance (**NMR**) **spectroscopy** is an analytical technique that you can use to work out the **structure** of an organic molecule. The way that NMR works is pretty **complicated**, but here are the **basics**:

1) A sample of a compound is placed in a **strong magnetic field** and exposed to a range of different **frequencies** of **radio waves**.

2) The **nuclei** of certain atoms within the molecule **absorb energy** from the radio waves.

3) The amount of energy that a nucleus absorbs at each frequency will depend on the **environment** that it's in — there's more about this further down the page.

4) The **pattern** of these absorptions gives you information about the **positions** of certain atoms within the molecule, and about **how many** atoms of that type the molecule contains.

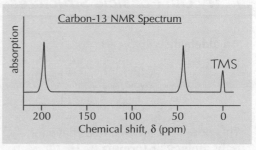
Radiowaves.

5) You can piece these bits of information together to work out the **structure of the molecule**.

The two types of NMR spectroscopy you need to know about are **carbon-13 NMR** and **high resolution proton NMR**.

Carbon-13 (or **^{13}C**) **NMR** gives you information about the **number of carbon atoms** that are in a molecule, and the **environments** that they are in.

High resolution proton NMR gives you information about the **number of hydrogen atoms** that are in a molecule, and the **environments** that they're in.

Nuclei in Different Environments Absorb Different Amounts of Energy

1) A nucleus is partly **shielded** from the effects of external magnetic fields by its **surrounding electrons**.

2) Any **other atoms** and **groups of atoms** that are around a nucleus will also affect its amount of electron shielding.
E.g. if a carbon atom bonds to a more electronegative atom (like oxygen) the amount of electron shielding around its nucleus will decrease.

3) This means that the nuclei in a molecule feel different magnetic fields depending on their **environments**. Nuclei in different environments will absorb **different amounts** of energy at **different frequencies**.

4) It's these **differences in absorption** of energy between environments that you're looking for in **NMR spectroscopy**.

5) An atom's **environment** depends on **all** the groups that it's connected to, going **right along the molecule** — not just the atoms it's actually bonded to. To be in the **same environment**, two atoms must be joined to **exactly the same things**.

Chloroethane has **2** carbon environments — its carbons are bonded to different atoms.

2-chloropropane has **2** carbon environments: • **1 C** in a CHCl group, bonded to $(CH_3)_2$ • **2 Cs** in CH_3 groups, bonded to $CHCl(CH_3)$

1-chlorobutane has **4** carbon environments. (The two carbons in CH_2 groups are **different distances** from the **electronegative** Cl atom — so their **environments** are **different**.)

Tetramethylsilane is Used as a Standard

The diagram below shows a typical **carbon-13 NMR spectrum**. The **peaks** show the **frequencies** at which **energy was absorbed** by the carbon nuclei. **Each peak** represents one **carbon environment** — so this molecule has two.

1) The **differences in absorption** are measured relative to a **standard substance** — **tetramethylsilane** (**TMS**).

2) TMS produces a **single absorption peak** in both types of NMR because all its carbon and hydrogen nuclei are in the **same environment**.

3) It's chosen as a standard because the **absorption peak** is at a **lower frequency** than just about everything else.

4) This peak is given a value of **0** and all the peaks in other substances are measured as **chemical shifts** relative to this.

Carbon-13 NMR Spectrum

absorption

TMS

200   150   100   50   0
Chemical shift, δ (ppm)

Chemical shift is the **difference in the radio frequency** absorbed by the nuclei (hydrogen or carbon) in the molecule being analysed and that absorbed by the same nuclei in **TMS**. It's given the symbol δ and is measured in **parts per million**, or **ppm**. A small amount of TMS is often added to samples to give a **reference peak** on the spectrum.

The chemical formula for TMS is $Si(CH_3)_4$.

TOPIC 19 — MODERN ANALYTICAL TECHNIQUES II

NMR Spectroscopy

¹³C NMR Spectra Tell You About Carbon Environments

It's very likely that you'll be given one or more **carbon-13 NMR spectra** to **interpret** in your exams. Here's a **step-by-step guide** to interpreting them:

1) Count the Number of Carbon Environments

First, count the **number of peaks** in the spectrum — this is the **number of carbon environments** in the molecule. If there's a peak at **δ = 0**, **don't count it** — it's the reference peak from **TMS**.

The spectrum on the right has **three peaks** — so the molecule must have **three different carbon environments**. This **doesn't** necessarily mean it only has **three carbons**, as it could have **more than one** in the **same environment**. In fact the molecular formula of this molecule is **$C_5H_{10}O$**, so it must have **several carbons** in the **same environment**.

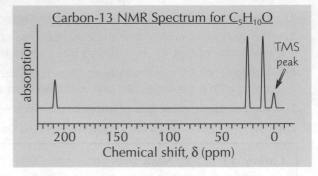
Carbon-13 NMR Spectrum for $C_5H_{10}O$
TMS peak

2) Look Up the Chemical Shifts in a Shift Diagram

In your exams you'll get a **data sheet** that will include a **diagram** a bit like the one below. The diagram shows the **chemical shifts** experienced by **carbon nuclei** in **different environments**. The boxes show the range of shift values a carbon in that environment could have, e.g. **C=C** could have a shift value anywhere between 115 – 140 ppm.

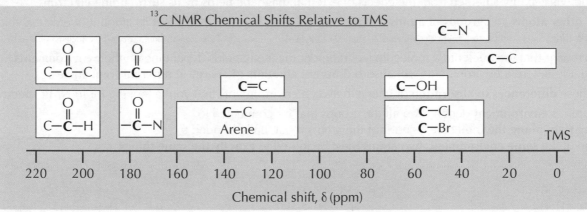
¹³C NMR Chemical Shifts Relative to TMS

You need to **match up** the **peaks** in the spectrum with the **chemical shifts** in the diagram to work out which **carbon environments** they could represent. For example, the peak at **δ ≈ 10** in the spectrum above represents a **C–C** bond. The peak at **δ ≈ 25** is also due to a **C–C** bond. The carbons causing this peak have a different chemical shift to those causing the first peak — so they must be in a slightly different environment. The peak at **δ ≈ 210** is due to a **C=O** group, but you don't know whether it could be an aldehyde or a ketone.

Matching peaks to the groups that cause them isn't always straightforward, because the chemical shifts can overlap. For example, a peak at δ ≈ 40 might be caused by C–C, C–Cl, C–N or C–Br.

3) Try Out Possible Structures

An **aldehyde** with 5 carbons:

This doesn't work — it does have the right **molecular formula** ($C_5H_{10}O$), but it also has **five carbon environments**.

A **ketone** with five carbons:

This works. **Pentan-3-one** has **three** carbon environments — two **CH₃** carbons, each bonded to $CH_2COCH_2CH_3$, two **CH₂** carbons, each bonded to CH_3 and $COCH_2CH_3$, and one **CO** carbon bonded to $(CH_2CH_3)_2$. It has the right **molecular formula** ($C_5H_{10}O$) too.

It can't be pentan-2-one — that has 5 carbon environments.

So, the molecule analysed was **pentan-3-one**.

TOPIC 19 — MODERN ANALYTICAL TECHNIQUES II

NMR Spectroscopy

Interpreting NMR Spectra Gets Easier with Practice

Example: The diagram shows the carbon-13 NMR spectrum of an alcohol with the molecular formula $C_4H_{10}O$.
Analyse and interpret the spectrum to identify the structure of the alcohol.

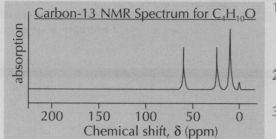

Carbon-13 NMR Spectrum for $C_4H_{10}O$

absorption

200   150   100   50   0
Chemical shift, δ (ppm)

1) Looking at the **diagram** on the **previous page**, the peak with a **chemical shift** of δ ≈ 65 is likely to be due to a **C–O** bond. Remember, the alcohol doesn't contain any **chlorine** or **bromine**, so you know the peak can't be caused by C–Cl or C–Br bonds.

2) The two peaks around **δ ≈ 20** probably both represent carbons in **C–C** bonds, but with slightly different environments.

3) The spectrum has **three peaks**, so the alcohol must have three **carbon environments**. There are **four carbons** in the alcohol, so two of the carbons must be in the **same environment**.

4) Put together all the **information** you've got so far, and try out some **structures**:

```
H  H  H  H
|  |  |  |
H–C–C–C–C–OH
|  |  |  |
H  H  H  H
```
This has a C–O bond, and some C–C bonds, which is right. But all four carbons are in different environments.

```
H  H  H  H
|  |  |  |
H–C–C–C–C–H
|  |  |  |
H  H  OHH
```
Again, this has a C–O bond, and some C–C bonds. But the carbons are still all in different environments.

```
      OH
      |
  H–C–H
  H  |  H
  |  |  |
H–C–C–C–H
  |  |  |
  H  H  H
```
This molecule has a C–O bond and C–C bonds and two of the carbons are in the same environment. So this must be the correct structure.

You'll also need to be able to predict what the carbon-13 NMR spectrum of a molecule may look like. This isn't as hard as it sounds — just identify the number of **unique carbon environments**, then use the **shift diagram** in your data booklet to work out **where** the peaks of each carbon environment would appear.

Practice Questions

Q1 What part of the electromagnetic spectrum does NMR spectroscopy use?

Q2 What is meant by chemical shift? What compound is used as a reference for chemical shifts?

Q3 How can you tell from a carbon-13 NMR spectrum how many carbon environments a molecule contains?

Q4 Which type of bond could a shift of δ ≈ 150 correspond to?

For these questions, use the shift values from the diagram on page 112.

Exam Questions

Q1 The carbon-13 NMR spectrum shown on the right was produced by a compound with the molecular formula C_3H_9N.

a) Explain why there is a peak at δ = 0. [1 mark]

b) The compound does not have the formula $CH_3CH_2CH_2NH_2$. Explain how the spectrum shows this. [2 marks]

c) Suggest and explain, using evidence from the carbon-13 NMR spectrum, a possible structure for the compound. [4 marks]

Carbon-13 NMR Spectrum

absorption

200   150   100   50   0
Chemical shift, δ (ppm)

Q2 Look at molecule X on the right. Which of the following statements is/are true?

1. The carbon-13 NMR spectrum of X has a peak in the region of 165 - 185.

2. Molecule X has three different carbon environments.

3. The carbon-13 NMR spectrum of X shows four peaks.

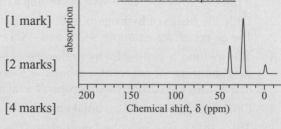

```
     H O        H
H\   | ||       |
  C=C–C–O–C–H
H/          |
            H
```

A 1, 2 and 3   B Only 1 and 2   C Only 1 and 3   D Only 3   [1 mark]

Why did the carbon peak? Because it saw the radio wave...

The ideas behind NMR are difficult, but don't worry too much if you don't really understand them. The important thing is to know how to interpret a spectrum — that's what will get you marks in the exam. If you're having trouble, go over the examples and practice questions a few more times. You should have the "ahh... I get it" moment sooner or later.

Proton NMR Spectroscopy

So, you know how to interpret carbon-13 NMR spectra — now it's time for some high resolution proton NMR spectra.

¹H NMR Spectra Tell You About Hydrogen Environments

Interpreting **proton** (or ¹H) **NMR spectra** is similar to interpreting carbon-13 NMR spectra:

1) Each peak represents one **hydrogen environment.**

2) Look up the **chemical shifts** on a **data diagram** to identify possible environments. They're different from ¹³C NMR, so make sure you're looking at the **correct data diagram.**

For example, **1-chloropropane** has **3 hydrogen environments.**

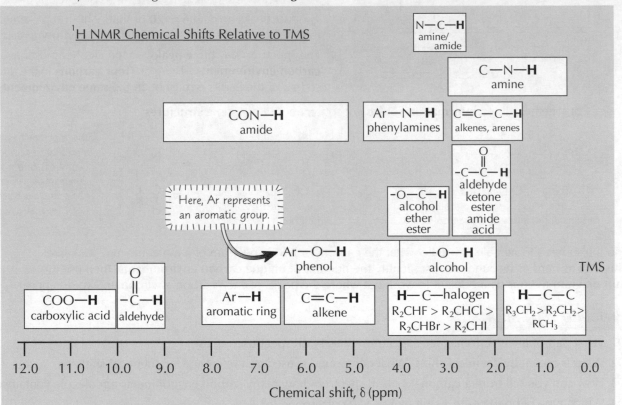

Spin-Spin Coupling Splits the Peaks in a Proton NMR Spectrum

1) The big difference between carbon-13 NMR and proton NMR spectra is that the peaks in a proton NMR spectrum **split** according to how the **hydrogen environments are arranged**.

2) Only the peaks of **hydrogens** bonded to **carbon** atoms split. The peaks of, for example, –OH and –NH hydrogens are not split.

3) The splitting is caused by the influence of hydrogen atoms that are bonded to **neighbouring** (or **adjacent**) **carbons** — these are carbons one along in the carbon chain from the carbon the hydrogen's attached to. This effect is called **spin-spin coupling**.

4) Only hydrogen nuclei on **adjacent** carbon atoms affect each other.

5) These **split peaks** are called **multiplets**. They always split into one more than the number of hydrogens on the neighbouring carbon atoms — it's called the **n+1 rule**. For example, if there are **2 hydrogens** on the adjacent carbon atoms, the peak will be split into 2 + 1 = 3.

The splitting of the peak for this H...

...tells you about the hydrogens on this adjacent carbon.

Type of Peak	Number of Hydrogens on Adjacent Carbon(s)
Singlet (not split)	0
Doublet (split into two)	1
Triplet (split into three)	2
Quartet (split into four)	3

6) You need to consider the hydrogens on **all** the adjacent carbons — if a hydrogen is attached to a carbon in the middle of a carbon chain, there could be **two neighbouring carbon atoms**, each bonded to hydrogens. They'll all contribute to the **splitting**.

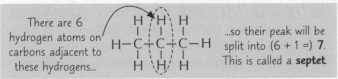

There are 6 hydrogen atoms on carbons adjacent to these hydrogens... ...so their peak will be split into (6 + 1 =) **7**. This is called a **septet**.

TOPIC 19 — MODERN ANALYTICAL TECHNIQUES II

Proton NMR Spectroscopy

Integration Traces Tell You the Ratio of Protons in Each Environment

1) In ^{1}H NMR, the **relative area** under each peak tells you the relative number of H atoms in each environment. For example, if the area under two peaks is in the **ratio** 2:1, there will be **two** H atoms in the first environment for every **one** in the second environment.

2) Areas can be shown using **numbers** above the peaks or with an **integration trace**.

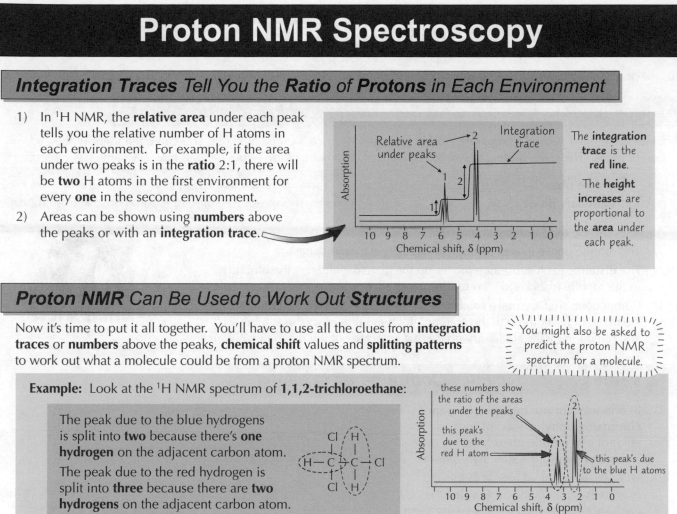

The **integration trace** is the **red line**.

The **height increases** are proportional to the **area** under each peak.

Proton NMR Can Be Used to Work Out Structures

Now it's time to put it all together. You'll have to use all the clues from **integration traces** or **numbers** above the peaks, **chemical shift** values and **splitting patterns** to work out what a molecule could be from a proton NMR spectrum.

You might also be asked to predict the proton NMR spectrum for a molecule.

Example: Look at the ^{1}H NMR spectrum of **1,1,2-trichloroethane**:

The peak due to the blue hydrogens is split into **two** because there's **one** hydrogen on the adjacent carbon atom.

The peak due to the red hydrogen is split into **three** because there are **two** hydrogens on the adjacent carbon atom.

these numbers show the ratio of the areas under the peaks

this peak's due to the red H atom

this peak's due to the blue H atoms

Practice Questions

Q1 What causes the peaks on a high resolution proton NMR spectrum to split?

Q2 What causes a triplet of peaks on a high resolution proton NMR spectrum?

Q3 What do the relative areas under each of the peaks on an NMR spectrum tell you?

Exam Questions

Q1 The proton NMR spectrum below is for an organic compound. Use the diagram of chemical shifts on page 114 to answer this question.

a) Explain the splitting patterns of the two peaks. [2 marks]

b) What is the likely environment of the protons with a shift of 3.6 ppm? [1 mark]

c) What is the likely environment of the protons with a shift of 1.3 ppm? [1 mark]

d) The molecular mass of the molecule is 64.5. Suggest a possible structure and explain your suggestion. [2 marks]

Q2 A sample of pure 3-chlorobut-1-ene was fed into a high resolution proton NMR spectroscopy machine.

a) Predict the number of peaks that will appear on the spectrum (excluding a TMS peak). [1 mark]

b) Predict the chemical shifts and splitting patterns of each peak. [4 marks]

Never mind splitting peaks — this stuff's likely to cause splitting headaches...

Is your head spinning yet? I know mine is. Round and round like a merry-go-round. It's a hard life when you're tied to a desk trying to get NMR spectroscopy firmly fixed in your head. You must be looking quite peaky by now... so go on, learn this stuff, take the dog around the block, then come back and see if you can still remember it all.

Chromatography

You've probably tried chromatography with a spot of ink on a piece of filter paper — it's a classic experiment.

Chromatography is Good for **Separating** and **Identifying** Things

Chromatography is used to **separate** stuff in a mixture — once it's separated out, you can often **identify** the components. There are quite a few different types of chromatography — but they all have the same basic set up:

- A **mobile phase** — where the molecules can move. This is always a liquid or a gas.
- A **stationary phase** — where the molecules can't move. This must be a solid, or a liquid on a solid support.

And they all use the same basic principle:

1) The mobile phase **moves through** or **over** the stationary phase.

2) The **distance** each substance moves up the plate depends on its **solubility** in the mobile phase and its **retention** by or **adsorption** to the stationary phase.

3) Components that are **more soluble** in the mobile phase will **travel further** up the plate, or faster through the column. It's these **differences** in solubility and retention by the stationary phase that **separate** out the different substances.

Claire was going through a bit of a stationery phase.

R_f Values Help to Identify **Components** in a **Mixture**

1) In **one-way chromatography** (or **paper chromatography**), a solvent such as ethanol (the mobile phase), moves over a **piece of paper** (the stationary phase).

2) You can work out what was in the mixture by calculating an R_f value for each spot on the paper and looking them up in a **table of known values**.

3) To work out R_f values, just use this formula:

$$R_f \text{ value} = \frac{\text{distance travelled by spot}}{\text{distance travelled by solvent}}$$

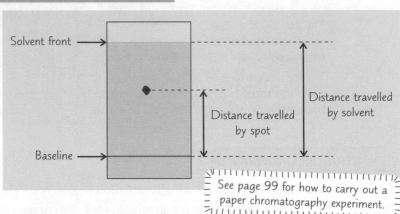

Solvent front
Distance travelled by solvent
Distance travelled by spot
Baseline

See page 99 for how to carry out a paper chromatography experiment.

4) R_f values are **always the same** no matter how big the paper is or how far the solvent travels — they're properties of the chemicals in the mixture and so can be used to identify those chemicals.

5) BUT if the composition of the paper, the solvent, or the temperature change even slightly, you'll get **different R_f values**.

6) It's hard to keep the conditions identical. So, if you suspect that a mixture contains, say, chlorophyll, it's best to put a spot of chlorophyll on the baseline of the **same paper** as the mixture and run them both at the **same time**.

HPLC is Done Under **High Pressure**

1) In **high-performance liquid chromatography** (HPLC) the stationary phase is small particles of a **solid** packed into a column (or tube). This is often **silica** bonded to various **hydrocarbons**.

2) The **liquid** mobile phase is often a **polar mixture** such as **methanol and water**. It's forced through the column under **high pressure**, which is why it used to be called high-pressure liquid chromatography. The mixture to be separated is injected into the stream of solvent and is carried through the column as a **solution**.

3) The mixture is separated because the different parts are **attracted** by **different amounts** to the solid, so they take different lengths of time to travel through the column.

4) As the liquid leaves the column, **UV light** is passed through it. The UV is **absorbed** by the parts of the mixture as they come through, and a **UV detector** measures the UV light absorbed by the mixture. A graph (called a **chromatogram**) is produced.

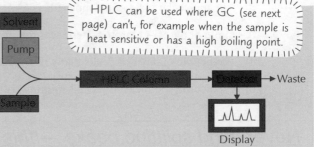

HPLC can be used where GC (see next page) can't, for example when the sample is heat sensitive or has a high boiling point.

Solvent
Pump
Sample
HPLC Column
Detector → Waste
Display

5) The chromatogram shows the **retention times** of the components of the mixture — this is the **time taken** for a **substance** to pass through the **column** and reach the **detector**. You can compare experimental retention times with those from **reference books** or **databases** to identify the different substances in the mixture.

Chromatography

In Gas Chromatography the Mobile Phase is a Gas

1) In **gas chromatography** (GC) the **sample** to be analysed is **injected** into a stream of **gas**, which carries it through a coiled **column** coated with a **viscous liquid** (such as an oil) or a **solid**.

2) The components of the mixture constantly **dissolve in the oil** or **adsorb onto the solid**, **evaporate back** into the gas and then **redissolve** as they travel through the **column**.

3) As with HPLC, the different components in the mixture can be **identified** by their time taken to travel through the column (their **retention times**).

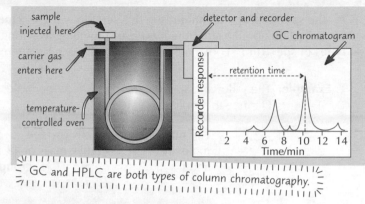

GC and HPLC are both types of column chromatography.

Mass Spectrometry can be Combined with GC and HPLC

1) **Mass spectrometry** is a technique used to identify substances from their mass/charge ratio (see your Year 1 notes). It's very good at **identifying** unknown compounds, but would give confusing results from a mixture of substances.

2) **Gas chromatography** and **HPLC**, on the other hand, are both very good at **separating** a mixture into its individual components, but not so good at identifying those components.

3) If you put HPLC or GC and mass spectrometry **together**, you get an **extremely useful** analytical tool. For example:

Gas chromatography-mass spectrometry (or GC-MS for short) **combines** the **benefits** of gas chromatography and mass spectrometry to make a super analysis tool.

The sample is **separated** using **gas chromatography**, but instead of going to a detector, the separated components are fed into a **mass spectrometer**.

The spectrometer produces a **mass spectrum** for each **component**, which can be used to **identify** each one and show what the original **sample** consisted of.

HPLC and GC combined with mass spectrometry are often used in forensics. Together, they can separate and detect trace amounts of illegal substances in samples, e.g. testing for drugs in blood samples of athletes.

Practice Questions

Q1 Explain what is meant by the terms 'mobile phase' and 'stationary phase'.
Q2 State the formula used to calculate the R_f value of a substance.

Exam Questions

Q1 Look at this diagram of a chromatogram produced using one-way chromatography on a mixture of substances A and B.

a) Calculate the R_f value of spot A. [2 marks]

b) Explain why substance A has moved further up the plate than substance B. [1 mark]

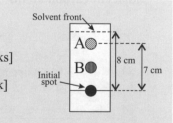

Q2 HPLC is a useful technique for separating mixtures.

a) Describe the key features of HPLC apparatus. [3 marks]

b) Explain how the resulting chromatogram may be used to identify the components of the mixture. [3 marks]

Q3 GC can be used to detect the presence and quantity of alcohol in the blood or urine samples of suspected drink-drivers.

a) What do the letters GC stand for? [1 mark]

b) Explain how 'retention time' is used to identify ethanol in a sample of blood or urine. [2 marks]

Cromer-tography — pictures from my holiday in Norfolk...

Loads of techniques to learn here, and don't forget to check p.99 to remind yourself about thin-layer chromatography and how to carry out a paper chromatography experiment. Good news is the theory behind all these different types of chromatography is the same. You've got a mobile phase, a stationary phase and a mixture that wants separating.

Combined Techniques

Yes, I know, it's yet another page on spectra — but it's the last one (alright, two) I promise.

You Can Use *Data From Several Spectra* to *Work Out a Structure*

All the **spectroscopy techniques** in this section will **give clues** to the **identity of a mystery molecule**, but you can be more **certain** about a structure (and avoid jumping to wrong conclusions) if you look at **data from several different types of spectrum**. Look back at your Year 1 notes for a reminder about mass spectroscopy, and IR spectra.

Example: The following spectra are all of the same molecule. Deduce the molecule's structure.

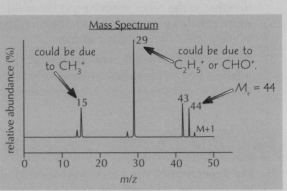

The **mass spectrum** tells you the molecule's got a **relative mass** of **44** and it's likely to contain a **CH₃ group**.

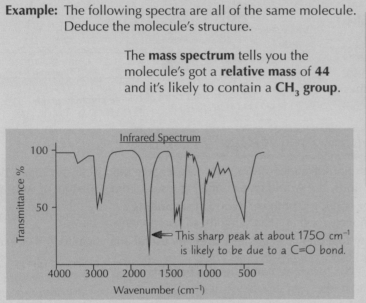

The **high resolution proton NMR spectrum** shows that there are **hydrogen nuclei in 2 environments**.

The peak at δ ≈ **9.5** is due to a **CHO group** and the one at δ ≈ **2.5** is probably the hydrogen atoms in **COCH₃**.

(You know that these can't be any other groups with similar chemical shifts thanks to the mass spectrum and IR spectrum.)

The **area** under the peaks is in the ratio **1 : 3**, which makes sense as there's **1 hydrogen in CHO** and **3 in COCH₃**.

The **splitting pattern** shows that the protons are on **adjacent carbon atoms**, so the group must be **HCOCH₃**.

The **IR spectrum** strongly suggests a **C=O** bond in an aldehyde, ketone, ester, carboxylic acid, amide, acyl chloride or acid anhydride.

But since it **doesn't** also have a broad absorption between 2500 and 3300, the molecule **can't** be a carboxylic acid. And there is no peak between 3300 and 3500, so it can't be an amide.

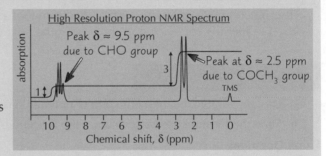

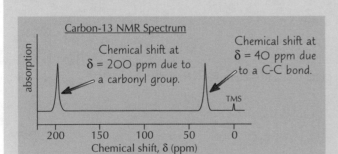

The **carbon-13 NMR spectrum** shows that the molecule has carbon nuclei in **2 different environments**.

The peak at δ = **200** corresponds to a carbon in a **carbonyl group** and the other peak is due to a **C–C bond**.

Putting all this together we have a molecule with a **mass of 44**, which contains a **CH₃** group, a **C=O** bond, and an **HCOCH₃** group.

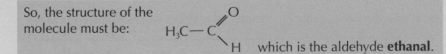

So, the structure of the molecule must be: $H_3C - C \overset{O}{\underset{H}{\diagup\hspace{-1mm}\diagdown}}$ which is the aldehyde **ethanal**.

You probably could have worked the molecule's structure out **without** using all the spectra, but in more **complex examples** you might well need all of them, so it's good practice.

Combined Techniques

Elemental Analysis also Helps to Work Out a Structure

1) In elemental analysis, experiments determine the **masses** or **percentage compositions** of different elements in a compound.

2) This data can help you to work out the **empirical** and **molecular formulae** of a compound. See page 108-109 to remind yourself how to do this.

3) Knowing the molecular formula is useful in working out the **structure** of the compound from different spectra.

Jim has a good knowledge of specs. Do you?

Practice Questions

Q1 Which type of spectrum gives you the relative mass of a molecule?

Q2 Which spectrum can tell you how many different hydrogen environments there are in a molecule?

Q3 Which spectrum can tell you how many carbon environments are in a molecule?

Exam Questions

Have a look at your exam data booklet or your Year 1 notes for the IR spectroscopy data you'll need to answer these questions.

Q1 The four spectra shown were produced by running different tests on samples of the same pure organic compound. Use them to work out:

a) The molecular mass of the compound. [1 mark]

b) The probable structure of the molecule. Explain your reasoning. [6 marks]

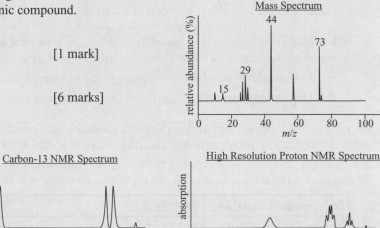

Q2 The four spectra shown were produced by running different tests on samples of the same pure organic compound. Use them to work out:

a) The molecular mass of the compound. [1 mark]

b) The probable structure of the molecule. Explain your reasoning. [6 marks]

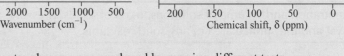
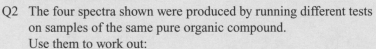

Spectral analysis — psychology for ghosts...

So that's analysis done and dusted, you'll be pleased to hear. But before you celebrate reaching the final topic in the book, take a moment to check that you really know how to interpret all the different spectra. You might want to have a look back at page 101 if you're struggling to remember what all the different functional groups look like.

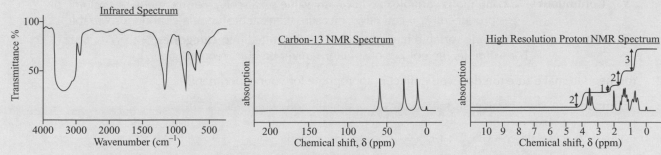

Planning Experiments

As well as doing practical work in class, you can get asked about it in your exams too. Harsh I know, but that's how it goes. You need to be able to plan the perfect experiment and make improvements to ones other people have planned.

Make Sure You **Plan** Your **Experiment Carefully**

It's really important to plan an experiment well if you want to get accurate and precise results. Here's how to go about it...

1) Work out the **aim** of the experiment — what are you trying to find out?
2) Identify the **independent**, **dependent** and other **variables** (see below).
3) Decide what **data** to collect.
4) Select **appropriate equipment** which will give you accurate results.
5) Make a **risk assessment** and plan any safety precautions.
6) Write out a **detailed method**.
7) Carry out **tests** — to gather **evidence** to address the aim of your experiment.

> Have a peek at page 126 to find out more about accurate and precise results.

Make it a **Fair Test** — Control your **Variables**

You probably know this all off by heart but it's easy to get mixed up sometimes. So here's a quick recap:

Variable — A variable is a **quantity** that has the **potential to change**, e.g. mass. There are two types of variable commonly referred to in experiments:

- **Independent variable** — the thing that you **change** in an experiment.
- **Dependent variable** — the thing that you **measure** in an experiment.

As well as the independent and dependent variables, you need to think of all the other variables in your experiment and plan ways to keep each of those the same.

For example, if you're investigating the effect of **temperature** on rate of reaction using the apparatus on the right, the variables will be:

Independent variable	Temperature
Dependent variable	Volume of gas produced — you can measure this by collecting it in a gas syringe.
Other variables	E.g. concentration and volume of solutions, mass of solids, pressure, the presence of a catalyst and the surface area of any solid reactants.

> You MUST control your other variables so they're always the same.

Collect the Appropriate **Data**

Experiments often involve collecting **data** and you need to decide what data to collect.

1) There are different types of data, so it helps to know what they are:

- **Discrete** — you get discrete data by **counting**. E.g. the number of bubbles produced in a reaction.
- **Continuous** — a continuous variable can have **any value** on a scale. For example, the volume of gas produced. You can never measure the exact value of a continuous variable.
- **Categoric** — a categoric variable has values that can be sorted into **categories**. For example, the colours of solutions might be blue, red and green.

2) You need to make sure the data you collect is appropriate for your experiment.

Example: A student suggests measuring the rate of the following reaction by observing how conductivity changes over the course of the reaction:
$NaOH_{(aq)} + CH_3CH_2Br_{(l)} \rightarrow CH_3CH_2OH_{(l)} + NaBr_{(aq)}$
Suggest what is wrong with the student's method, and how it could be improved.

You couldn't collect data about how the **conductivity changes** over the course of the reaction, because there are **salts** in both the reactants and the products.

Instead you could use a **pH meter** to measure how the **pH changes** from basic (due to sodium hydroxide) to neutral.

Planning Experiments

Choose *Appropriate* Equipment — *Think about* Size *and* Precision

Selecting the right apparatus may sound easy but it's something you need to think carefully about.

1) The equipment has to be **appropriate** for the specific experiment.

> For example, if you want to measure the volume of gas produced in a reaction, you need to make sure you use apparatus which will collect the gas, without letting any escape.

2) The equipment needs to be the right **size**.

> For example, if you're using a gas syringe to collect a gas, it needs to be big enough to collect **all** the gas produced during the experiment, or the plunger will just fall out the end. You might need to do some **calculations** to work out what size of syringe to use.

3) The equipment needs to be the right level of **precision**.

> If you want to measure 10 cm^3 of a liquid, it will be more precise to use a measuring cylinder that is graduated to the nearest 0.5 cm^3 than to the nearest 1 cm^3. A burette would be most precise though (they can measure to the nearest 0.1 cm^3).

Risk Assessments *Help You to Work* Safely

1) When you're planning an experiment, you need to carry out a **risk assessment**. To do this, you need to identify:
   - All the **dangers** in the experiment, e.g. any hazardous compounds or naked flames.
   - **Who** is at **risk** from these dangers.
   - What can be done to **reduce the risk**, such as wearing goggles or working in a fume cupboard.

2) You need to make sure you're working **ethically** too. This is most important if there are other people or animals involved. You have to put their welfare first.

Methods Must be *Clear* and *Detailed*

When **writing** or **evaluating** a method, you need to think about all of the things on these two pages. The method must be **clear** and **detailed** enough for anyone to follow — it's important that **other people** can recreate your experiment and get the **same** results. Make sure your method includes:

1) All **substances** and **quantities** to be used.
2) How to **control** variables.
3) The exact **apparatus** needed (a diagram is usually helpful to show the set up).
4) Any **safety precautions** that should be taken.
5) What **data** to collect and **how** to collect it.

Results Should be *Repeatable* and *Reproducible*

1) **Repeatable** means that if the **same** person does the experiment again using the same methods and equipment, they'll get the same results. **Reproducible** means that if someone **else** does the experiment, or a different **method** or piece of **equipment** is used, the results will still be the same.

2) To make sure your results can be consistently repeated and reproduced, you need to **minimise** any **errors** that might sneak into your data. This includes:
   - using **apparatus** and **techniques** correctly,
   - taking **measurements** correctly,
   - **repeating** your experiments and calculating a **mean**.

Revision time — independent variable. Exam mark — dependent variable...

I wouldn't advise you to investigate the effect of revision on exam marks. Just trust me — more revision = better marks. But if you were to investigate it, there are all manner of variables that you'd need to control. The amount of sleep you had the night before, how much coffee you drank in the morning, your level of panic on entering the exam hall...

Carrying Out Experiments

The way you carry out your experiment is important, so here's a nice round up of some of the techniques chemists use and some information about recording results. I don't know about you, but I can't wait to get started on these pages...

Make Sure You **Measure** Substances **Correctly**

The **state** (solid, liquid or gas) that your substance is in will determine **how** you decide to measure it.

1) You weigh **solids** using a **balance**. Here are a couple of things to look out for:
   - Put the container you are weighing your substance into on the balance, and make sure the balance is set to exactly zero before you start weighing out your substance.
   - If you need to **transfer** the solid into another container, make sure that it's **all** transferred. For example, if you're making up a standard solution you could wash any remaining solid into the new container using the solvent. Or, you could **reweigh** the weighing container after you've transferred the solid so you can work out **exactly** how much you added to your experiment.

2) There are a few methods you might use to measure the volume of a liquid. Whichever method you use, always read the volume from the **bottom** of the **meniscus** (the curved upper surface of the liquid) when it's at **eye level**.

Read volume from here — the bottom of the meniscus.

Pipettes are long, narrow tubes that are used to **suck up** an **accurate volume** of liquid and transfer it to another container. They are often **calibrated** to allow for the fact that the last drop of liquid stays in the pipette when the liquid is ejected. This reduces transfer errors.

Burettes measure from **top** to **bottom** (so when they are **full**, the scale reads **zero**). They have a **tap** at the bottom which you can use to release the liquid into another container (you can even release it drop by drop). To use a burette, take an **initial reading**, and once you've released as much liquid as you want, take a **final reading**. The **difference** between the readings tells you how much liquid you used.

Burettes are used a lot for titrations. There's loads more about titrations on pages 42-47.

Volumetric flasks allow you to **accurately** measure a very **specific** volume of liquid. They come in various **sizes** (e.g. 100 cm³, 250 cm³) and there's a **line** on the neck that marks the volume that they measure. They're used to make **accurate dilutions** and **standard solutions**. To use them, first measure out and add the liquid or solid that is being diluted or dissolved. Rinse out the measuring vessel into the volumetric flask with a little solvent to make sure everything's been transferred. Then fill the flask with solvent to the **bottom** of the neck. Fill the neck **drop by drop** until the bottom of the meniscus is **level** with the line.

10 cm³

500 cm³

A standard solution is a solution with a precisely known concentration. You learnt how to make them in Year 1.

3) Gases can be measured with a **gas syringe**. They should be measured at **room temperature** and **pressure** as the **volume** of a gas **changes** with temperature and pressure. Before you use the syringe, you should make sure it's completely **sealed** and that the **plunger** moves **smoothly**.

Once you've measured a quantity of a substance you need to be careful you don't **lose** any. In particular, think about how to minimise losses as you transfer it from the measuring equipment to the reaction container.

Measure **Temperature** Accurately

I'm sure you've heard this before, so I'll be quick... You can use a **thermometer** or a **temperature probe** to measure the temperature of a substance (a temperature probe is like a thermometer but it will always have a **digital display**).

- Make sure the **bulb** of your thermometer or temperature probe is **completely submerged** in any mixture you're measuring.
- Wait for the temperature to **stabilise** before you take an initial reading
- If you're using a thermometer with a scale, read off your measurement at **eye level** to make sure it's accurate.

Carrying Out Experiments

Qualitative Tests Can be Harder to Reproduce

Qualitative tests measure **physical qualities** (e.g. colour) while **quantitative** tests measure numerical data, (e.g. mass).

So if you carried out a reaction and noticed that heat was produced, this would be a **qualitative** observation. If you **measured** the temperature change with a thermometer, this would be **quantitative**.

Qualitative tests can be harder to **reproduce** because they're often **subjective** (based on **opinion**), such as describing the **colour** or **cloudiness** of a solution. There are ways to **reduce** the subjectivity of qualitative results though. For example:

- If you're looking for a **colour change**, put a **white background** behind your reaction container.
- If you're looking for a **precipitate** to form, mark an **X** on a piece of paper and place it under the reaction container. Your solution is 'cloudy' when you can **no longer see** the X.

Organise Your Results in a Table

It's a good idea to set up a table to **record** the **results** of your experiment in. When you draw a table, make sure you **include** enough **rows** and **columns** to **record all of the data** you need. You might also need to include a column for **processing** your data (e.g. working out an average).

Make sure each **column** has a **heading** so you know what's going to be recorded where.

The **units** should be in the **column heading**, not the table itself.

Temperature (°C)	Time (s)	Volume of gas evolved (cm³) Run 1	Run 2	Run 3	Average volume of gas evolved (cm³)
20	10	8.1	7.6	8.5	$(8.1 + 7.6 + 8.5) \div 3 = 8.1$
	20	17.7	19.0	20.1	$(17.7 + 19.0 + 20.1) \div 3 = 18.9$
	30	28.5	29.9	30.0	$(28.5 + 29.9 + 30.0) \div 3 = 29.5$

You'll need to repeat each test **at least three** times to check your results are **repeatable**.

You can find the **mean result** by **adding up** the data from each repeat and **dividing** by the number of repeats.

Watch Out For Anomalous Results

1) Anomalous results are ones that **don't fit** in with the other values and are likely to be wrong.
2) They're often due to **random errors**, e.g. if a drop in a titration is too big and shoots past the end point, or if a syringe plunger gets stuck whilst collecting gas produced in a reaction.
3) When looking at results in tables or graphs, you always need to look to see if there are any anomalies — you need to **ignore** these results when calculating means or drawing lines of best fit.

Example: Calculate the mean volume from the results in the table below.

Titration Number	1	2	3	4
Titre Volume (cm³)	15.20	15.30	15.25	15.50

Titre **4** isn't **concordant** (doesn't match) the other results so you need to ignore it and just use the other three:
$$\frac{15.20 + 15.30 + 15.25}{3} = \textbf{15.25 cm}^3$$

There won't always be an anomalous result, but sometimes there can be more than one — don't be afraid to ignore more than one result.

My mate Steve gave me a beaker with a hole in — he's a practical joker...

Practicals come up the whole way through your course, so you should be familiar with some practical techniques before now. It might seem like there's a lot to do to with all this measuring malarkey, but I have faith in you my dear chemist pal. Before long you'll be measuring temperatures and volumes with your eyes shut (metaphorically speaking).

Presenting Results

Results tables are all well and good, but graphs and other pretty charts can be better...

Graphs: **Scatter** or **Bar** — Use the **Best Type**

You can often make a **graph** of your results. Graphs make your data **easier to understand** — if you choose the right type.

Scatter plots are great for showing how two sets of continuous data are related (or **correlated** — see page 125) Don't try to join all the points on a scatter plot — draw a straight or curved **line of best fit** to show the **trend**.

Graph to show the relationship between
M_r and melting point in straight-chain alcohols

Melting point (K): 0, 100, 150, 200, 250, 300
M_r: 0, 25, 50, 75, 100, 125, 150, 175

Graph to show volume of gas
evolved against time

Volume of gas (cm^3): 0, 20, 40, 60, 80, 100
Time (s): 0, 15, 30, 45, 60, 75, 90, 105, 120

When drawing graphs, the dependent variable should go on the y-axis, the independent on the x-axis.

You should use a **bar chart** when one of your data sets is **categoric**. For example:

Graph to Show
Chlorine Concentration
in Water Samples

Chlorine concentration (ppm): 0, 0.1, 0.2, 0.3, 0.4, 0.5
Water samples: A, B, C

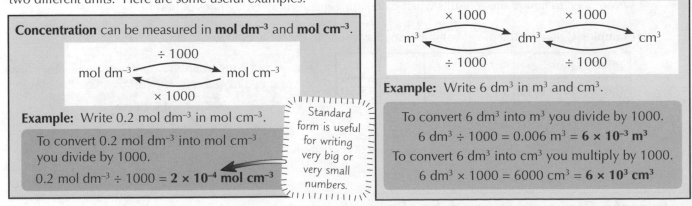

Apple and blackberry
was number one on
Jane's pie chart

Whatever type of graph you make, you'll ONLY get full marks if you:

- Choose a sensible **scale** — don't do a tiny graph in the corner of the paper, or massive axes where the data only takes up a tiny part of the graph.
- **Label** both **axes** — including units.
- Plot your points accurately — use a **sharp pencil**.

Sometimes you might need to work out the gradient of a graph, e.g. to work out the rate of a reaction. There are details of how to do this on page 61.

Pie charts are also used to display categoric data.

Don't Forget About **Units**

Units are very important — 10 g is a bit different from 10 kg, so make sure you don't forget to add them to your **tables** and **graphs**. It's often a good idea to write down the units on each line of any **calculations** you do — it makes things less confusing, particularly if you need to convert between two different units. Here are some useful examples:

Concentration can be measured in **mol dm⁻³** and **mol cm⁻³**.

$$mol\ dm^{-3} \underset{\times 1000}{\overset{\div 1000}{\rightleftharpoons}} mol\ cm^{-3}$$

Example: Write 0.2 mol dm⁻³ in mol cm⁻³.

To convert 0.2 mol dm⁻³ into mol cm⁻³ you divide by 1000.

0.2 mol dm⁻³ ÷ 1000 = **2 × 10⁻⁴ mol cm⁻³**

Standard form is useful for writing very big or very small numbers.

Volume can be measured in **m³**, **dm³** and **cm³**.

$$m^3 \underset{\div 1000}{\overset{\times 1000}{\rightleftharpoons}} dm^3 \underset{\div 1000}{\overset{\times 1000}{\rightleftharpoons}} cm^3$$

Example: Write 6 dm³ in m³ and cm³.

To convert 6 dm³ into m³ you divide by 1000.

6 dm³ ÷ 1000 = 0.006 m³ = **6 × 10⁻³ m³**

To convert 6 dm³ into cm³ you multiply by 1000.

6 dm³ × 1000 = 6000 cm³ = **6 × 10³ cm³**

Popstar unit conversions — 10¹² microphones = 1 megaphone...

When you draw graphs, always be careful to get your axes round the right way. The thing you've been changing (the independent variable) goes on the x-axis, and the thing you've been measuring (the dependent variable) is on the y-axis.

Drawing Conclusions and Evaluating

And so we conclude our delightful journey through the world of practical skills. And what better way to conclude than with some conclusions. It's as if I planned it isn't it? Well, read on to the very end, but beware — there are errors about.

Round to the **Lowest Number** of **Significant Figures**

You may need to do a few calculations before you can start drawing conclusions from your data. When doing this, you need to be aware of **significant figures**.

1) The rule is the same for when doing calculations with the results from your experiment, or when doing calculations in the exam — you have to round your answer to the **lowest number of significant figures** (s.f.) given in the question

2) It always helps to write down the number of significant figures you've rounded to after your answer — it shows you really know what you're talking about.

3) If you're converting between **standard** and **ordinary form**, you have to keep the **same number** of significant figures. For example, 0.0060 mol dm⁻³ is the same as 6.0×10^{-3} mol dm⁻³ — they're both given to 2 s.f..

> The first significant figure of a number is the first digit that isn't a zero. The second, third and fourth significant figures follow on immediately after the first (even if they're zeros).

Example: 13.5 cm³ of a 0.51 mol dm⁻³ solution of sodium hydroxide reacts with 1.5 mol dm⁻³ hydrochloric acid. Calculate the volume of hydrochloric acid required to neutralise the sodium hydroxide.

3 s.f.　　　　2 s.f.

No. of moles of NaOH: $(13.5 \text{ cm}^3 \times 0.51 \text{ mol dm}^{-3}) \div 1000 = 6.885 \times 10^{-3}$ mol

Volume of HCl: (6.885×10^{-3}) mol $\times 1000 \div 1.5$ mol dm⁻³ $= 4.59 \text{ cm}^3 =$ **4.6 cm³ (2 s.f.)**

Final answer should be rounded to 2 s.f.

> You don't need to round intermediate answers. Rounding too early will make your final answer less accurate.

> Make sure all your units match when you're doing calculations.

Scatter Graphs Show The **Relationship** Between Variables

Correlation describes the **relationship** between two variables — the independent one and the dependent one. Data can show:

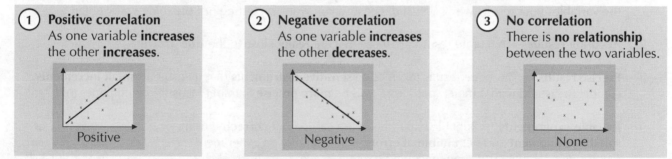

(1) **Positive correlation**
As one variable **increases** the other **increases**.

Positive

(2) **Negative correlation**
As one variable **increases** the other **decreases**.

Negative

(3) **No correlation**
There is **no relationship** between the two variables.

None

Correlation **Doesn't** Mean **Cause** — Don't Jump to Conclusions

1) Ideally, only **two** quantities would **ever** change in any experiment — everything else would remain **constant**.

2) But in experiments or studies outside the lab, you **can't** usually control all the variables. So even if two variables are correlated, the change in one may **not** be causing the change in the other. Both changes might be caused by a **third variable**.

Example:

Some studies have found a correlation between **drinking chlorinated tap water** and the risk of developing certain cancers. So some people argue that water shouldn't have chlorine added.

BUT it's hard to control all the **variables** between people who drink tap water and people who don't. It could be due to other lifestyle factors.

Or, the cancer risk could be affected by something else in tap water — or by whatever the non-tap water drinkers drink instead...

PRACTICAL SKILLS

Drawing Conclusions and Evaluating

Don't Get **Carried Away** When Drawing Conclusions

The **data** should always **support** the conclusion. This may sound obvious but it's easy to **jump** to conclusions. Conclusions have to be **specific** — not make sweeping generalisations.

Example: The rate of an enzyme-controlled reaction was measured at **10 °C**, **20 °C**, **30 °C**, **40 °C**, **50 °C** and **60 °C**. All other variables were kept constant, and the results are shown in the graph below.

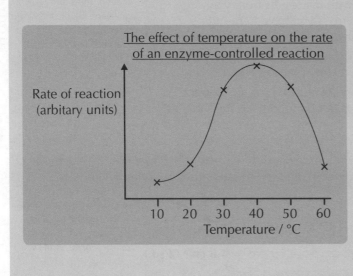

The effect of temperature on the rate of an enzyme-controlled reaction

Rate of reaction (arbitary units)

Temperature / °C

1) A science magazine **concluded** from this data that this enzyme works best at **40 °C**.

2) The data **doesn't** support this. The enzyme **could** work best at 42 °C or 47 °C but you can't tell from the data because **increases** of **10 °C** at a time were used. The rate of reaction at in-between temperatures **wasn't** measured.

3) All you know is that it's faster at **40 °C** than at any of the other temperatures tested.

4) The experiment **ONLY** gives information about this particular enzyme-controlled reaction. You can't conclude that **all** enzyme-controlled reactions happen faster at a particular temperature — only this one. And you can't say for sure that doing the experiment at, say, a different constant pressure, wouldn't give a different optimum temperature.

You Need to Look **Critically** at Your Experiment

There are a few terms that'll come in handy when you're evaluating how convincing your results are...

1) **Valid results** — Valid results answer the **original question**. For example, if you haven't **controlled all the variables** your results won't be valid, because you won't be testing just the thing you wanted to.

2) **Accurate results** — Accurate results are those that are **really close** to the **true** answer.

3) **Precise results** — These are results taken using **sensitive instruments** that measure in **small increments**, e.g. pH measured with a meter (pH 7.692) will be **more precise** than pH measured with paper (pH 7).

4) **Reliable experiments** — Reliable experiments are carried out **correctly**, using **suitable equipment** and with **minimal errors**. For example, an experiment measuring a temperature change would be set up to avoid any heat loss and temperature changes would be measured using a thermometer or temperature probe.

Repeating an experiment won't make your results more reliable.

Uncertainty is the Amount of **Error** Your **Measurements** Might Have

1) Any measurements you make will have **uncertainty** in them due to the limits to the **precision** of the equipment you used.

2) If you use a weighing scale that measures to the nearest 0.1 g, then the **true** weight of any substance you weigh could be up to 0.05 g **more than** or **less than** your reading. Your measurement has an **uncertainty** (or error) of ±0.05 g in either direction.

3) The ± sign tells you the **range** in which the true value could lie. The range can also be called the **margin of error**.

4) For any piece of equipment you use, the uncertainty will be **half** the **smallest increment** the equipment can measure, in either direction.

5) If you're **combining measurements**, you'll need to combine their **uncertainties**. For example, if you're calculating a temperature change by measuring an initial and a final temperature, the **total** uncertainty for the temperature change will be the uncertainties for both measurements added together.

PRACTICAL SKILLS

Drawing Conclusions and Evaluating

The **Percentage Uncertainty** in a Result Should be Calculated

You can calculate the **percentage uncertainty** of a measurement using this equation:

$$\text{percentage uncertainty} = \frac{\text{uncertainty}}{\text{reading}} \times 100$$

You may see percentage uncertainty called percentage error.

Example: A balance measures to the nearest 0.2 g, and is used to measure the **mass** of a substance. The mass is zeroed so it reads 0.0 g. Then, 18.4 g of a solid are weighed. Calculate the percentage uncertainty.

The balance measures to the nearest 0.2 g, so **each reading** has an uncertainty of ±0.1 g. There is an error of ±0.1 g associated with when the balance reads 0.0 g (when it's zeroed), and when the mass of solid has been weighed out. Therefore, there are two sources of error, so the **total uncertainty** is 0.1 × 2 = 0.2 g.

So for this mass measurement, percentage uncertainty $= \frac{0.2}{18.4} \times 100 = \textbf{1.1\%}$

You Can **Minimise** the **Percentage Uncertainty**

1) One obvious way to **reduce errors** in your measurements is to use the most **precise equipment** available to you.

2) A bit of clever **planning** can also improve your results. If you measure out **5 cm³** of liquid in a measuring cylinder that has increments of 0.1 cm³ then the percentage uncertainty is (0.05 ÷ 5) × 100 = **1%**. But if you measure **10 cm³** of liquid in the same measuring cylinder the percentage uncertainty is (0.05 ÷ 10) × 100 = **0.5%**. Hey presto — you've just halved the percentage uncertainty. So the percentage uncertainty can be reduced by planning an experiment so you use a **larger volume** of liquid.

3) The general principle is that the **smaller** the measurement, the **larger** the percentage uncertainty.

Errors Can Be **Systematic** or **Random**

1) **Systematic errors** are the same every time you repeat the experiment. They may be caused by your **set-up** or **equipment**. For example, if the 10.00 cm³ pipette you used to measure out a sample for titration actually only measured 9.95 cm³, your sample would have been about 0.05 cm³ too small **every time** you repeated the experiment.

2) **Random errors** vary — they're what make the results a bit **different** each time you repeat an experiment. The errors when you make a reading from a burette are random. You have to estimate or round the level when it's between two marks — so sometimes your figure will be **above** the real one, and sometimes it will be **below**.

3) **Repeating an experiment** and finding the mean of your results helps to deal with **random errors**. The results that are a bit high will be **cancelled out** by the ones that are a bit low. But repeating your results won't get rid of any **systematic errors**, so your results won't get more **accurate**.

Think About How the Experiment Could Be **Improved**

In your evaluation you need to think about anything that you could have done differently to improve your results. Here are some things to think about...

1) **Whether your method gives you valid results.**
   - Will the data you collected answer the question your experiment aimed to answer?
   - Did you control all your variables?

2) **How you could improve the accuracy of your results.**
   - Was the apparatus you used on an appropriate scale for your measurements?
   - Could you use more precise equipment to reduce the random errors and uncertainty of your results?

3) **Whether your results are repeatable and reproducible.**
   - Did you repeat the experiment, and were the results you got similar?

There's more about repeatable and reproducible results on page 121.

Repeat your results: Your results, your results, your results, your results...

Watch out for errors creeping in to your experimental methods. It may not seem obvious that there's an error when you're taking a measurement that's zero (e.g. on a balance), so remember to include this when calculating errors.

Do Well In Your Exams

Revision is really important when it comes to exams, but it's not the only thing that can help. Good exam technique and knowing what to expect in each exam can make a big difference to your mark, so you'd better check this out...

Make Sure You Know the **Structure** of Your **Exams**

For A-Level Chemistry, you'll be sitting **three papers**. Knowing what's going to come up in each paper and how much time you'll have will be really useful when you are preparing for your exams, so here's what you'll be up against:

Paper		Time	No. of marks	% of total mark	Topics assessed	Paper details
1	Advanced Inorganic and Physical Chemistry	1 hr 45 mins	90	30	1-5, 8 and 10-15	A mixture of multiple choice, short answer, calculations and extended writing questions.
2	Advanced Organic and Physical Chemistry	1 hr 45 mins	90	30	2, 3, 5-7, 9 and 16-19	A mixture of multiple choice, short answer, calculations and extended writing questions.
3	General and Practical Principles in Chemistry	2 hrs 30 mins	120	40	All topics, including Practical Skills.	A mixture of multiple choice, short answer, calculations and extended writing questions.

1) **All three papers** cover theory from **both years** of your course — this means you need to make sure you **revise** your **Year 1 topics** (**1-10**) as well as your **Year 2 topics** (**11-19**) for these exams.

2) Each paper will include some **extended writing questions** which are marked on the **quality** of the response, as well as their **scientific content**. These questions will be shown by an **asterisk** (*) next to their number. Your answer needs to:

- Have a **clear** and **logical structure**.
- Include the right **scientific terms**, spelt correctly.
- Include **detailed information** that's **relevant** to the question.

Some Questions Will Test Your Knowledge of **Carrying Out Practicals**

Some of the marks in your A-Level Chemistry exams will focus on how to carry out **experiments**, analyse **data** and **work scientifically**. This means you will be given questions where you're asked to do things like comment on the **design** of **experiments**, make **predictions**, **draw graphs**, **calculate** percentage **errors** — basically, anything related to planning experiments or analysing results. These skills are covered in the Practical Skills section of this book on pages 120-127, and in the relevant topics.

Although Paper 3 covers the Practical Skills section of this book, you could be asked about practical techniques in any of your exams.

Manage Your Time Sensibly

1) **How long** you spend on **each question** is important in an exam — it could make all the difference to your grade.

2) The **number of marks** tells you roughly **how long** to spend on a question. But some questions will require **lots of work** for a few marks while others will be **quicker**.

> **Example:** 1) Define the term 'enthalpy change of neutralisation'. (2 marks)
>
> 2) Compounds A and B are hydrocarbons with relative molecular masses of 78 and 58 respectively. In their ^1H NMR spectra, A has only one peak and B has two peaks. Draw a possible structure for each compound. (2 marks)

Question 1 only requires you to write down a **definition** — if you can remember it this shouldn't take too long.

Question 2 requires you to **apply your knowledge** of NMR spectra and **draw the structure** of two compounds — this may take you a lot longer, especially if you have to draw out a few structures before getting it right.

So if **time's running out**, it makes sense to do questions like Q1 **first** and **come back** to Q2 if there's time at the end.

3) If you get stuck on a question for too long, it may be best to **move on** and come back to it later. If you skip any questions the first time round, don't forget to **go back** to do them.

4) You don't have to work through the paper **in order** — you might decide not to do all the multiple choice questions first, or leave questions on topics you find harder till the end.

Do Well In Your Exams

Make Sure You *Read the Question*

1) It sounds obvious, but it's really important you read each question **carefully**, and give an answer that fits.

2) **Command words** in the question give you an idea of the **kind of answer** you should write. You'll find answering exam questions much easier if you understand exactly what they mean. Here's a summary of the **common** ones:

Command word	What to do
Give / Name / State	Give a brief one or two word answer, or a short sentence.
Identify	Say what something is.
Compare / Contrast	Look at the similarities and differences between two or more things.
Explain	Give an explanation, including reasoning, for something.
Predict	Use your scientific knowledge to work out what the answer might be.
Describe	Write an account or a description of something, e.g. an experiment, some observations or a chemical trend.
Calculate	Work out the solution to a mathematical problem.
Deduce / Determine	Use the information given in the question to work something out.
Discuss	Explore and investigate a topic, as presented in the question.
Sketch	Produce a rough drawing of a diagram or graph.

From the looks on his classmates' faces, Ivor deduced that he had gone a bit overboard when decorating his lucky exam hat.

Remember to Use the **Data Booklet**

When you sit your exams, you'll be given a data booklet. It will contain lots of **useful information**, including:

- the **characteristic infrared absorptions**, ^{13}C NMR shifts and ^1H NMR shifts of some common functional groups.
- some electronegativity information, including the **Pauling electronegativity index**.
- some useful **scientific constants**.
- the **standard electrode potentials** of some electrochemical half-cells.
- some information about the **colours** and **pH ranges** of common **indicators**.
- a copy of the **periodic table**.

Use a copy of the data booklet while you're revising. It will get you used to using it, and show you the facts you don't need to memorise.

Be *Careful With Calculations*

20% of the marks up for grabs in A-Level Chemistry will require maths skills, so make sure you know your stuff.

1) In calculation questions you should always **show your working** — you may get some marks for your **method** even if you get the answer wrong.

2) Don't **round** your answer until the **very end**. Some of the calculations in A-Level Chemistry can be quite **long**, and if you round too early you could introduce errors into your final answer.

3) Be careful with **units**. Lots of formulae require quantities to be in specific units (e.g. temperature in kelvin), so it's best to **convert** any numbers you're given into these before you start. And obviously, if the question **tells** you which units to give your **answer** in, don't throw away marks by giving it in different ones.

4) You should give your final answer to the correct number of **significant figures**. This is usually the same as the data with the **lowest number** of significant figures in the question — see p.125 for more on significant figures.

5) It can be easy to mistype numbers into your calculator when you're under pressure in an exam, so always **double-check** your calculations and make sure that your answer looks **sensible**.

I'd tell you another Chemistry joke, but I'm not sure it'd get a good reaction...

The key to preparing for your exams is to practise, practise, practise. Get your hands on some practice papers and try to do each of them in the time allowed. This'll flag up any topics that you're a bit shaky on, so you can go back and revise.

Answers

Topic 11 — Equilibrium II

Page 3 — Calculations Involving K_c

1   C *[1 mark]*

2   $K_c = \dfrac{[Cu^{2+}]}{[Ag^+]^2}$ *[1 mark]* $= \dfrac{0.193}{(0.431)^2} = \mathbf{1.04\ mol^{-1}dm^3}$

   [2 marks — 1 mark for correct value of K_c, 1 mark for correct units]

   (Units = (mol dm^{-3})/ (mol dm^{-3})^2 = 1/mol dm^{-3} = mol^{-1} dm^3)

   Don't forget, solids aren't included in the expression for the equilibrium constant.

3 a) i) mass ÷ M_r = 42.5 ÷ 46.0 = **0.923...** *[1 mark]*

      ii) moles of O_2 = mass ÷ M_r = 14.1 ÷ 32.0 = 0.440... *[1 mark]*

          moles of NO = 2 × moles of O_2 = 0.881... *[1 mark]*

          moles of NO_2 = 0.923... – 0.881... = **0.0427** *[1 mark]*

  b) Concentration of O_2 = 0.441 ÷ 22.8 = 0.0193... mol dm^{-3}

      Concentration of NO = 0.881 ÷ 22.8 = 0.0386... mol dm^{-3}

      Concentration of NO_2 = 0.0427 ÷ 22.8 = 0.00187... mol dm^{-3}

      $K_c = \dfrac{[NO]^2[O_2]}{[NO_2]^2}$ *[1 mark]* $\Rightarrow K_c = \dfrac{(0.0386...)^2 \times (0.0193...)}{(0.00187...)^2}$ *[1 mark]*

      = **8.23 mol dm^{-3}** *[2 marks — 1 mark for correct value of K_c, 1 mark for correct units]*

      (Units = (mol dm^{-3})^2 × (mol dm^{-3}) /(mol dm^{-3})^2 = mol dm^{-3})

      You might get a slightly different answer depending on how you rounded your intermediate answers throughout this question. As long as your answer is between 8.16 and 8.23, you'll still get the mark.

Page 5 — Gas Equilibria

1 a) $K_p = \dfrac{p(SO_2)p(Cl_2)}{p(SO_2Cl_2)}$ *[1 mark]*

  b) Cl_2 and SO_2 are produced in equal amounts so

      $p(Cl_2) = p(SO_2) = 0.594$ atm *[1 mark]*

      Total pressure = $p(SO_2Cl_2) + p(Cl_2) + p(SO_2)$ so

      $p(SO_2Cl_2) = 1.39 - 0.594 - 0.594 = \mathbf{0.202\ atm}$ *[1 mark]*

  c) $K_p = \dfrac{0.594 \times 0.594}{0.202} = \mathbf{1.75\ atm}$

      [2 marks — 1 mark for correct value of K_p, 1 mark for correct units]

      (Units = (atm × atm)/ atm = atm)

2 a) $p(O_2) = ½ × 0.36 = 0.18$ atm *[1 mark]*

  b) $p(NO_2)$ = total pressure – $p(NO)$ – $p(O_2)$

                = 0.98 – 0.36 – 0.18 = **0.44 atm** *[1 mark]*

  c) $K_p = \dfrac{p(NO_2)^2}{p(NO)^2p(O_2)}$ *[1 mark]*

      $= \dfrac{0.44^2}{0.36^2 \times 0.18} = \mathbf{8.3\ atm^{-1}}$ *[2 marks — 1 mark for correct value of K_p, 1 mark for correct units]*

      (Units = atm^2/(atm^2 × atm) = atm^{-1})

Page 7 — Le Chatelier's Principle and Equilibrium Constants

1 a) T_2 is lower than T_1 *[1 mark]*. A decrease in temperature shifts the position of equilibrium in the exothermic direction, producing more product *[1 mark]*. More product (and less reactant) means K_c increases *[1 mark]*.

      A negative ΔH means the forward reaction is exothermic — it gives out heat.

  b) A decrease in volume means an increase in pressure. This shifts the equilibrium position to the right where there are fewer moles of gas. The yield of ammonia increases *[1 mark]*.

      K_c is unchanged *[1 mark]*.

2 a) $K_p = \dfrac{p(CO)p(H_2)^3}{p(CH_4)p(H_2O)}$ *[1 mark]*

  b) A *[1 mark]*

Topic 12 — Acid-Base Equilibria

Page 9 — Acids and Bases

1 a) $HCN \rightleftharpoons H^+ + CN^-$ OR $HCN + H_2O \rightleftharpoons H_3O^+ + CN^-$ *[1 mark]*

  b) Strongly to the left *[1 mark]* as it is a weak acid so it is only partially dissociated *[1 mark]*.

  c) CN^- *[1 mark]*

2 a) The enthalpy of neutralisation is the enthalpy change when solutions of an acid and a base react together, under standard conditions *[1 mark]*, to produce 1 mole of water *[1 mark]*.

  b) He is incorrect/the values for the enthalpy change of neutralisation will be different *[1 mark]*. This is because nitric acid is a strong acid, so will fully dissociate in solution. Therefore, the value for the standard enthalpy of neutralisation for the reaction of nitric acid and potassium hydroxide only includes the enthalpy of reaction between the H^+ and OH^- ions *[1 mark]*. Ethanoic acid is a weak acid, so only dissociates slightly in solution. Therefore, the value for the enthalpy change of neutralisation for the reaction of ethanoic acid and potassium hydroxide includes the enthalpy of dissociation of the ethanoic acid, as well as enthalpy for the reaction of the H^+ and OH^- ions *[1 mark]*.

Page 11 — pH

1 a) It's a strong monobasic acid, so $[H^+] = [HBr] = 0.32$ mol dm^{-3}.

      pH = $-\log_{10} 0.32 = \mathbf{0.49}$ *[1 mark]*

  b) HF is a weaker acid than HCl, so will be less dissociated in solution. This means the concentration of hydrogen ions will be lower, so the pH will be higher *[1 mark]*.

2 a) $K_a = \dfrac{[H^+][A^-]}{[HA]}$ *[1 mark]*

  b) $K_a = \dfrac{[H^+]^2}{[HA]}$ $[H^+] = \sqrt{(5.60 \times 10^{-4}) \times 0.280} = 0.0125...$ *[1 mark]*

      pH = $-\log_{10}[H^+] = -\log_{10}(0.0125...) = \mathbf{1.90}$ *[1 mark]*

3   $[H^+] = 10^{-2.65} = 2.23... \times 10^{-3}$ mol dm^{-3} *[1 mark]*

    $K_a = \dfrac{[H^+]^2}{[HX]}$ *[1 mark]* $= \dfrac{(2.23... \times 10^{-3})^2}{0.150}$

               = **3.34 × 10^{-5} mol dm^{-3}** *[1 mark]*

Page 13 — The Ionic Product of Water

1 a) Moles of NaOH = 2.50 ÷ 40.0 = 0.0625 moles *[1 mark]*

      1 mole of NaOH gives 1 mole of OH^-.

      So $[OH^-] = [NaOH] = \mathbf{0.0625\ mol\ dm^{-3}}$ *[1 mark]*.

  b) $K_w = [H^+][OH^-]$

      $[H^+] = 1 \times 10^{-14} ÷ 0.0625 = 1.60 \times 10^{-13}$ *[1 mark]*

      pH = $-\log_{10}(1.60 \times 10^{-13}) = \mathbf{12.80}$ *[1 mark]*

2   $K_w = [H^+][OH^-]$

    $[OH^-] = [NaOH] = 0.0370$

    $[H^+] = K_w ÷ [OH^-] = (1 \times 10^{-14}) ÷ 0.0370 = 2.70 \times 10^{-13}$ *[1 mark]*

    pH = $-\log_{10}[H^+] = -\log_{10}(2.70 \times 10^{-13}) = \mathbf{12.57}$ *[1 mark]*

3   $K_a = 10^{-pK_a} = 10^{-4.20} = 6.3 \times 10^{-5}$ *[1 mark]*

    $K_a = \dfrac{[H^+]^2}{[HA]}$ so $[H^+] = \sqrt{K_a \times [HA]}$

      $= \sqrt{(6.3 \times 10^{-5}) \times (1.60 \times 10^{-4})} = \sqrt{1.0 \times 10^{-8}}$

      $= 1.0 \times 10^{-4}$ mol dm^{-3} *[1 mark]*

    pH = $-\log_{10}[H^+] = -\log_{10} 1.0 \times 10^{-4} = \mathbf{4.00}$ *[1 mark]*

Answers

Page 15 — Experiments Involving pH

1 a) E.g. pH meter / pH probe connected to a data logger *[1 mark]*
  b) Substance A is a acidic, and $[H^+] = 10^{-3.20} = 0.00063$ mol dm^{-3}, which means only a tiny fraction of the molecules in A dissociate *[1 mark]*.
   Substance B is alkali, so $[H^+] = 10^{-13.80} = 1.58... \times 10^{-14}$ mol dm^{-3}.
   Since $K_w = [H^+][OH^-] = 1.0 \times 10^{-14}$,
     $[OH^-] = 1.0 \times 10^{-14} \div 1.58... \times 10^{-14} = 0.63$ mol dm^{-3}.
   This means there's more dissociation in B than in A / a larger number of molecules dissociate in B than in A *[1 mark]*.
   Substance C is slightly acidic, so $[H^+] = 10^{-6.80}$
     $= 1.6 \times 10^{-7}$ mol dm^{-3}.
   This means a tiny fraction of molecules dissociate in C *[1 mark]*.
   So, substance B dissociates the most in solution *[1 mark]*.

2 a) Moles of benzoic acid in solution $= 1.22 \div 122 = 0.0100$ moles
   Concentration of benzoic acid solution $= \dfrac{0.0100 \times 1000}{100}$
     $= 0.100$ mol dm^{-3} *[1 mark]*
   $[H^+] = 10^{-2.60} = 0.00251...$ mol dm^{-3} *[1 mark]*
   Assume that [HA] at equilibrium is 0.100 because only a very small amount of HA will dissociate *[1 mark]*.
   $K_a = \dfrac{[H^+]^2}{[C_6H_5COOH]}$ *[1 mark]* $= \dfrac{(0.00251...)^2}{0.100}$
     $= 6.309... \times 10^{-5} = $ **6.31 $\times 10^{-5}$ mol dm^{-3}** *[1 mark]*
  b) $[H^+] = \sqrt{K_a[C_6H_5COOH]}$ *[1 mark]*
     $= \sqrt{(6.309... \times 10^{-5}) \times 0.0100} = 7.94... \times 10^{-4}$
       $= $ **7.94 $\times 10^{-4}$ mol dm^{-3}** *[1 mark]*
  c) pH $= -\log_{10}[H^+] = -\log(7.94... \times 10^{-4}) = $ **3.1** *[1 mark]*
  d) $[H^+] = \sqrt{(6.309... \times 10^{-5}) \times 1.00} = 0.00794...$ mol dm^{-3} *[1 mark]*
     So pH $= -\log(0.00794...) = $ **2.1** *[1 mark]*
  e) The pH would be $(3.1 + 0.5 =)$ 3.6 *[1 mark]* since, as the solution is diluted by 10, the pH increases by 0.5 *[1 mark]*.

Page 18 — Titration Curves and Indicators

1 Nitric acid:

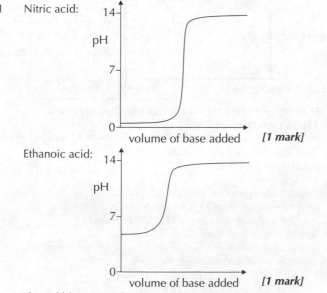

    volume of base added   *[1 mark]*

  Ethanoic acid:

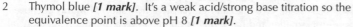

    volume of base added   *[1 mark]*

2 Thymol blue *[1 mark]*. It's a weak acid/strong base titration so the equivalence point is above pH 8 *[1 mark]*.

3 a) 9 (accept values in the range 8 – 10) *[1 mark]*
  b) 15 cm^3 *[1 mark]*
  c) E.g. phenolphthalein *[1 mark]* because the pH range where it changes colour lies entirely on the vertical part of the titration curve *[1 mark]*.
  d)

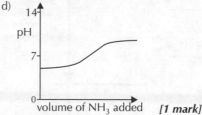

    volume of NH$_3$ added   *[1 mark]*

  e) The change in pH is gradual, so is difficult to see with an indicator *[1 mark]*.
4 a) i) 8 (accept values in the range 7 – 9) *[1 mark]*
    ii) 3.5 (accept values in the range 3.0 – 4.0) *[1 mark]*
  b) $K_a = \dfrac{[H^+][HCOO^-]}{[HCOOH]}$ *[1 mark]*
  c) It is reduced to half its original value, 0.05 mol dm^{-3} *[1 mark]*.
  d) At the half-equivalence point $pK_a = $ pH $= 3.5$ *[1 mark]*
     so $K_a = 10^{-3.5} = $ **3 $\times 10^{-4}$ mol dm^{-3}** *[1 mark — allow marks for correct method with value from 2a)ii) if answer is not 3.5]*

Page 21 — Buffers

1 a) $K_a = \dfrac{[C_6H_5COO^-][H^+]}{[C_6H_5COOH]}$ *[1 mark]*
   $[H^+] = 6.40 \times 10^{-5} \times \dfrac{0.400}{0.200} = 0.000128$ mol dm^{-3} *[1 mark]*
   pH $= -\log_{10}(0.000128) = 3.892... = $ **3.893** *[1 mark]*
  b) The buffer solution contains benzoic acid and benzoate ions in equilibrium: $C_6H_5COOH \rightleftharpoons H^+ + C_6H_5COO^-$ *[1 mark]*.
   Adding H_2SO_4 increases the concentration of H^+ *[1 mark]*.
   The equilibrium shifts left to reduce concentration of H^+, so the pH will only change very slightly *[1 mark]*.
2 a) $CH_3(CH_2)_2COOH \rightleftharpoons H^+ + CH_3(CH_2)_2COO^-$ *[1 mark]*
  b) $[CH_3(CH_2)_2COOH] = [CH_3(CH_2)_2COO^-]$,
   so $[CH_3(CH_2)_2COOH] \div [CH_3(CH_2)_2COO^-] = 1$ and $K_a = [H^+]$.
   pH $= -\log_{10}(1.5 \times 10^{-5})$ *[1 mark]* $= $ **4.8** *[1 mark]*
   If the concentrations of the weak acid and the salt of the weak acid are equal, they cancel from the K_a expression and the buffer pH $= pK_a$.

Topic 13 — Energetics II

Page 23 — Lattice Energy

1 a)

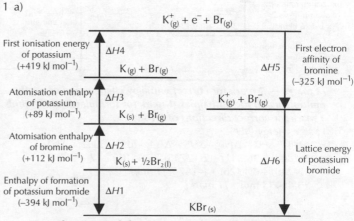

   [3 marks — 1 mark for correct enthalpy changes, 1 mark for formulae/state symbols, 1 mark for correct directions of arrows]
  b) Lattice energy, $\Delta H6 = -\Delta H5 - \Delta H4 - \Delta H3 - \Delta H2 + \Delta H1$
     $= -(-325) - (+419) - (+89) - (+112) + (-394)$ *[1 mark]*
     $= $ **−689 kJ mol^{-1}** *[1 mark]*

Answers

2 a)

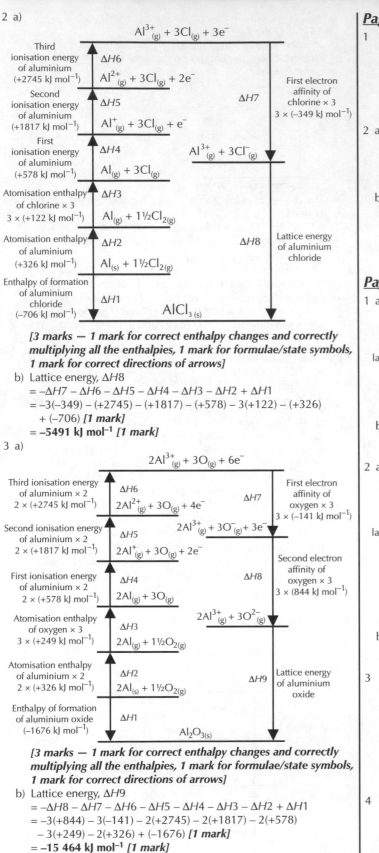

[3 marks — 1 mark for correct enthalpy changes and correctly multiplying all the enthalpies, 1 mark for formulae/state symbols, 1 mark for correct directions of arrows]

b) Lattice energy, $\Delta H8$
$= -\Delta H7 - \Delta H6 - \Delta H5 - \Delta H4 - \Delta H3 - \Delta H2 + \Delta H1$
$= -3(-349) - (+2745) - (+1817) - (+578) - 3(+122) - (+326)$
$\quad + (-706)$ **[1 mark]**
$= \mathbf{-5491\ kJ\ mol^{-1}}$ **[1 mark]**

3 a)

The Born-Haber cycle for $Al_2O_{3(s)}$:
$2Al^{3+}_{(g)} + 3O_{(g)} + 6e^-$

Third ionisation energy of aluminium × 2, $2 \times (+2745\ kJ\ mol^{-1})$ — $\Delta H6$
$2Al^{2+}_{(g)} + 3O_{(g)} + 4e^-$
First electron affinity of oxygen × 3, $3 \times (-141\ kJ\ mol^{-1})$ — $\Delta H7$
$2Al^{3+}_{(g)} + 3O^-_{(g)} + 3e^-$

Second ionisation energy of aluminium × 2, $2 \times (+1817\ kJ\ mol^{-1})$ — $\Delta H5$
$2Al^+_{(g)} + 3O_{(g)} + 2e^-$
Second electron affinity of oxygen × 3, $3 \times (844\ kJ\ mol^{-1})$ — $\Delta H8$
$2Al^{3+}_{(g)} + 3O^{2-}_{(g)}$

First ionisation energy of aluminium × 2, $2 \times (+578\ kJ\ mol^{-1})$ — $\Delta H4$
$2Al_{(g)} + 3O_{(g)}$

Atomisation enthalpy of oxygen × 3, $3 \times (+249\ kJ\ mol^{-1})$ — $\Delta H3$
$2Al_{(g)} + 1\frac{1}{2}O_{2(g)}$

Atomisation enthalpy of aluminium × 2, $2 \times (+326\ kJ\ mol^{-1})$ — $\Delta H2$
$2Al_{(s)} + 1\frac{1}{2}O_{2(g)}$
Lattice energy of aluminium oxide — $\Delta H9$

Enthalpy of formation of aluminium oxide $(-1676\ kJ\ mol^{-1})$ — $\Delta H1$
$Al_2O_{3(s)}$

[3 marks — 1 mark for correct enthalpy changes and correctly multiplying all the enthalpies, 1 mark for formulae/state symbols, 1 mark for correct directions of arrows]

b) Lattice energy, $\Delta H9$
$= -\Delta H8 - \Delta H7 - \Delta H6 - \Delta H5 - \Delta H4 - \Delta H3 - \Delta H2 + \Delta H1$
$= -3(+844) - 3(-141) - 2(+2745) - 2(+1817) - 2(+578)$
$\quad - 3(+249) - 2(+326) + (-1676)$ **[1 mark]**
$= \mathbf{-15\ 464\ kJ\ mol^{-1}}$ **[1 mark]**

Page 25 — Polarisation

1 Al^{3+} has a high charge/volume ratio (or a small radius AND a large positive charge) **[1 mark]**, so it has a high polarising ability **[1 mark]** and can pull electron density away from Cl^- **[1 mark]** to create a bond with mostly covalent characteristics **[1 mark]**. (Alternatively Cl^- is relatively large **[1 mark]** and easily polarised **[1 mark]** so its electrons can be pulled away from Cl^- **[1 mark]** to create a bond with mostly covalent characteristics **[1 mark]**.)

2 a) Increasing covalent character: $NaBr$, $MgBr_2$, MgI_2 **[1 mark]**. Covalent character is greatest when cations are small and have large charge, which applies more to Mg^{2+} than to Na^+ **[1 mark]**, and when anions are large, which applies more to I^- than to Br^- **[1 mark]**.

b) Experimental and theoretical lattice energies match well when a compound has a high degree of ionic character **[1 mark]**. NaI has a higher degree of ionic character than MgI_2 because Na^+ has a smaller charge density / smaller charge and isn't much smaller than Mg^{2+} **[1 mark]**.

Page 27 — Dissolving

1 a)

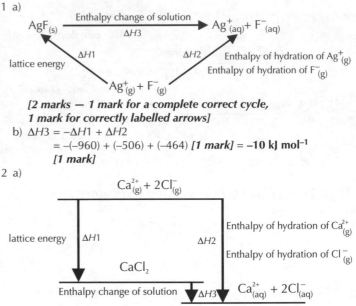

[2 marks — 1 mark for a complete correct cycle, 1 mark for correctly labelled arrows]

b) $\Delta H3 = -\Delta H1 + \Delta H2$
$= -(-960) + (-506) + (-464)$ **[1 mark]** $= \mathbf{-10\ kJ\ mol^{-1}}$
[1 mark]

2 a)

$Ca^{2+}_{(g)} + 2Cl^-_{(g)}$
lattice energy — $\Delta H1$
Enthalpy of hydration of $Ca^{2+}_{(g)}$
Enthalpy of hydration of $Cl^-_{(g)}$ — $\Delta H2$
$CaCl_2$
Enthalpy change of solution — $\Delta H3$ $Ca^{2+}_{(aq)} + 2Cl^-_{(aq)}$

[2 marks — 1 mark for complete, correct energy levels, 1 mark correctly labelled arrows]

b) $-(-2258) + (-1579) + (2 \times -364)$ **[1 mark]** $= \mathbf{-49\ kJ\ mol^{-1}}$ **[1 mark]**
Don't forget — you have to double the enthalpy of hydration for Cl^- because there are two Cl^- ions in $CaCl_2$.

3 By Hess's law:
Enthalpy change of solution $(MgCl_{2(s)})$
$= -$lattice energy $(MgCl_{2(s)})$ + enthalpy of hydration $(Mg^{2+}_{(g)})$
$\quad + [2 \times$ enthalpy of hydration $(Cl^-_{(g)})]$ **[1 mark]**
So enthalpy of hydration $(Cl^-_{(g)})$
$= [$enthalpy change of solution $(MgCl_{2(s)})$ + lattice energy $(MgCl_{2(s)})$
$\quad -$ enthalpy of hydration $(Mg^{2+}_{(g)})] \div 2$
$= [(-122) + (-2526) - (-1920)] \div 2$ **[1 mark]**
$= -728 \div 2 = \mathbf{-364\ kJ\ mol^{-1}}$ **[1 mark]**

4 Ca^{2+} will have a greater enthalpy of hydration **[1 mark]** because it is smaller and has a higher charge / has a higher charge density than K^+ **[1 mark]**. This means there is a stronger attraction between Ca^{2+} and the water molecules, so more energy is released when bonds are formed between them **[1 mark]**.

Page 29 — Entropy

1 a) The reaction is not likely to be feasible **[1 mark]** because there are fewer moles of product than moles of reactants / there's a gas in the reactants and only a solid product, and therefore a decrease in entropy **[1 mark]**.
Remember — more particles means more entropy. There's 1½ moles of reactants and only 1 mole of product.

Answers

b) $\Delta S = 26.9 - [32.7 + (\frac{1}{2} \times 205)]$ *[1 mark]*
   = **−108 J K⁻¹ mol⁻¹** *[1 mark]*

c) The reaction is not likely to be feasible because ΔS is negative/there is a decrease in entropy *[1 mark]*.

2 a) $\Delta S = 48 - 70 = $ **−22 J K⁻¹ mol⁻¹** *[1 mark]*

   b) Despite the negative entropy change, the reaction might still be feasible because other factors such as enthalpy, temperature and kinetics also play a part in whether or not a reaction occurs *[1 mark]*.

Page 31 — More on Entropy Change

1 a) You would expect an increase in the entropy of the system *[1 mark]* because a solid is combining with a substance in solution to produce another solution, a liquid and a gas — this leads to an increase in disorder *[1 mark]*. There is also an increase in the number of molecules which will also lead to an increase in disorder *[1 mark]*.

   b) The reaction is endothermic, so the entropy change of the surroundings will be negative *[1 mark]*. However, if the entropy change of the system has a large enough positive value then this will override the negative entropy change of the surroundings and result in an overall positive entropy change *[1 mark]*.

2 a) $\Delta S_{system} = S_{products} - S_{reactants}$ *[1 mark]*
   $= (2 \times 26.9) - ((2 \times 32.7) + 205) = 53.8 - 270.4$ *[1 mark]*
   = **−217 J K⁻¹ mol⁻¹** (3 s.f.) *[1 mark, include units]*

   b) $\Delta S_{surroundings} = -\Delta H / T = -(-1\,204\,000 \div 298)$ *[1 mark]*
   = **+4040 J K⁻¹ mol⁻¹** (3 s.f.) *[1 mark]*
   $\Delta S_{total} = \Delta S_{system} + \Delta S_{surroundings} = (-216.6) + 4040.3$ *[1 mark]*
   = **+3824 J K⁻¹ mol⁻¹** (3 s.f.) *[1 mark]*

Page 33 — Free Energy

1 a) $\Delta S = [214 + (2 \times 69.9)] - [186 + (2 \times 205)]$
   $= -242.2$ J K⁻¹ mol⁻¹ *[1 mark]*
   $\Delta G = -730\,000 - (298 \times -242.2)$
   $\approx$ **−658 000 J mol⁻¹** (3 s.f.) (= **−658 kJ mol⁻¹**) *[1 mark]*

   b) The reaction is feasible at 298 K because ΔG is negative *[1 mark]*.

   c) $T = \dfrac{\Delta H}{\Delta S} = -730\,000 \div -242.2 = $ **3010 K** (3 s.f.) *[1 mark]*

2 a) $\Delta G = -[8.31 \times 723] \times \ln (60)$
   $= $ **−24600 J mol⁻¹** (3 s.f.) (= **−246 kJ mol⁻¹**) *[1 mark]*

   b) As $\Delta G = \Delta H - T\Delta S$ *[1 mark]* and the change in entropy for the reaction is negative, an increase in temperature will result in a less negative value for the free energy change of reaction *[1 mark]*.

Topic 14 — Redox II

Page 35 — Electrochemical Cells

1 a) Get a strip each of zinc and iron metal. Clean the surfaces of the metals using a piece of emery paper (or sandpaper). Clean any grease or oil from the electrodes using some propanone *[1 mark]*. Place each electrode into a beaker filled with a solution containing ions of that metal (e.g. $ZnSO_{4(aq)}$ and $FeSO_{4(aq)}$) *[1 mark]*. Create a salt bridge to link the two solutions together by soaking a piece of filter paper in salt solution, e.g. $KCl_{(aq)}$ or $KNO_{3(aq)}$, and draping it between the two beakers. The ends of the filter paper should be immersed in the solutions *[1 mark]*. Connect the electrodes to a voltmeter, using crocodile clips and wires *[1 mark]*.

b)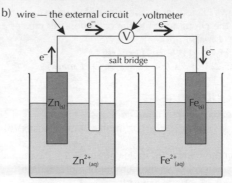

[4 marks — 1 mark for complete circuit of wires and salt bridge, 1 mark for zinc electrode drawn on the left, 1 mark for a correct aqueous solution of ions in each half-cell, 1 mark for correct direction of electron flow]

2 a) The salt bridge completes the circuit *[1 mark]* and allows the salt ions to flow between the half-cells to balance the charges *[1 mark]*.

   b) E.g. Soak a piece of filter paper in a salt solution, e.g. $KNO_{3(aq)}$ *[1 mark]*.

   c) silver *[1 mark]*

Page 37 — Electrode Potentials

1 a) Iron *[1 mark]* as it has a more negative electrode potential/it loses electrons more easily than lead *[1 mark]*.

   b) Standard cell potential = $-0.13 - (-0.44) = $ **+0.31 V** *[1 mark]*

2 a) $+0.80$ V $- (-0.76$ V$) = $ **+1.56 V** *[1 mark]*

   b) The concentration of Zn^{2+} ions or Ag^+ ions was not 1.00 mol dm⁻³ *[1 mark]*. The pressure wasn't 100 kPa *[1 mark]*.

Page 39 — The Electrochemical Series

1 a) $Zn_{(s)} + Ni^{2+}_{(aq)} \rightleftharpoons Zn^{2+}_{(aq)} + Ni_{(s)}$ *[1 mark]*
   $E^{\ominus} = (-0.25) - (-0.76) = $ **+0.51 V** *[1 mark]*

   b) $2MnO_4^{-}_{(aq)} + 16H^+_{(aq)} + 5Sn^{2+}_{(aq)} \rightleftharpoons$
   $2Mn^{2+}_{(aq)} + 8H_2O_{(l)} + 5Sn^{4+}_{(aq)}$ *[1 mark]*
   $E^{\ominus} = (+1.51) - (+0.14) = $ **+1.37 V** *[1 mark]*

   c) No reaction *[1 mark]*. Both reactants are in their oxidised form *[1 mark]*.

2 $KMnO_4$ *[1 mark]* because it has a more positive/less negative electrode potential *[1 mark]*.

3 a) $Cu^{2+}_{(aq)} + Ni_{(s)} \rightleftharpoons Cu_{(s)} + Ni^{2+}_{(aq)}$ *[1 mark]*

   b) If the copper solution was more dilute, the $E^{\ominus}$ of the copper half-cell would be lower (the equilibrium would shift to the left/ the copper would lose electrons more easily), so the overall cell potential would be lower *[1 mark]*.

Page 41 — Storage and Fuel Cells

1 a) i) and ii)

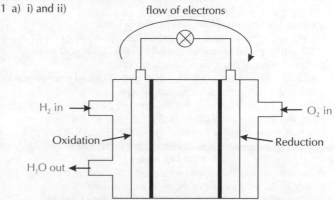

[2 marks — 1 mark for labelling the sites of reduction and oxidation correctly, 1 mark for drawing the arrow showing the direction of electron flow correctly]

b) Negative electrode: $H_{2(g)} + 4OH^-_{(aq)} \rightarrow 4H_2O_{(l)} + 4e^-$ *[1 mark]*
   Positive electrode: $O_{2(g)} + 2H_2O_{(l)} + 4e^- \rightarrow 4OH^-_{(aq)}$ *[1 mark]*

c) It only allows the OH^- across and not O_2 and H_2 gases *[1 mark]*.

Answers

2 a) The PEM only allows H^+ ions across it *[1 mark]*, forcing the electrons around the circuit to get to the cathode. This creates an electrical current *[1 mark]*.
  b) Anode reaction: $H_2 \rightarrow 2H^+ + 2e^-$ *[1 mark]*
     Cathode reaction: $2H^+ + \frac{1}{2}O_2 + 2e^- \rightarrow H_2O$ *[1 mark]*

Page 44 — Redox Titrations

1 a) 15.0 cm³ of manganate(VII) solution contains:
     $(15.0 \times 0.00900) \div 1000 = 1.35 \times 10^{-4}$ moles of manganate(VII) ions *[1 mark]*
     From the equation the number of moles of iron = 5 × the number of moles of manganate(VII). So the number of moles of iron =
     $5 \times 1.35 \times 10^{-4} = \mathbf{6.75 \times 10^{-4}}$ *[1 mark]*
  b) In the tablet there will be $250 \div 25.0 = 10$ times this amount
     $= \mathbf{6.75 \times 10^{-3}}$ **moles** *[1 mark]*
  c) 1 mole of iron has a mass of 55.8 g, so the tablet contains:
     $6.75 \times 10^{-3} \times 55.8 = 0.37665$ g of iron *[1 mark]*
     The percentage of iron in the tablet = $(0.37665 \div 3.20) \times 100$
     $= \mathbf{11.8\%}$ *[1 mark]*

2 a) A redox reaction *[1 mark]*.
  b) Number of moles = (concentration × volume) ÷ 1000
     $= (0.500 \times 10.0) \div 1000$ *[1 mark]* $= \mathbf{0.00500}$ **moles** *[1 mark]*
  c) Number of moles = (concentration × volume) ÷ 1000
     $= (0.100 \times 20.0) \div 1000$ *[1 mark]* $= \mathbf{0.00200}$ **moles** *[1 mark]*
  d) 1 mole of MnO_4^- ions needs 5 moles of electrons to be reduced. So to reduce 0.00200 moles of MnO_4^-, you need $(0.00200 \times 5) = 0.0100$ moles of electrons *[1 mark]*.
     The 0.00500 moles of tin ions must have lost 0.0100 moles of electrons as they were oxidised OR all of these electrons must have come from the tin ions *[1 mark]*. Each tin ion changed its oxidation number by $0.01 \div 0.005 = 2$ *[1 mark]*. So, the oxidation number of the oxidised tin ions is $(+2) + 2 = \mathbf{+4}$ *[1 mark]*.

Page 47 — More on Redox Titrations

1 a) $IO_3^- + 5I^- + 6H^+ \rightarrow 3I_2 + 3H_2O$ *[1 mark]*
  b) Number of moles = (concentration × volume) ÷ 1000
     Number of moles of thiosulfate = $(0.150 \times 24.0) \div 1000$
     $= \mathbf{3.60 \times 10^{-3}}$ *[1 mark]*
  c) 2 moles of thiosulfate react with 1 mole of iodine, so there were $(3.60 \times 10^{-3}) \div 2 = \mathbf{1.80 \times 10^{-3}}$ moles of iodine *[1 mark]*
  d) 1/3 mole *[1 mark]*
  e) There must be $1.80 \times 10^{-3} \div 3 = \mathbf{6.00 \times 10^{-4}}$ **moles** of iodate(V) in the solution *[1 mark]*. So concentration of potassium iodate(V)
     $= (6.00 \times 10^{-4}) \div (10.0 \div 1000) = \mathbf{0.0600}$ **mol dm⁻³** *[1 mark]*

2 Number of moles = (concentration × volume) ÷ 1000
     Number of moles of thiosulfate = $(0.300 \times 12.5) \div 1000$
     $= 3.75 \times 10^{-3}$ *[1 mark]*
     2 moles of thiosulfate react with 1 mole of iodine.
     So there must have been $(3.75 \times 10^{-3}) \div 2 = 1.875 \times 10^{-3}$ moles of iodine produced *[1 mark]*
     2 moles of manganate(VII) ions produce 5 moles of iodine molecules, so there must have been $(1.875 \times 10^{-3}) \times (2 \div 5) = 7.50 \times 10^{-4}$ moles of manganate(VII) in the solution *[1 mark]*
     Concentration of potassium manganate(VII)
     $= (7.50 \times 10^{-4}$ moles$) \div (18.0 \div 1000) = \mathbf{0.0417}$ **mol dm⁻³** *[1 mark]*

3 a) The number of moles of thiosulfate used =
     $(19.3 \times 0.150) \div 1000 = 0.002895$ moles *[1 mark]*
     From the iodine-thiosulfate equation, the number of moles of I_2 = half the number of moles of thiosulfate, so in this case the number of moles of $I_2 = 0.002895 \div 2 = 0.0014475$
     $= \mathbf{0.00145}$ **moles** *[1 mark]*
  b) From the equation, 2 copper ions produce 1 iodine molecule *[1 mark]*, so the number of moles of copper ions
     $= 0.0014475 \times 2 = 0.002895 = \mathbf{0.00290}$ **moles** *[1 mark]*
  c) In 250 cm³ of the copper solution there are:
     $(250 \div 25.0) \times 0.002895 = 0.02895$ moles of copper *[1 mark]*
     1 mole of copper has a mass of 63.5 g, so in the alloy there are:
     $0.02895 \times 63.5 = 1.8383...$ g of copper *[1 mark]*
     % of copper in alloy = $(1.8383... \div 4.20) \times 100 = \mathbf{43.8\%}$ *[1 mark]*

Topic 15 — Transition Metals

Page 49 — Transition Metals

1 Manganese has the electronic configuration [Ar] $4s^2 3d^5$ so its outer electrons are in the 4s and 3d subshells. These subshells are very close in energy *[1 mark]*, so there is no great difference between removing electrons from the 4s subshell (e.g. to make Mn^{2+}) or from the 3d subshell (e.g. to make MnO_4^-) *[1 mark]*. The energy released when manganese forms compounds or complexes containing manganese in variable oxidation numbers is greater than the energy required to remove these outer electrons *[1 mark]*, (so manganese can exist with variable oxidation numbers).

2 a) Iron: $1s^2 2s^2 2p^6 3s^2 3p^6 3d^6 4s^2$ OR [Ar] $3d^6 4s^2$ *[1 mark]*
     Copper: $1s^2 2s^2 2p^6 3s^2 3p^6 3d^{10} 4s^1$ OR [Ar] $3d^{10} 4s^1$ *[1 mark]*
  b) Copper has only one 4s electron *[1 mark]* because it is more stable with a full 3d subshell *[1 mark]*.
  c) Iron loses the 4s electrons to form Fe^{2+} *[1 mark]*.
     It loses the 4s electrons and an electron from the 3d orbital containing 2 electrons to form Fe^{3+} *[1 mark]*.

Page 51 — Complex Ions

1 a) Coordination number: 6 *[1 mark]*
     Shape: octahedral *[1 mark]*
  b) Coordination number: 4 *[1 mark]*
     Shape: tetrahedral *[1 mark]*
     Bond angles: 109.5° *[1 mark]*
     Formula: $[CuCl_4]^{2-}$ *[1 mark]*
  c) Cl^- ligands are larger than water ligands *[1 mark]*, so only 4 Cl^- ligands can fit around the Cu^{2+} ion *[1 mark]*.

Page 53 — Complex Ions and Colour

1 a) i) [Ar] $3d^{10}$ *[1 mark]*
     ii) [Ar] $3d^9$ *[1 mark]*
  b) Cu^{2+} because it has an incomplete d-subshell *[1 mark]*.

2 ***A maximum of two marks can be awarded for structure and reasoning of the written response:***
     2 marks: The answer is constructed logically, and displays clear reasoning and links between points throughout.
     1 mark: The answer is mostly logical, with some reasoning and links between points.
     0 marks: The answer has no structure and no links between points.
     Here are some points your answer may include:
     Normally, all the 3d orbitals have the same energy. When ligands form dative covalent bonds with a metal ion, the 3d electron orbitals split in energy. Electrons tend to occupy the lower orbitals and energy is required to move an electron from an lower 3d orbital to a higher one. The energy needed to make an electron jump from the lower 3d orbital to the higher 3d orbital is equal to a certain frequency of light. This frequency gets absorbed. All the other frequencies are transmitted and it is these frequencies that give the transition metal colour.
     [4 marks — 4 marks if 6 points mentioned covering all areas of the question, 3 marks if 4-5 points covered, 2 marks if 2-3 points covered, 1 mark if 1 point covered]

Page 55 — Chromium

1 a) The solution changes from orange to green *[1 mark]*.
  b) Cr is reduced from +6 to +3 *[1 mark]*.
     Zn is oxidised from 0 to +2 *[1 mark]*.
     $Cr_2O_7^{2-} + 14H^+ + 3Zn \rightarrow 2Cr^{3+} + 7H_2O + 3Zn^{2+}$ *[1 mark]*
  c) The solution turns blue *[1 mark]* because the Cr^{3+} is reduced further to Cr^{2+} *[1 mark]*. It is not oxidised back to Cr^{3+} because it is in an inert atmosphere *[1 mark]*.

Answers

2 a) Amphoteric means something can react with both an acid and a base *[1 mark]*.
   In acid: $[Cr(OH)_3(H_2O)_3]_{(s)} + 3H^+_{(aq)} \rightarrow [Cr(H_2O)_6]^{3+}_{(aq)}$ *[1 mark]*
   In base: $[Cr(OH)_3(H_2O)_3]_{(s)} + 3OH^-_{(aq)} \rightarrow$
   $[Cr(OH)_6]^{3-}_{(aq)} + 3H_2O_{(l)}$ *[1 mark]*
 b) $[Cr(OH)_3(H_2O)_3]_{(s)} + 6NH_{3(aq)} \rightarrow$
   $[Cr(NH_3)_6]^{3+}_{(aq)} + 3OH^-_{(aq)} + 3H_2O_{(l)}$ *[1 mark]*
   The grey-green precipitate would dissolve to form a purple solution *[1 mark]*.

Page 57 — Reactions of Ligands

1 a) $[Fe(H_2O)_6]^{3+} + EDTA^{4-} \rightarrow [FeEDTA]^- + 6H_2O$ *[1 mark]*
 b) The formation of $[FeEDTA]^-$ results in an increase in entropy, because the number of particles increases from two to seven *[1 mark]*.
2 a) $[Co(H_2O)_6]^{2+}_{(aq)}$ *[1 mark]*
 b) $[Co(H_2O)_6]^{2+}_{(aq)} + 2NH_{3(aq)} \rightarrow$
   $[Co(OH)_2(H_2O)_4]_{(s)} + 2NH_4^+_{(aq)}$ *[1 mark]*
   This is an acid-base reaction *[1 mark]*.
   $[Co(OH)_2(H_2O)_4]_{(s)} + 6NH_{3(aq)} \rightarrow$
   $[Co(NH_3)_6]^{2+}_{(aq)} + 2OH^-_{(aq)} 4H_2O_{(l)}$ *[1 mark]*
   This is a ligand exchange reaction *[1 mark]*.

Page 59 — Transition Metals and Catalysts

1 a) Heterogeneous means 'in a different phase from the reactants'. Homogeneous means 'in the same phase as the reactants' *[1 mark]*.
 b) The orbitals allow reactant molecules to make weak bonds to the catalyst *[1 mark]*.
 c) By changing oxidation state easily, transition metals can take in or give out electrons *[1 mark]* and so they can help transfer electrons from one reactant to another *[1 mark]*.
   You could also give an answer that describes a catalyst in terms of helping to oxidise and reduce.
2   The overall equation for the reaction is:
   $2MnO_4^-_{(aq)} + 16H^+_{(aq)} + 5C_2O_4^{2-}_{(aq)} \rightarrow$
   $2Mn^{2+}_{(aq)} + 8H_2O_{(l)} + 10CO_{2(g)}$ *[1 mark]*
   This is slow to begin with, because the MnO_4^- and $C_2O_4^{2-}$ ions are both negatively charged, so repel each other and don't collide very frequently *[1 mark]*. The Mn^{2+} product, however, is able to catalyse the reaction. It reduces MnO_4^- to Mn^{3+}:
   $MnO_4^-_{(aq)} + 4Mn^{2+}_{(aq)} + 8H^+_{(aq)} \rightarrow 5Mn^{3+}_{(aq)} + 4H_2O_{(l)}$ *[1 mark]*.
   The Mn^{3+} ions are reduced back to Mn^{2+} by reaction with $C_2O_4^{2-}$:
   $2Mn^{3+}_{(aq)} + C_2O_4^{2-}_{(aq)} \rightarrow 2Mn^{2+}_{(aq)} + 2CO_{2(g)}$ *[1 mark]*.
   This means the reaction is an autocatalysis reaction. As more Mn^{2+} is produced, there is more catalyst available and so the reaction rate will increase *[1 mark]*.
3 a) When molecules stick to the surface of a solid *[1 mark]*.
 b) The surface of the catalyst activates the molecules, weakening the bonds between the atoms in the reactants *[1 mark]*, making them easier to break and reform as the products *[1 mark]*.

Topic 16 — Kinetics II

Page 61 — Reaction Rates

1 a) E.g there is an increase in number of ions so follow the reaction by measuring electrical conductivity *[1 mark]*.
 b) Plot a graph of concentration of propanone against time *[1 mark]* and find out the rate at any time by working out the gradient of the graph at that time *[1 mark]*.

c)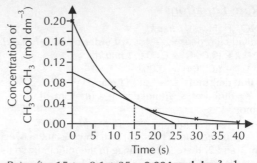
Rate after 15 s = 0.1 ÷ 25 = **0.004 mol dm^{-3} s^{-1}**
[3 marks — 1 mark for labelled axes the correct way round, 1 mark for points plotted accurately, smooth best-fit curve and a tangent drawn at 15 s, 1 mark for rate within range 0.004 ±0.001 and correct units]

Page 63 — Orders of Reactions

1 a)
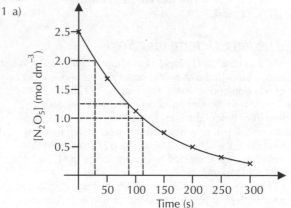
[2 marks — 1 mark for $[N_2O_5]$ on y-axis, time on x-axis, and points plotted accurately, 1 mark for a smooth best-fit curve]
 b) i) Time value = 85 s *[1 mark, allow 85 ±2]*
   (Horizontal line from 1.25 on *y*-axis to curve and vertical line from curve to *x*-axis.)
   ii) Time value difference = 113 (±2) – 28 (±2) = **85 s** *[1 mark, allow 85 ±4]*
   (Vertical lines from curve at 2.0 mol dm^{-3} and 1.0 mol dm^{-3}.)
 c) Half life for 0.625 mol dm^{-1} from 1.25 mol dm^{-1}= 170 – 85 = 85 s
   Half life for 1.25 mol dm^{-1} from 2.5 mol dm^{-1} = 85 – 0 = 85 s
   So, the half lives remain constant and are independent of concentration so the order of reaction is 1 *[1 mark]*.
2 a) The reaction rate would double *[1 mark]*.
 b) The overall order is 3 *[1 mark]*.

Page 65 — The Initial Rates Method

1 a) All the sodium thiosulfate that has been added has been used up so any more iodine that is formed will stay in solution turning the starch indicator blue-black *[1 mark]*
 b) The time it would take for the colour change to occur would increase as there would be a greater amount of thiosulfate instantaneously removing iodine from solution meaning it would take longer for it to be used up *[1 mark]*.
2   Take samples of the reaction mixture at regular intervals and stop the reaction using sodium hydrogen carbonate *[1 mark]*. Titrate the samples against sodium thiosulfate, using starch as the indicator, to calculate the concentration of iodine *[1 mark]*. Repeat the experiment several times changing the concentration of the iodine *[1 mark]*.

Answers

Page 67— Rate Equations

1 a) Rate = $k[NO_{(g)}]^2 [H_{2(g)}]$ *[1 mark]*
Sum of individual orders = 2 + 1 = **3rd order overall** *[1 mark]*.
   b) i) $0.0027 = k \times (0.004)^2 \times 0.002$ *[1 mark]*
$k = 0.0027 \div ((0.004)^2 \times 0.002)$
$k = $ **84 000 dm^6 mol^{-2} s^{-1}** (2 s.f.) *[1 mark]*
(Units: $k = $ mol dm^{-3} s^{-1}/[(mol dm^{-3})$^2 \times$ (mol dm^{-3})]
$= $ dm^6 mol^{-2} s^{-1})
   ii) The rate constant would decrease *[1 mark]*.
2 a) When [X] is doubled and [Y] and [Z] remain constant between
experiment 1 and 2, there is no change in the initial rate so the
rate is zero order with respect to [X] *[1 mark]*.
When [Y] is doubled and [X] and [Z] remain constant between
experiment 1 and 3, the initial rate quadruples so the rate is
second order with respect to [Y] *[1 mark]*.
When [Z] is doubled and [X] and [Y] remain constant between
experiment 3 and 4, the initial rate doubles so the rate is first
order with respect to [Z] *[1 mark]*.
   b) $1.30 \times 10^{-3} \times 3 = $ **3.90×10^{-3} mol dm^{-3} s^{-1}** *[1 mark]*
   c) rate = $k[Z][Y]^2$ *[1 mark]*

Page 69— The Rate-Determining Step

1   H$^+$ is acting as a catalyst *[1 mark]*. You know this because it is not
one of the reactants in the chemical equation, but it does affect
the rate of reaction/appear in the rate equation *[1 mark]*.
2 a) If the molecule is in the rate equation, it must be involved in
the reaction in or before the rate-determining step. The orders
of the reaction tell you how many molecules of each reactant
are involved up to the rate-determining step *[1 mark]*. So the
rate-determining step is affected by one molecule of H$_2$ and one
molecule of ICl *[1 mark]*.
   b) Incorrect *[1 mark]*. H$_2$ and ICl are both in the rate equation,
so they must both be involved in the reaction in or before the
rate-determining step. / The order of the reaction with respect
to ICl is 1, so there must be only one molecule of ICl in the
rate-determining step *[1 mark]*.

Page 71 — Halogenoalkanes and Reaction Mechanisms

1   D *[1 mark]*
1-chloropropane is a primary halogenoalkane, which means it will react
using an S$_N$2 mechanism. So both 1-chloropropane and sodium hydroxide
must be in the rate equation, as the rate will depend on the concentration
of both them.
2 a) 1-iodobutane is a primary iodoalkane *[1 mark]*.
   b) Rate = $k[CH_3CH_2CH_2CH_2I] [OH^-]$ *[1 mark]*
   c) Mechanism is S$_N$2 *[1 mark]*
   d)
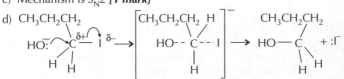
   **[3 marks — 1 mark for each curly arrow, 1 mark for correct
   transition molecule]**
3 a) Rate = $k[CH_3CBr(CH_3)C_3H_7]$
   b) Step 1—
   Rate determining step
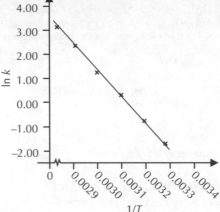
   Step 2
   **[3 marks — 1 mark for each correct step in the mechanism,
   1 mark for correct identification of rate determining step]**

Page 73 — Activation Energy

1 a)

T (K)	k	$1/T$ (K^{-1})	ln k
305	0.181	0.00328	-1.709
313	0.468	**0.00319**	**-0.759**
323	1.34	**0.00310**	**0.293**
333	3.29	0.00300	1.191
344	10.1	**0.00291**	**2.313**
353	22.7	**0.00283**	**3.127**

[2 marks — 1 mark for all 1/T values, 1 mark for all ln k values]

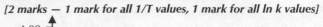

*[2 marks — 1 mark for at least 5 accurate points, 1 mark for line
of best fit]*
   b) Value = −10750 ±250 *[1 mark]*
   c) $−E_a/R = −10750$ *[1 mark]*
$E_a = 10750 \times 8.31 = $ **89 300 J mol^{-1}** OR **89.3 kJ mol^{-1}** *[1 mark]*
2   Homogeneous catalysts are in the same state as the reactants,
homogeneous however, are in a different physical state than the
reactants *[1 mark]*.

Topic 17 — Organic Chemistry II

Page 75 — Optical Isomerism

1 a)
[1 mark]
It doesn't really matter how you mark the chiral centre, as long as
you've made it clear which carbon you've marked.
   b) Since the butan-2-ol solution is a racemic mixture, it must contain
equal amounts of both optical isomers. The two optical isomers
will exactly cancel out each other's light-rotating effect *[1 mark]*.
   c) The reaction has proceeded via an S$_N$1 mechanism *[1 mark]*.
You know this because the original solution contained a single
optical isomer, but the product is a racemic mixture *[1 mark]*.

Page 77 — Aldehydes and Ketones

1 a) C *[1 mark]*
   b) B and C *[1 mark]*
   c) Compound B is a ketone and is therefore not oxidised by acidified
dichromate(VI) ions and no colour change occurs *[1 mark]*.

Page 79 — Reactions of Aldehydes and Ketones

1 a) E.g.
[1 mark]
The reaction with 2,4-DNPH tells you that the molecule contains
a carbonyl group *[1 mark]*. The reduction to a secondary alcohol
tells you it must be a ketone *[1 mark]*. The result of the reaction
with iodine tells you that the molecule contains a methyl carbonyl
group *[1 mark]*.

Answers

b) You can measure the melting point of the precipitate formed with 2,4-DNPH *[1 mark]*. Each carbonyl compound gives a precipitate with a specific melting point which can be looked up in tables *[1 mark]*.

c) E.g.

H H H H H OH H
H−C−C−C−C−C−C−C−H
H H H H H H H   *[1 mark]*

2 a) Nucleophilic addition *[1 mark]*

b) i)

OH
$H_3C−C−CH_3$
C≡N *[1 mark]*

ii)

$H_3C−C^{\delta+}$ ⟶ $H_3C−C−CH_3$ ⟶ $H_3C−C−CH_3$
(with O:, H⁺, CH₃, :CN⁻, C≡N labels)

[4 marks — 1 mark for correct structures, 1 mark for each correct curly arrow]

c) Depending on which side the CN⁻ attacks from, one of two optical isomers is formed *[1 mark]*. Because the groups around the C=O bond are planar, there is an equal chance that the CN⁻ will attack from either direction *[1 mark]*, meaning an equal amount of each optical isomer, i.e. a racemic mixture, will form *[1 mark]*.

Page 81 — Carboxylic Acids

1 a) Reflux *[1 mark]* propan-1-ol with acidified potassium dichromate(VI) *[1 mark]*.

b) Add a carbonate/hydrogencarbonate *[1 mark]*. Propan-1-ol will show no reaction, but propanoic acid will produce bubbles of carbon dioxide *[1 mark]*.

2 a)

H H H H   O
H−C−C−C−C−C   C
H H H H OH *[1 mark]*   H OH *[1 mark]*

b) Pentanoic acid has a longer carbon chain than methanoic acid *[1 mark]*. This means the chain is more likely to get in the way of the hydrogen bonds forming between pentanoic acid and water. The energy released from formation of the water–acid hydrogen bonds for pentanoic acid is less than that for methanoic acid . This leads to less energy to compensate for the breaking of water–water hydrogen bonds and therefore a reduction in solubility *[1 mark]*.

c) $C_7H_{14}O_2 + PCl_5 \rightarrow C_7H_{14}OCl + POCl_3 + HCl$ *[1 mark]*

Page 83 — Esters

1 a) 2-methylpropyl ethanoate *[1 mark]*

b)

H   O
H−C−C
H   OH *[1 mark]* Ethanoic acid *[1 mark]*

H H H
HO−C−C−C−H
H CH₃ H *[1 mark]* 2-methylpropan-1-ol *[1 mark]*

This is an acid hydrolysis reaction *[1 mark]*.

2 a)

O   H
H−C
O−C−CH₃
CH₃ *[1 mark]*

b) $HCOOH + CH_3CH(CH_3)OH \underset{H^+}{\rightleftharpoons} HCOOCH(CH_3)_2 + H_2O$
[1 mark for correct reactants, 1 mark for correct products, 1 mark for reversible reaction]

c) An esterification reaction *[1 mark]*.

Page 84 — Acyl Chlorides

1 a)

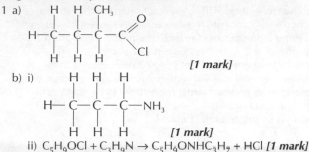

H H CH₃   O
H−C−C−C−C
H H H   Cl   *[1 mark]*

b) i)

H H H
H−C−C−C−NH₃
H H H   *[1 mark]*

ii) $C_5H_9OCl + C_3H_9N \rightarrow C_5H_9ONHC_3H_7 + HCl$ *[1 mark]*

Topic 18 — Organic Chemistry III

Page 87 — Aromatic Compounds

1 a) i) 2 moles *[1 mark]*
   ii) $2 \times 120 = $ **240 kJ** *[1 mark]*

b) You would expect 3 moles of H_2 to react with a molecule with the Kekulé structure. Each mole should release 120 kJ, so there should be $3 \times 120 = 360$ kJ released in the reaction *[1 mark]*.

c) The delocalisation of electrons makes benzene more stable (it lowers the energy of the molecule) *[1 mark]* and so it releases less energy when it reacts *[1 mark]*.

d) E.g. The Kekulé structure cannot explain why the bonds between carbons in benzene are all the same length *[1 mark]*, since C=C double bonds are shorter than single bonds *[1 mark]*. The benzene molecule represented by the Kekulé structure should react in the same way as alkenes *[1 mark]* (i.e. by electrophilic addition), but benzene is actually much less reactive *[1 mark]* (and tends to react via electrophilic substitution).

2 Cyclohexene would decolourise the brown bromine water, benzene would not *[1 mark]*. This is because bromine water reacts in an electrophilic addition reaction with cyclohexene, due to the localised electrons in the double bond *[1 mark]*, to form a colourless dibromocycloalkane, leaving a clear solution. Benzene has a ring of delocalised π-bonds which spreads out the negative charge and makes it very stable, so it doesn't react with bromine water and the solution stays brown *[1 mark]*.

Page 90 — Electrophilic Substitution Reactions

1 a) i) A: Nitrobenzene *[1 mark]*
   B + C: Concentrated nitric acid *[1 mark]*
   and concentrated sulfuric acid *[1 mark]*
   D: Warm, not more than 55 °C *[1 mark]*
   When you're asked to name a compound, write the name, not the formula.
   ii) $HNO_3 + H_2SO_4 \rightarrow H_2NO_3^+ + HSO_4^-$ *[1 mark]*
   $H_2NO_3^+ \rightarrow NO_2^+ + H_2O$ *[1 mark]*
   iii)

⁺NO₂   O₂N H   NO₂
(benzene ring) → (intermediate) → (nitrobenzene) + H⁺

[2 marks — 1 mark for each step]

b) i) J: Bromobenzene *[1 mark]*
   ii) E + F: Bromine *[1 mark]* and FeBr₃ *[1 mark]*
   G: Room temperature *[1 mark]*

2 a) Conditions: non-aqueous solvent (e.g. dry ether), reflux *[1 mark]*

b) The acyl chloride molecule isn't polarised enough/isn't a strong enough electrophile to attack the benzene *[1 mark]*. The halogen carrier makes the acyl chloride electrophile stronger *[1 mark]*.

c) $H_3C−C^+$
   O *[1 mark]*

Answers

Page 91 — Phenols

1 a) With benzene, there will be no reaction but with phenol a reaction will occur which decolourises the brown bromine water and forms a precipitate *[1 mark]*. The product from the reaction with phenol is 2,4,6-tribromophenol *[1 mark]*.
b) Electrons from one of oxygen's p-orbitals overlap with the benzene ring's delocalised system, increasing its electron density *[1 mark]*. This makes the ring more likely to be attacked by electrophiles *[1 mark]*.
c) Electrophilic substitution *[1 mark]*.

Page 94 — Amines

1 a) The amine molecules remove protons/H^+/H ions from the water molecules *[1 mark]*. This gives alkyl ammonium ions and hydroxide ions, which make the solution alkaline *[1 mark]*.
b) $CH_3COCl + C_4H_9NH_2 \rightarrow CH_3CONH(C_4H_9) + HCl$ *[1 mark]*
   $C_4H_9NH_2 + HCl \rightarrow C_4H_9NH_3^+ + Cl^-$ *[1 mark]*
2 a) The lone pair of electrons on the nitrogen atom can accept protons/H^+ ions, or it can donate a lone pair of electrons *[1 mark]*.
b) Methylamine is stronger, as the methyl group/CH_3 pushes electrons onto/increases electron density on the nitrogen, making the lone pair more available *[1 mark]*. Phenylamine is weaker, as the nitrogen lone pair is less available — nitrogen's electron density is decreased as it's partially delocalised around the benzene ring *[1 mark]*.
3 a) $LiAlH_4$ and a non-aqueous solvent (e.g. dry ether), followed by dilute acid *[1 mark]*.
b) Hydrogen gas *[1 mark]*, metal catalyst such as platinum or nickel or high temperature and pressure *[1 mark]*.

Page 95 — Amides

1 a) N-propylbutanamide *[1 mark]*
b) Butanoyl chloride *[1 mark]*, propan-1-amine ($CH_3CH_2CH_2NH_2$) *[1 mark]*, room temperature *[1 mark]*.

Page 97 — Condensation Polymers

1 a) E.g.

—C—(CH₂)₂—C—O—C—(CH₂)₂—C—O—

[2 marks — 1 mark for ester link correct, 1 mark for rest of structure correct]

The oxygen atom at the right-hand end of the repeat unit could just as easily go on the left-hand end instead. As long as you have it there, it doesn't really matter which side it's on.

b) ester link *[1 mark]*
2 a) E.g.

—C—(CH₂)₄—C—N—(CH₂)₆—N—

[2 marks — 1 mark for amide link correct, 1 mark for rest of structure correct]

b) For each link formed, one small molecule (water) is eliminated *[1 mark]*.

Page 99 — Amino Acids

1 a) Cysteine is chiral but glycine isn't *[1 mark]*. So a mixture containing just one enantiomer of cysteine will rotate the plane of plane-polarised light, but glycine won't *[1 mark]*.
b) *A maximum of two marks can be awarded for structure and reasoning of the written response:*
   2 marks: The answer is constructed logically, and displays clear reasoning and links between points throughout.
   1 mark: The answer is mostly logical, with some reasoning and links between points.
   0 marks: The answer has no structure and no links between points.

Here are some points your answer may include:
Draw a line near the bottom of a piece of chromatography paper, and put a spot of the amino acid mixture on it. Put the paper into a beaker containing a small amount of solvent that lies below the level of the spot of mixture. Put a watch glass on the beaker and leave until the solvent has nearly reached the top of the paper, then remove the paper and mark the distance the solvent has moved. Each amino acid will have a different solubility in the solvent, so as the solvent spreads up the paper the different amino acids will separate out. Leave the paper to dry and spray with ninhydrin (to reveal location of spots), then measure how far the solvent front and the spots have travelled. Calculate the R_f values of the amino acid spots using the equation

$$R_f \text{ value} = \frac{\text{distance travelled by spot}}{\text{distance travelled by solvent}}$$ and compare to a table of

known amino acid R_f values *[1 mark]*.
[4 marks — 4 marks if 6 points mentioned covering all areas of the question, 3 marks if 4-5 points covered, 2 marks if 2-3 points covered, 1 mark if 1 point covered]

2 a) An amino acid's isoelectric point is the pH where its average overall charge is zero *[1 mark]*.
b) i)
   CH₂OH
   |
   H₂N—C—COOH
   |
   H
   [1 mark]
   ii)
   CH₂OH
   |
   H₂N—C—COO⁻
   |
   H
   [1 mark]

It might seem a bit obvious to say this, but if you've drawn these out in more detail — like drawing the NH_2 group out with all its bonds shown — you'd get the mark.

Page 100 — Grignard Reagents

1 a) 1-bromobutane, magnesium, dry ether *[1 mark]*
b) i) Ethanal and dry ether *[1 mark]*, then dilute HCl *[1 mark]*.
   ii) CO_2 and dry ether *[1 mark]*, then dilute HCl *[1 mark]*.

Page 103 — Organic Synthesis

1 E.g. Step 1: The methanol is refluxed with $K_2Cr_2O_7$ and acid to form methanoic acid *[1 mark]*.
   Step 2: The methanoic acid is heated with ethanol using an acid catalyst to make ethyl methanoate *[1 mark]*.
2 E.g. Step 1: React propane with bromine in the presence of UV light to form bromopropane *[1 mark]*.
   Step 2: Bromopropane is then refluxed with aqueous sodium hydroxide solution to form propanol *[1 mark]*.
3 a) Heat under reflux *[1 mark]*.
b) $K_2Cr_2O_7$/potassium dichromate and H_2SO_4/sulfuric acid *[1 mark]*, reflux *[1 mark]*.
4 E.g. Step 1:

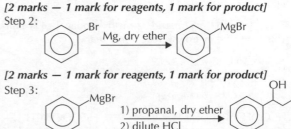

[2 marks — 1 mark for reagents, 1 mark for product]
Step 2:

[2 marks — 1 mark for reagents, 1 mark for product]
Step 3:

[2 marks — 1 mark for reagents at each stage]

Answers

Page 105 — Practical Techniques

1 a)

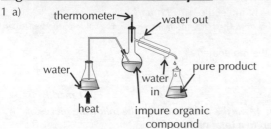

thermometer→
water out
water
water in
pure product
heat
impure organic compound

[3 marks — 1 mark showing steam distillation apparatus, 1 mark for a correct set-up, 1 mark for correct labels]

b) Put the mixture in a separating funnel and add ether *[1 mark]*. Add some salt (e.g. NaCl) to the mixture, as this makes the aqueous layer very polar, ensuring that all the phenylamine is dissolved in the ether layer *[1 mark]*. Put a stopper on the funnel, and shake it, then remove the stopper and let the mixture settle into layers *[1 mark]*. Open the tap and run each layer off into a separate container *[1 mark]*.

Page 107 — More Practical Techniques

1 a) The purer sample will have the higher melting point, so the sample that melts at 69 °C is purer *[1 mark]*.
   b) E.g. recrystallisation in propanone *[1 mark]*.
   c) E.g. the purity could be checked by measuring the melting point and comparing it against the known melting point of stearic acid *[1 mark]*.
2 a) The scientist used the minimum possible amount of hot solvent to make sure that the solution would be saturated *[1 mark]*.
   b) Filter the hot solution through a heated funnel to remove any insoluble impurities *[1 mark]*. Leave the solution to cool down slowly until crystals of the product have formed *[1 mark]*. Filter the mixture under reduced pressure *[1 mark]*. Wash the crystals with ice-cold solvent *[1 mark]*. Leave the crystals to dry *[1 mark]*.
   c) The melting point range of the impure product will be lower and broader than that of the pure product *[1 mark]*.
3   B *[1 mark]*

Page 109 — Empirical and Molecular Formulae

1 a) 0.100 g of the carbonyl gives 0.228 g of CO_2.
   $0.228 \div 44.0 = 0.00518$ moles of CO_2.
   1 mole of CO_2 contains 1 mole of carbon, so 0.100 g of the carbonyl must contain 0.00518 moles of C *[1 mark]*.
   0.100 g of the carbonyl makes 0.0930 g of H_2O.
   $0.0930 \div 18.0 = 0.00517$ moles of H_2O.
   1 mole of H_2O contains 2 moles of H, so 0.100 g of the carbonyl must contain $2 \times 0.00517 = 0.0103$ moles of H *[1 mark]*.
   0.00518 moles of C has a mass of $0.00518 \times 12.0 = 0.0622$ g
   0.0103 moles of H has a mass of $0.0103 \times 1.0 = 0.0103$ g
   $0.0622 + 0.0103 = 0.0725$ g
   So 0.100 g of the compound contains $0.100 - 0.0725 = 0.0275$ g of O *[1 mark]*.
   0.0275 g of O $= 0.0275 \div 16.0 = 0.00172$ moles
   So the mole ratio is C = 0.00518, H = 0.0103, O = 0.00172
   Divide by the smallest (0.00172): The ratio of C:H:O is 3:6:1.
   So the empirical formula = C_3H_6O *[1 mark]*.
   b) Mass of empirical formula: $(3 \times 12.0) + 6.0 + 16.0 = 58.0$ *[1 mark]*
   So by mass, hydrogen is $(6.0 \div 58.0) \times 100 = $ **10.3%** *[1 mark]*
   c) Molecular formula is the same as the empirical formula as they have the same mass *[1 mark]*.
   d) The carbonyl reacts with Tollens' reagent to form a silver mirror, so it must be an aldehyde. So, the structure is:

   H H H
   H–C–C–C=O
   H H
   [1 mark]

2 a) To get the mole ratio, divide each % by atomic mass:
   C: $37.0 \div 12.0 = 3.08$ H: $2.2 \div 1.0 = 2.2$
   N: $18.5 \div 14.0 = 1.32$ O: $42.3 \div 16.0 = 2.64$ *[1 mark]*
   Then divide by the smallest (1.32):
   The ratio of C:H:N:O is $2.33:1.67:1:2$ *[1 mark]*
   Multiply by 3 to get whole numbers: C:H:N:O = $7:5:3:6$
   So the empirical formula = $C_7H_5N_3O_6$ *[1 mark]*
   The molecular mass = 227
   The empirical mass = $(7 \times C) + (5 \times H) + (3 \times N) + (6 \times O)$
   $= (7 \times 12.0) + (5 \times 1.0) + (3 \times 14.0) + (6 \times 16.0) = 227$
   The empirical formula is the same as the molecular formula as they have the same mass *[1 mark]*.
   b) E.g.

   O_2N — CH_3 — NO_2
   NO_2

   [1 mark, allow different placing of groups around ring]

3 a) $25X_{(g)} + 125O_{2(g)} \rightarrow 75CO_{2(g)} + ?H_2O$
   Dividing by 25 gives: $X_{(g)} + 5O_2 \rightarrow 3CO_2 + nH_2O$
   5 moles of O_2 reacts to give 3 moles of CO_2 and n moles of H_2O, so $n = (5 \times 2) - (3 \times 2) = 4$.
   $X_{(g)} + 5O_2 \rightarrow 3CO_2 + 4H_2O$ *[1 mark]*
   All the C atoms in CO_2 come from X, so X contains 3 C atoms.
   All the H atoms in H_2O come from X, so X contains $(4 \times 2) = 8$ H atoms. The molecular formula of X is C_3H_8 *[1 mark]*.
   b) The empirical mass is $(3 \times 12.0) + (8 \times 1.0) = 44$ *[1 mark]*. The mass spectrum of X has an M peak at $m/z = 88$, so the molecular mass of X is 88. So X contains $88 \div 44 = 2$ empirical units. The molecular formula of X is C_6H_{16} *[1 mark]*.

Topic 19 — Modern Analytical Techniques II

Page 110 — High Resolution Mass Spectrometry

1 a) C *[1 mark]*
   The relative molecular mass of the compound = the m/z value of the molecular ion, so calculate the precise M_r of each possible molecular formula:
   A: $(3 \times 12.0000) + (6 \times 1.0078) + (2 \times 15.9990) = 74.0448$
   B: $(4 \times 12.0000) + (10 \times 1.0078) + 15.9990 = 74.077$
   C: $(3 \times 12.0000) + (10 \times 1.0078) + (2 \times 14.0064) = 74.0908$
   D: $(2 \times 12.0000) + (6 \times 1.0078) + (2 \times 14.0064) + 15.9990$
   $= 74.0586$
   b) The four options given in part a) all have the same M_r to the nearest whole number, so their molecular ions would all have the same m/z value on a low resolution mass spectrum *[1 mark]*.

2   E.g.

   H H
   H–C–C–C=C(H)(H)   OR   H–C–C=C–C–H
   H H H   H H H H
   but-1-ene   but-2-ene

   OR   H–C–C=C(H)(H)
        H CH_3
   methylpropene

   [2 marks — 1 mark for correct structure, 1 mark for correct name]
   Answering questions like this can involve a bit of trial and error. Here, there was a big clue in the question — it's a hydrocarbon, so it only contains H and C atoms. There are actually two other hydrocarbons with the formula C_4H_8, so well done if you thought of cyclobutane or methylcyclopropane.

Page 113 — NMR Spectroscopy

1 a) The peak at $\delta = 0$ is produced by the reference compound, tetramethylsilane/TMS *[1 mark]*.
   b) All three carbon atoms in the molecule $CH_3CH_2CH_2NH_2$ are in different environments *[1 mark]*. There are only two peaks on the carbon-13 NMR spectrum shown *[1 mark]*.
   The ^{13}C NMR spectrum of $CH_3CH_2CH_2NH_2$ would have three peaks because this molecule has three carbon environments.

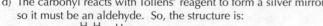

Answers

c) The peak at $\delta \approx 25$ represents carbons in C–C bonds *[1 mark]*. The peak at $\delta \approx 40$ represents a carbon in a C–N bond *[1 mark]*. The spectrum has two peaks, so the molecule must have two carbon environments *[1 mark]*.
So the structure of the molecule must be:

$$\begin{array}{c}
\text{H} \quad \text{NH}_2 \text{H} \\
\overset{|}{\text{H}} \;\; \overset{|}{\text{H}} \;\; \overset{|}{\text{H}} \\
\text{H}-\overset{|}{\underset{|}{\text{C}}}-\overset{|}{\underset{|}{\text{C}}}-\overset{|}{\underset{|}{\text{C}}}-\text{H} \\
\text{H} \quad \text{H} \quad \text{H}
\end{array}$$ *[1 mark]*

The two carbon environments are CH_3–$CH(NH_2)$–CH_3 and $CH(NH_2)$–$(CH_3)_2$.

2 C *[1 mark]*

Page 115 — Proton NMR Spectroscopy

1 a) The quartet at 3.6 ppm is caused by 3 protons on the adjacent carbon. The n+1 rule tells you that 3 protons give 3 + 1 = 4 peaks *[1 mark]*.
Similarly the triplet at 1.3 ppm is due to 2 adjacent protons giving 2 + 1 = 3 peaks *[1 mark]*.

b) A CH_2 group adjacent to a halogen or oxygen (in an alcohol, ether or ester) or a CH_2 group adjacent to a nitrogen (in an amine or amide) *[1 mark]*.

c) A CH_3 group *[1 mark]*.

d) CH_2 added to CH_3 gives a mass of 29, which leaves a mass of 64.5 – 29 = 35.5 for the rest of the molecule. This is the relative atomic mass of chlorine *[1 mark]*, so a likely structure is CH_3CH_2Cl *[1 mark]*.

2 a) 4 *[1 mark]*
With questions like this, it really helps to draw out the structure of the molecule you're dealing with. That way you can clearly see how many different H environments there are.
Here's the structure of 3-chlorobut-1-ene:

$$\begin{array}{c}
\quad\quad\quad \text{H} \;\; \text{H} \;\; \text{H} \\
\quad\quad\quad \overset{|}{\;} \;\; \overset{|}{\;} \;\; \overset{|}{\;} \\
\text{H}\;\;\;\;\;\; \\
\text{C}=\text{C}-\text{C}-\text{C}-\text{H} \\
\text{H}\;\;\;\;\;\; \overset{|}{\;} \;\; \overset{|}{\;} \\
\quad\quad\quad\quad \text{Cl} \;\; \text{H}
\end{array}$$

b) There will be a doublet with a chemical shift of $\delta \approx 4.5$-6.5 ppm (corresponding to the H in the alkene environment) *[1 mark]*, a quartet with a chemical shift of $\delta \approx 4.5$-6.5 ppm (corresponding to the other H in the alkene environment) *[1 mark]*, a quintet with a chemical shift of $\delta \approx 2.0$-4.0 ppm (corresponding to the H in the halogen environment) *[1 mark]* and a doublet with a chemical shift of $\delta \approx 0.2$-1.9 ppm (corresponding to the H in the alkane environment) *[1 mark]*.

Page 117 — Chromatography

1 a) R_f value $= \dfrac{\text{Distance travelled by spot}}{\text{Distance travelled by solvent}}$ *[1 mark]*

R_f value of spot A = 7 ÷ 8 = 0.875 *[1 mark]*
The R_f value has no units, because it's a ratio.

b) Substance A has moved further up the plate because it's less strongly adsorbed onto the surface / more soluble in the solvent than substance B *[1 mark]*.

2 a) E.g. the stationary phase consists of small solid particles packed in a tube *[1 mark]*. The sample is injected into a stream of high pressure liquid — this is the mobile phase *[1 mark]*. The detector monitors the output from the tube *[1 mark]*.

b) The chromatogram shows a peak for each component of the mixture *[1 mark]*. UV light is passed through the liquid leaving the tube and the detector measures the absorbance *[1 mark]*. From these, the retention time can be seen and compared to reference books or databases to identify the substances *[1 mark]*.

3 a) Gas chromatography *[1 mark]*

b) Different substances have different retention times *[1 mark]*. The retention time of substances in the sample is compared against that for ethanol *[1 mark]*.

Page 119 — Combined Techniques

1 a) Relative mass of molecule = 73 *[1 mark]*
You can tell this from the mass spectrum — the m/z value of the molecular ion is 73.

b) Structure of the molecule:

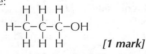

[1 mark]

Explanation: *[Award 1 mark each for the following pieces of reasoning, up to a total of 5 marks]*:
The infrared spectrum of the molecule shows a strong absorbance at about 3200 cm^{-1}, which suggests that the molecule contains an amine or amide group.
It also has a trough at about 1700 cm^{-1}, which suggests that the molecule contains a C=O group.
The ^{13}C NMR spectrum tells you that the molecule has three carbon environments.
One of the ^{13}C NMR peaks has a chemical shift of about 170, which corresponds to a carbonyl group in an amide.
The ^1H NMR spectrum has a quartet at $\delta \approx 2$, and a triplet at $\delta \approx 1$ — to give this splitting pattern the molecule must contain a CH_2CH_3 group.
The ^1H NMR spectrum has a singlet at $\delta \approx 6$, corresponding to H atoms in an amine or amide group.
The mass spectrum shows a peak at m/z = 15 which corresponds to a CH_3^+ group.
The mass spectrum shows a peak at m/z = 29 which corresponds to a $CH_2CH_3^+$ group.
The mass spectrum shows a peak at m/z = 44 which corresponds to a $CONH_2^+$ group.

2 a) Relative mass of molecule = 60 *[1 mark]*
You can tell this from the mass spectrum — the m/z value of the molecular ion is 60.

b) Structure of the molecule:

$$\begin{array}{c}
\text{H} \;\; \text{H} \;\; \text{H} \\
\overset{|}{\;} \;\; \overset{|}{\;} \;\; \overset{|}{\;} \\
\text{H}-\text{C}-\text{C}-\text{C}-\text{OH} \\
\overset{|}{\;} \;\; \overset{|}{\;} \;\; \overset{|}{\;} \\
\text{H} \;\; \text{H} \;\; \text{H}
\end{array}$$ *[1 mark]*

Explanation: *[Award 1 mark each for the following pieces of reasoning, up to a total of 5 marks]*:
The ^{13}C NMR spectrum tells you that the molecule has three carbon environments.
One of the ^{13}C NMR peaks has a chemical shift of 60 — which corresponds to a C–O group.
The infrared spectrum of the molecule has a trough at about 3300 cm^{-1}, which suggests that the molecule contains an alcoholic OH group.
It also has a trough at about 1200 cm^{-1}, which suggests that the molecule also contains a C–O group.
The mass spectrum shows a peak at m/z = 15 which corresponds to a CH_3^+ group.
The mass spectrum shows a peak at m/z = 17 which corresponds to an OH^+ group.
The mass spectrum shows a peak at m/z = 29 which corresponds to a $C_2H_5^+$ group.
The mass spectrum shows a peak at m/z = 31 which corresponds to a CH_2OH^+ group.
The mass spectrum shows a peak at m/z = 43 which corresponds to a $C_3H_7^+$ group.
The ^1H NMR spectrum has 4 peaks, showing that the molecule has 4 proton environments.
The ^1H NMR spectrum has a singlet at $\delta \approx 2$, corresponding to H atoms in an OH group.
The ^1H NMR spectrum has a sextet with an integration trace of 2 at $\delta \approx 1.5$, a triplet with an integration trace of 2 at $\delta \approx 3.5$, and a triplet with an integration trace of 3 at $\delta \approx 0.5$ — to give this splitting pattern the molecule must contain a $CH_3CH_2CH_2$ group.

Index

Index